ALL THE WORLD'S ANIMALS

BIRDS: OWLS, PARROTS & WADERS

ALL THE WORLD'S ANIMALS

BIRDS: OWLS, PARROTS & WADERS

TORSTAR BOOKS
New York · Toronto

CONTRIBUTORS

MEB Michael E. Birkhead DPhil
Edward Grey Institute of Field
Ornithology
University of Oxford
England

TRB Timothy R. Birkhead BSc
DPhil
University of Sheffield
England

DB Dieter Blume
Gladenbach
West Germany

PRC P.R. Colston
British Museum (Natural
History)
Sub-department of
Ornithology
Tring, Hertfordshire
England

AWD A.W. Diamond PhD
Canadian Wildlife Service
Ottawa, Ontario
Canada

EKD Euan K. Dunn PhD
Edward Grey Institute of Field
Ornithology
University of Oxford
England

RME R. Michael Erwin PhD
Patuxent Wildlife Research
Center
Laurel, Maryland
USA

CHF C. Hilary Fry PhD
University of Aberdeen
Scotland

RWF Robert W. Furness PhD
University of Glasgow
Scotland

LGG Llewellyn G. Grimes BSc MSc
PhD
Warwick
England

JWH John W. Hardy PhD
Florida State Museum
Gainesville, Florida
USA

GJMH Graham J.M. Hirons DPhil
University of Southampton
England

JAH John A. Horsfall BA DPhil
Edward Grey Institute of Field
Ornithology
University of Oxford
England

AK Alan Kemp PhD
Transvaal Museum
Pretoria
South Africa

GLM Gordon L. Maclean DSc
University of Natal
Pietermaritzburg
South Africa

CJM Christopher J. Mead PhD
British Trust for Ornithology
Tring, Hertfordshire
England

CMP Christopher M. Perrins DPhil
Edward Grey Institute of Field
Ornithology
University of Oxford
England

MWP Michael W. Pienkowski PhD
University of Durham
England

ASR Andrew S. Richford DPhil
London
England

HR Hugh Robertson DPhil
Edward Grey Institute of Field
Ornithology
University of Oxford
England

JAS James A. Serpell PhD
University of Cambridge
England

AFS Alexander F. Skutch PhD
San Isidro
Costa Rica

BKS Barbara K. Snow BSc
British Museum (Natural
History)
Sub-department of
Ornithology
Tring, Hertfordshire
England

DWS David W. Snow DSc
British Museum (Natural
History)
Sub-department of
Ornithology
Tring, Hertfordshire
England

GT Gareth Thomas PhD
Royal Society for the
Protection of Birds
Sandy, Bedfordshire
England

ALL THE WORLD'S ANIMALS
BIRDS: OWLS, PARROTS & WADERS

TORSTAR BOOKS INC.
41 Madison Avenue
Suite 2900
New York, NY 10010

Project Editor: Graham Bateman
Editors: Peter Forbes, Bill MacKeith, Robert Peberdy
Art Editor: Jerry Burman
Art Assistant: Carol Wells
Picture research: Alison Renney
Production: Barry Baker
Design: Chris Munday

Originally planned and produced by:
Equinox (Oxford) Ltd
Littlegate House
St Ebbe's Street
Oxford OX1 1SQ, England

On the cover: Scarlet macaw
Page 1: Barn owl
Pages 2–3: Australian jacanas
Pages 4–5: Eclectus parrots
Pages 6–7: Malachite kingfisher
Pages 8–9: Eagle owl

Editors:
Dr Christopher M. Perrins
Edward Grey Institute of Field Ornithology
University of Oxford, England

Dr L. A. Middleton
Associate Professor of Zoology
University of Guelph, Ontario, Canada

Artwork Panels
Norman Arlott   Peter Harrison
Trevor Boyer   Sean Milne
Ad Cameron   Laurel Tucker
Robert Gillmor   Ian Willis

Library of Congress Cataloging in Publication Data

Owls, parrots & waders.
(All the world's animals)
Edited by Christopher M. Perrins and L. A. Middleton.
Bibliography: p.
Includes index.
1. Birds. I. Perrins, Christopher M.
II. Middelton, L. A. III. Title: Owls, parrots, and
waders. IV. Series.
QL673.094   1985   598   86-4333

ISBN 0-920269-71-9 (Series: All the World's Animals)
ISBN 0-920269-84-2 (Birds: Owls, Parrots & Waders)

In conjunction with *All the World's Animals*
Torstar Books offers a 12-inch raised relief
world globe.
For more information write to:
Torstar Books Inc.
41 Madison Avenue
Suite 2900
New York, NY 10010

CONTENTS

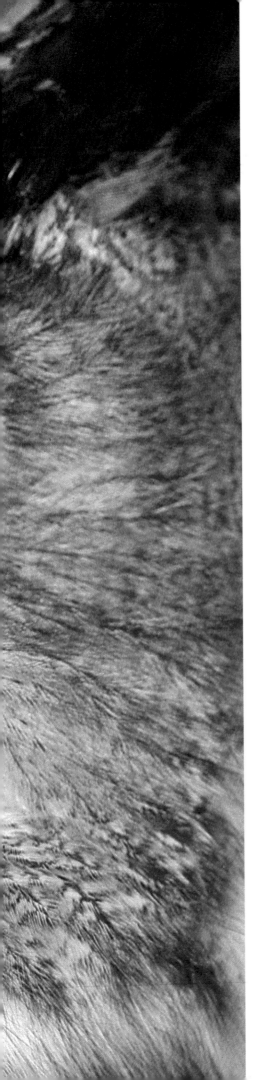

FOREWORD

The world of birds is breathtaking in its diversity. From owls to oystercatchers, from parrots to potoos, this magnificent volume journeys far beyond the birds of its title, to encapsulate much of ornithology's splendor. Superb color photographs, taken on location, show subjects most readers will never have seen in the wild.

Besides being visually spectacular, *Owls, Parrots & Waders* offers an absorbing study of the physiology, behavior and social dynamics of a wide range of birds. Many have familiar everyday names—gulls, kingfishers, toucans and plovers; others—honeyguides, hoatzin, hoopoes—are less familiar.

The parrot's vibrant beauty and imitative vocal powers may not be matched by the drab little honeyguide, but the latter's retiring disposition disguises perhaps the most extraordinary behavior of any bird: as its name implies, the honeyguide will actually guide people, as well as other large mammals, to bees' nests. Another example of the amazing weave of Nature's tapestry is the mutual dependence of certain hummingbirds and the plants on which they feed.

More than a highly authoritative reference work, *Owls, Parrots & Waders* also presents the latest and most exciting work from the field in a vivid and very readable fashion.

How this book is organized

Bird classification, even for professional ornithologists, can be a thorny problem. Here we have used a widely accepted classification, based, with only a few exceptions, on the so-called Wetmore order employed in *Checklist of Birds of the World* by J. L. Peters. Other taxonomic works referred to are listed in the Bibliography.

The layout of the book follows a fairly simple structure. Each article deals with a single family or with several related families or subfamilies. The text gives details, where relevant, of physical features, distribution, evolutionary history, classification, breeding, diet and feeding behavior typical of that family. Social dynamics and spatial organization, conservation and relationships with man are also covered. Color artwork shows representative species engaged in typical activities.

Preceding the discussion of each family or group of families is a panel of text that provides basic data about size, habitat, plumage, voice, nests, eggs and diet. Where a number of families are considered, a supplementary table gives this detailed information for each family (or in some cases subfamilies). For each family, there is a map of natural distribution (not introductions to other areas by man). Unless otherwise stated, this is the global distribution of the family and includes breeding and wintering grounds for migratory birds. For each family, there is a scale drawing comparing the size of a representative species with that of a six-foot man or a 12-inch human foot. Where there are two silhouettes, they are of the largest and smallest representatives of the family. Generally, dimensions given are for both males and females. Where sexes differ in size, the scale drawings show the larger.

Every so often a really remarkable study of a species or behavior pattern emerges. Some of these studies are so distinctive that they have been allocated two whole pages, enabling the authors to develop their stories. The topics of these special features give insight into evolutionary processes at work and span social organization, foraging behavior, breeding biology and conservation. Similar themes are developed in smaller "box features" alongside the main text.

As you read these pages, you will marvel as each story unfolds. But as well as relishing the beauty of these birds you should also be fearful for them. Again and again authors return to the need to conserve species threatened with extinction. The following symbols are used to show the status accorded to species at risk as listed by the International Council for Bird Preservation (ICBP) at the time of going to press. E = Endangered—in danger of extinction unless causal factors (such as habitat destruction) are modified. V = Vulnerable—likely to become endangered in the near future. R = Rare, but neither endangered nor vulnerable at present. I = Indeterminate—insufficient information available, but known to be in one of the above categories. (Some species that have become extinct within the past 100 years are indicated by the symbol Ex.)

However, not all the species listed as threatened by the ICBP are discussed in this book, and information about the total number of threatened species in each family is included as follows: where all such species are included in the summary panel or table of species devoted to a particular family, no further comment is added. Otherwise, a figure for the "total threatened species" is given, either at the end of the list of representative species or, where the list is divided into subfamilies or other groups, at the head of the tabulated information on the family.

PLOVERS AND SANDPIPERS

Families: Charadriidae, Scolopacidae, Recurvirostridae, Phalaropodidae
Order: Charadriiformes (suborder: Charadrii, part).
One hundred and fifty-three species in 33 genera.
Distribution: see maps and table.

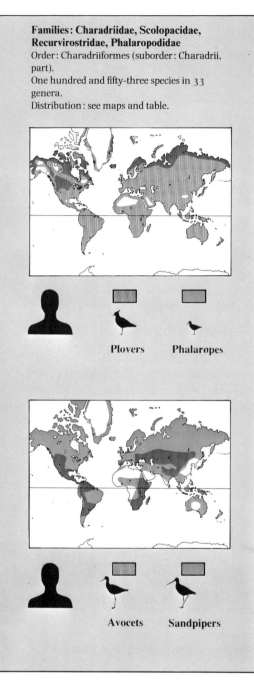

Plovers   Phalaropes

Avocets   Sandpipers

▶ **Defending its nest,** a south Australian Banded plover (*Vanellus tricolor*) challenges an intruder. Within the egg, the unhatched but noisy chicks fall silent when they hear their parents' alarm call.

THE noisy cries of **plovers** ring out in open spaces the world over, from the killdeer repeating the call for which it was named, in North America, to the sad "peewit" of its Eurasian counterpart, the lapwing. In southern Africa the Blacksmith plover breaks its silence with a loud, metallic "klink, klink" when disturbed.

The plovers are a large family of small to medium-sized plumpish shorebirds with rounded heads and large eyes. The "true plovers" (*Charadrius*) are at the lower end of the size range, the "lapwings" (*Vanellus*) in the middle and the *Pluvialis* species at the top. Unlike other waders, plovers have "pigeon-like" bills, with the upper mandible swollen toward the tip. They have medium to long legs and all are quick runners and strong fliers. The hind toe is small or absent, and most have three relatively short, unwebbed front toes. Leg colors may be black, flesh-colored, or striking reds and yellows.

Despite the bold color patterns of most species, the plumage is disruptive, and individuals blend easily into the background as soon as they stand still. The body feathers are molted twice, and the flight feathers at

▶ **Common on farm and marsh,** the Eurasian lapwing is immediately known by its tumbling flight, mournful call and, close up, its long wispy crest.

least once, a year during molts—the timings of which can be complex. There is usually a complete post-breeding molt. Juvenile plovers molt a few weeks after fledging.

The 22 species of *Vanellus* are mostly found inland. They are widespread in all tropical and temperate areas except North America, and are well represented in Africa. The breeding distribution ranges from the tideline to above the treeline—the Puna plover is found up to 14,750ft (4,500m) in the high Andes. The habitats include marshlands, lake edges, grasslands, steppes and sometimes arid areas well away from water. Among lapwing species, but not other members of the family, a crest, wattles and wing spurs are common.

The 30 species of true plovers or sand plovers (*Charadrius*) are found along sandy or muddy shores and along rivers and inland on fields. The Ringed plover is widespread along the coasts of the Old World and breeds up to the arctic tundra; the main wintering grounds are along the eastern Mediterranean and African coasts. Most true plovers show a black chest band, black forehead, and black line from eye to bill.

The largest plovers are the three species of *Pluvialis*, which breed at freshwater marshes and grasslands in the upland and tundra regions of the Northern Hemisphere. The Eurasian golden plover acquires a beautiful nuptial plumage in the spring which includes a coal black "face," breast and belly to accompany the golden spots on the upperparts. It breeds in northern Europe and is replaced in Siberia and North America by the American golden plover, which is a true long-distance migrant, journeying from the arctic tundra across the

Atlantic to Argentina and across the Pacific to Australia. One population flies directly from Alaska to Hawaii, a flight of some 2,800mi (4,500km). The Black-bellied plover (or Gray plover) breeds in the high Arctic of North America and Siberia, and although many individuals winter in temperate latitudes, some fly as far as Chile and Australia.

The wrybill from New Zealand has a bill that is bent laterally to the right at an angle of about 12°. This lateral asymmetry is unique among birds. So far there is no satisfactory explanation for this: there does not seem to be any benefit gained while feeding.

Most plovers do not wade in water in the same ways or to the same extent as other shorebirds. Typically they forage by walking in damp areas or at the water's edge and some species are adapted to feeding in arid zones well away from water. An exception is the White-tailed lapwing which, as well as feeding on land, wades in flooded areas taking prey from the surface or sometimes by submerging its head. Plovers have relatively large eyes which testify to the importance of sight during feeding. The range of food taken is broad, and includes adult and larval insects, beetles, crustaceans, mollusks, worms and sometimes berries. Typically they locate their prey by sight on the surface and quickly run forward a short distance to catch it. The Ringed plover, for example, largely feeds on crustaceans picked off mud or sand especially at the edge of the tide. It quickly runs in and out of the areas vacated by receding waves.

The diets of migratory species at their wintering grounds probably differ widely from their diets at the breeding grounds, but only a few species have been investigated. In Britain the Eurasian golden plover takes crane flies and other insects at its upland breeding grounds. On the lowland grasslands during the winter it feeds largely on earthworms and insect larvae. At this time the golden plovers are frequently found in fairly large flocks often mixed with lapwings. Black-headed gulls (p38) may also station themselves among these flocks, and as soon as they see a bird capture an earthworm they fly over and try to steal it. This feeding off others by theft, or kleptoparasitism, seems to be more successful against lapwings because they are slower at taking and ingesting worms than are the golden plovers. The Eurasian lapwing is noted for its cold weather movements. Large flocks fly south and west ahead of cold weather fronts and quickly return to areas after a thaw.

Plovers may be paired on arrival at the breeding grounds or form pairs very shortly

The 4 Families of Plovers and Sandpipers   E Endangered.   R Rare.

Plovers
Family: Charadriidae
Sixty-two species in 10 genera.

Worldwide except for permanently frozen areas. Most species migratory. Coastal, marshland, inland water, rivers, grassland to mountains and tundra regions. Size: Length 5.5–16in (14–41cm); weight 1.2–10.5oz (34–296g). Males usually slightly larger than females. Plumage: usually light-colored below, often marked features on head and neck. Voice: a variety of mono- to tri-syllabic calls often repeated. Nests: simple scrape on bare or open ground. Eggs: typically 4 (range 2–6); variable backgrounds, small flecks to large dark blotches; 0.2–1.2oz (5.3–33g); incubation 18–38 days; young precocial, fledging at 21–42 days. Diet: wide range of terrestrial and aquatic invertebrates, sometimes berries.

Species include: the **American golden plover** (*Pluvialis dominica*), **Black-bellied** or **Gray plover** (*P. squatarola*), **Blacksmith plover** (*Vanellus armatus*), **Eurasian golden plover** (*Pluvialis apricaria*), **Greater sand plover** (*Charadrius leschenaultii*), **killdeer** (*C. vociferus*), **Kittlitz's plover** (*C. pecuarius*), **lapwing** or **peewit** (*Vanellus vanellus*), **Masked plover** (*V. miles*), **New Zealand shore plover** E (*Charadrius novaeseelandiae*), **Puna plover** (*C. alticola*), **Red-wattled lapwing** (*Vanellus indicus*), **Ringed plover** (*Charadrius hiaticula*), **Wattled plover** (*Vanellus senegallus*), **White-tailed lapwing** (*V. leucurus*), **wrybill**

(*Anarhynchus frontalis*). Total threatened species: 2.

Sandpipers
Family: Scolopacidae
Eighty-one species in 18 genera.

Most species breed in N Hemisphere. a few in tropics, Africa and S America. Most species migratory. Breed in wetlands and grasslands, mainly in tundra, boreal and temperate zones. Winter along coasts, estuaries and other wetlands. Size: length 5–26in (13–66cm); weight 0.6–37oz (18–1,040g). Plumage: upperparts mottled browns and grays; underparts light; markings cryptic. Voice: variety of twitterings, rattles, shrill calls and whistles. Nests: made in tussocks or on dry ground, exceptionally in trees or holes. Eggs: typically 4 (range 2–4, rarely more), buff or greenish backgrounds with variable markings, pear-shaped, 0.2–2.8oz (5.8–80g); incubation 18–30 days; young precocial, fledging at 16–50 days. Diet: mollusks, crustaceans, aquatic worms and flies, some plant material at times.

Species include: **Black-tailed godwit** (*Limosa limosa*), **Bristle-thighed curlew** (*Numenius tahitiensis*), **Broad-billed sandpiper** (*Limicola falcinellus*), **Common sandpiper** (*Tringa hypoleucos*), **Common snipe** (*Gallinago gallinago*), **Curlew sandpiper** (*Calidris ferruginea*), **dunlin** (*C. alpina*), **Eskimo curlew** E (*Numenius borealis*), **Eurasian curlew** (*N. arquata*), **Eurasian woodcock** (*Scolopax*

rusticola), **Green sandpiper** (*Tringa ochropus*), **Little stint** (*Calidris minuta*), **Long-billed curlew** (*Numenius americanus*), **Long-billed dowitcher** (*Limnodromus scolopaceus*), **Pectoral sandpiper** (*Calidris melanotos*), **Red knot** or **knot** (*C. canutus*), **redshank** (*Tringa totanus*), **Ruddy turnstone** (*Arenaria interpres*), **ruff** (*Philomachus pugnax*), **sanderling** (*Calidris alba*), **Sharp-tailed sandpiper** (*C. acuminata*), **Solitary sandpiper** (*Tringa solitaria*), **Spoon-billed sandpiper** (*Eurynorhynchus pygmeus*), **Subantarctic snipe** R (*Coenocorypha aucklandica*), **Upland sandpiper** (*Bartramia longicauda*), **Western sandpiper** (*Calidris mauri*), **Wood sandpiper** (*Tringa glareola*). Total threatened species: 5.

Avocets and stilts
Family: Recurvirostridae
Seven species in 4 genera.

Europe, Asia, Australasia, Africa, N and S America. Fresh, brackish and saline waters. Size: 12–18in (30–46cm) long and 4.9–15.3oz (140–435g). Females usually slightly smaller. Plumage: basically brown or black and white on body and wings. Sexes similar. Voice: mostly mono- or di-syllabic yelping calls. Nests: scrapes, sometimes lined, on bare ground or short vegetation near water. Eggs: usually 4 (range 2–5), light background with dark markings: 0.8–1.6oz (22–44g); incubation 22–28 days; young precocial, fledging at 28–35 days.

Diet: wide range of aquatic invertebrates or small vertebrates.

Species: the **American avocet** (*Recurvirostra americana*), **Andean avocet** (*R. andina*), **Banded stilt** (*Cladorhynchus leucocephalus*), **Eurasian avocet** (*Recurvirostra avosetta*), **Ibisbill** (*Ibidorhyncha struthersii*), **Red-necked avocet** (*Recurvirostra novaehollandiae*), **stilt** or **Black-winged** or **Black-necked stilt** (*Himantopus himantopus*). Total threatened species: 1.

Phalaropes
Family: Phalaropodidae
Three species of the genus *Phalaropus*.

Breed in N Hemisphere, winter in tropics or S Hemisphere. Breed beside shallow water bodies; in winter 2 species oceanic, 1 in inland waters. Size: 6.5–7.5in (16.5–19cm) long and 1–3oz (29–85g) weight. Females larger than males. Plumage: breeding—reds, white, buff, gray and black, males considerably duller; non-breeding—dark above and light underparts. Voice: some short calls, noisy at times. Nests: in tussocks near water. Eggs: usually 4, oval to pear-shaped, olive-buff with irregular black or brown spots and blotches; 0.2–0.3oz (6–9.4g); incubation 16–24 days; young precocial, fledging at 18–21 days. Diet: chiefly insects and plankton in oceans.

Species: **Gray** or **Red phalarope** (*Phalaropus fulicarius*), **Red-necked** or **Northern phalarope** (*P. lobatus*), **Wilson's phalarope** (*P. tricolor*).

◄ **A simple scrape on bare ground** is the nest of the Black-fronted plover (*Charadrius melanops*) of Australia. The disruptive plumage of the adult makes an incubating bird hard for a predator to spot. Even harder to detect may be the eggs. Plovers that nest on sand or gravel produce eggs covered with small dark flecks or spots. Other species nesting on bare earth or among sparse vegetation lay eggs that are mottled, while eggs of moorland and tundra species have large spots and blotches. These inherited egg color characters may even vary within a species according to the terrain of different populations.

Faced with danger, the young can run within an hour or so of hatching, or they may crouch close to the ground, their first plumage rendering them practically invisible.

▶ **Displays of breeding plovers** include sometimes spectacular aerial advertisement of the territory, as (1) in the tumbling flight of the lapwing. On the ground, when warning off rivals from the mate or territory, the effect of the display may be enhanced by vocalizations and the display of plumage, including crests, colored wattles, and wing spurs. (2) "Song duel" between Eurasian golden plovers. (3) Spur-winged plover (*Vanellus spinosus*) in challenge or threat posture, and (4) running at opponent.

after arrival. They have some very aggressive and highly vocal displays. Aerial displays often contain spectacular twisting, plunging, diving and hovering movements. On the ground there may be displays involving quick running, wing-dropping, tail-fanning and much bowing and curtseying, especially by the males during scrape making. The importance of displays in this family is emphasized by the presence of a crest in some species, such as the Eurasian lapwing, of prominent red and yellow facial wattles in species such as the Wattled plover of southern Africa and, in several species, well-developed wing spurs growing at the bend of the wing (carpal joint). These are particularly long in the Masked plover of Australia.

The males create many scrapes on open, bare or slightly vegetated ground and the female appears to choose one in which to lay her eggs. The four eggs of the usual-sized clutch are commonly produced at intervals of $1\frac{1}{2}$–4 days. Among the few exceptions, Kittlitz's plover and the wrybill lay only two eggs. The eggs and young are highly camouflaged and are well defended by their parents. Nests may be flooded out if they are made near water and they are often subject to heavy predation. A completed clutch of the large, pear-shaped eggs represents some 50–70 percent of the female's body weight. Incubation, typically by both sexes, begins after the last egg is laid and lasts for some 18–22 days in the smaller species and 28–38 days in the larger species.

Most species are noticeably gregarious. Migrating flocks can number thousands. Within a species some populations, especially northern ones, can be highly migratory while other southern ones can be virtually sedentary, eg redshank and golden plovers. Prior to migration birds put on a lot of subcutaneous body fat. Breeding densities vary between species. Some nest in colonies of several hundred pairs, others nest in small groups and defend fairly large territories.

The family contains one of the rarest members of the order Charadriiformes, and certainly the most restricted wader or shorebird in the world—the New Zealand shore plover. Formerly found along New Zealand's many coasts, it is now an endangered species limited to one small island of about 0.9sq mi (220ha) in the Chatham Islands some 500mi (800km) to the east. It was probably never very numerous but was seriously affected by commercial collectors at the turn of this century. By 1937 the population was down to about 70 pairs and today there may be slightly fewer than 100 birds. They are sedentary, docile and highly vulnerable to mammalian predators. The removal of sheep from the coastal areas of the island has allowed the vegetation to grow unchecked which has probably reduced the amount of appropriate habitat. In the early 1970s the introduction of adults and juveniles (some partially wing-clipped) onto a nearby predator-free island failed, because of the strong homing abilities of the birds. Further research into its ecological requirements may make it possible to devise a successful management plan for this plover, whose plight is so typical of many other birds found on remote islands.

Plovers' eggs used to be collected in large

numbers in Europe. Indeed, bird protection laws were often framed to allow the taking of lapwings' eggs into the spring to satisfy the demand of epicures. Plovers were also extensively trapped after the breeding season and sold at many markets. Areas of grassland would be temporarily flooded to provide food, and the arriving birds, mostly lapwings, then caught in large clap nets. Live decoys were used by the trappers to lure the birds to the precise area as efficiently as possible.

In the northern winter, the estuaries of Atlantic Europe hold over 2 million waders, mostly members of the **sandpiper** family. Nearly half the wintering birds are to be found in Britain, with concentrations of 100,000 in larger estuaries, such as the Wash in the east and Morecambe Bay in the west, which are of immense importance as feeding and roosting sites. Flocks, sometimes of tens of thousands, of dunlin and Red knot, together with smaller numbers of other species, are marveled at by birdwatchers. At low tides all are widely dispersed over the sands and muds and are busy feeding. As the tide comes in and the feeding grounds become covered, the waders are concentrated into tighter and larger groups. They are forced into the high salt marshes or arable farmland to roost or rest during the high tide period. Before settling, the large flocks wheel and turn in the sky like billowing plumes of smoke. The roosting flocks break up when the tide recedes and the birds then stream back to the shore to start another feeding cycle.

The sandpiper family (Scolopacidae) comprises the largest family of shorebirds. Most species breed in the Northern Hemisphere, especially in the arctic and subarctic regions. The breeding range of many species encircles the Pole, and only a few sandpiper species are adapted to breed in tropical areas. Most are highly migratory and the most northerly breeders tend to undertake the longest journeys. Sandpipers breed in all types of wetlands and grasslands, ranging from coastal salt marshes to mountainous moorland. Temporary pools and areas of tundra freed from winter snows are favored by many species. Some nest on prairies and along rivers. Wintering areas are mainly sand and mudflats in estuaries, although some species use inland freshwaters, pastures, or rocky shores.

All sandpipers have relatively long wings and a short tail. Their legs and neck are often long. All have three fairly long front toes and, except for the sanderling, a short hind toe. There is a great variety of bill shapes and sizes (see p17). The bill is at least the length of the head in all species, but is usually much longer. Plumage patterns are generally cryptic—mottled browns

▶ ▼ **Representative species of plovers, sandpipers and phalaropes.** (1) Golden plover (*Pluvialis apricaria*) on nest. (2) Killdeer (*Charadrius vociferus*) in "broken wing" distraction display. (3) Wattled plover (*Vanellus senegallus*) in alert posture, showing spurs on carpel joint of wing. (4) Common snipe (*Gallinago gallinago*) in "drumming" display flight. (5) Redshank (*Tringa totanus*) in courtship display. (6) Eurasian curlew (*Numenius arquata*) feeding. (7) Sanderling (*Calidris alba*) foraging along waterline. (8) Red-necked or Northern phalarope (*Phalaropus lobatus*) "spinning" on water while feeding.

and grays above, with paler underparts sometimes with streaks and spots. The sexes look alike but in some species there may be some sexual differences in breeding plumage. All are quick runners, can wade in water and swim if necessary.

The main foods of most species during the breeding season are two-winged (dipterous) flies, especially crane flies and midges. Sometimes plant foods are taken before the insects emerge. The main foods of the shore feeders in winter are mollusks such as tellins and spire snails, crustaceans such as *Corophium*, and marine worms such as ragworms and lugworms. Snipes and woodcocks mostly take oligochaete worms from damp soils, the snipes from marshy ground, the woodcocks often in damp woodland. Surface foods may be located by sight and picked up, but those beneath the surface are probed for and located by touch. The Bristle-thighed curlew is, somewhat unusually, fond of eating the eggs of other birds, particularly seabirds. The eyes are so placed in the head to give feeding waders a wide field of view; this adaptation is so complete in the woodcock that it has a 360° field of view.

Arctic-nesting species either arrive at the breeding grounds already paired or pair within 2–10 days, in order to take advantage of the short time available for breeding. Temperate-nesting species have a more protracted breeding season and individuals may spend several weeks at the breeding grounds before nesting. All species have elaborate display flights or song flights and there are ground displays involving wing-lifting prior to copulation. Sandpiper calls may be mono- to tri-syllabic and range from the noisy piping calls made by the redshank to twittering calls made by the true sandpipers. Most species nest in tussocks on dry ground or amid ground vegetation, where they are well concealed. The Black-tailed godwit often fashions the vegetation into a cupola over its nest to give increased cover. The Sub-antarctic snipe nests in burrows made by other birds. Green sandpipers, Solitary sandpipers and occasionally Wood sandpipers lay their eggs in abandoned songbird nests in trees and bushes. Green sandpipers seek out well-wooded areas in which to breed. Most species are highly territorial, at least in the early part of the breeding season, and nesting densities range from 2.6 pairs per sq mi (1/sq km) in the Long-billed curlew to 12–25 pairs per acre (5–10/ha) in Sharp-toed sandpipers and Western sandpipers.

Eggs are laid at 1–2 day intervals; incubation begins after the last egg is laid, and for most species lasts for 21–24 days. The markedly pear-shaped eggs are relatively large and neatly "fit together" in the nest bowl. The eggs are proportionally very large in the stints and a clutch represents some 90 percent of the female's body weight. Typically, both male and female incubate, but the division of labor varies between species. However, in the ruff and Pectoral sandpiper only the females incubate. The female of the Arctic-nesting sanderling lays two clutches, one of which she incubates herself, the other incubated by her mate.

The chicks hatch out within 24 hours of each other. They are well camouflaged and are able to fend for themselves. Once dry, they are typically tended by both parents and are led to suitable feeding grounds. However, only the female Pectoral and Curlew sandpipers tend their young. The dowitchers are most unusual, if not unique, in that only the females incubate the eggs and only the males tend to the young. Female dunlins may leave the males to tend the chicks with the assistance of non- or failed breeding birds. Male and female Common snipes may split up the newly hatched

brood between them. Woodcocks and red-shanks are known to transport their young in flight, holding the chicks between their thighs. The fledging period varies from about 16 days in the smaller species to some 35–50 days in the curlews.

Male ruffs take part in complex communal displays or "tournaments" prior to mating. At this time they acquire elaborately colored "collar" feathers and also long ear-tufts of various colors. This color range between individual males is perhaps the most extreme case of sexual polymorphism in plumage. The males gather at a display ground, or lek, which is usually an open, slightly raised spot. Some of the dark-colored ruffs are known as independent males and defend small patches of ground at the lek. Other dark-colored males are kept at the edge of the lek and do not defend any ground. White-collared males do not defend any ground but, unlike marginal dark birds, are allowed to wander among the territories of the independent males. These "satellite" white males may serve to attract females for the independent males. There are short periods of frenzied activity at the lek, as the males spar, posture, leap and flap, followed by periods of calm. Females ("reeves") are allowed to walk through the lek. The successful males copulate with several females

in a short space of time. No true pairs are formed and subsequently the females undertake all the incubation of the eggs and tending the chicks.

Displaying Common snipes are vociferous (notably, "chipping" noises) but are best known for their aerial "drumming" display. They dive at an angle of about 45° with the tail fanned out. The two outer tail feathers have highly asymmetrical vanes, the leading edges comprising very narrow strips. When the diving speed reaches about 40mph (65km/h) the air passing over these feathers causes them to vibrate and give off the resonating bleat or drumming sound which can be heard some distance away. Most drumming is done by the males, although the females may drum early in the

▷ **Skulking through damp undergrowth** OVERLEAF in search of worms, its main food, this Jack snipe (*Lymnocryptes minima*) is distinguished from other snipes by its small size (length 7.5in/19cm), shorter bill, and more pointed tail lacking white feathers.

◀ **Marbled godwit** (*Limosa fedoa*) ABOVE of North America probing for marine worms along the tide edge.

◀ **The Sharp-tailed sandpiper** BELOW breeds in Siberia. Among sandpipers the longest migrations are often undertaken by the most northerly breeding species. Thus, Sharp-tailed sandpipers winter in tidal estuaries and natural harbors in Australasia.

Fitting the Bill

Sandpipers' bills show a great variety of forms, which is related to variation in feeding behavior between species. They range from the short, straight bill (1.7cm/0.7in) of the Little stint (1) to the outsized down-curved bill of the Long-billed curlew (2) (20cm/8in in females). The short, thin bills of the stints allow them to pick at surface prey, such as crustaceans, which they detect by sight. The Curlew sandpiper's (3) is the largest and most decurved bill of the small true sandpipers and is used to probe for a variety of marine animals including small mollusks.

The Broad-billed sandpiper has a heavy bill (4) which allows it to feed on relatively large prey which includes mollusks. The Spoon-billed sandpiper has a broad and flattened tip to both mandibles (5) but the function of this design is not properly understood. The head and bill are sometimes moved from side to side when the bird feeds (eg on insects and other larvae)—sometimes in quite deep water. The two turnstones have short, thickset bills (6)

which they use adeptly to turn over stones and seaweed to expose such foods as sandhoppers and crabs.

The curlews probe with their long, decurved bills for such animals as the deeper-burrowing shellfish and marine worms which are out of reach of most other shore feeders. Godwits, with their long straight bills (7), also probe, often rapidly, deep into wet substrates for prey such as aquatic worms. The dowitches (8), woodcocks (9) and snipes (10) have long, straight bills which are proportionately longer than in all other waders. In these, and other deep-probing species, the parts of the bill towards the tip are well endowed with Herbst's corpuscles. These touch-sensitive organs are essential in helping to locate the buried prey. Another adaptation in some of the long-billed waders is the ability to move the portion of the bill near the tip independently of the rest. This is very useful when manipulating prey, either on the surface or while probing underground.

breeding season. Drumming continues in the rain, but it is curtailed by windy conditions.

Migrating birds may travel singly or in small groups (eg Common sandpipers), but most species are gregarious and travel in flocks of several hundred. On the wintering grounds some species, eg Red knot and dunlin, are highly gregarious and are found in mixed-species flocks numbering tens of thousands. Species which nest in the high Arctic, such as the Ruddy turnstone and sanderling, migrate south over most of the coasts of the world as far south as Australia, Chile and southern Africa. Ruffs breeding in Siberia fly westward to northwest Europe and then continue on a remarkable journey over the Mediterranean and Sahara deserts. Up to one million have been recorded in the Senegal delta in West Africa.

Several species have been extensively taken by hunters in both the Old and New worlds and some have never recovered their former numbers. Upland sandpipers, now scarce in their prairie breeding grounds, were extensively shot in North America in the 1880s–90s and large numbers used to be packed in barrels and shipped to the cities for sale as food. (In part, this hunting pressure was brought about by the failing supply of Passenger pigeons, which were being hunted to extinction.) Vast numbers of Eskimo curlews were shot in the 1870s–80s, particularly when they made their northward journey from the Argentine pampas to the tundra breeding grounds. Today no wintering or breeding sites are known for this near-extinct species, but there have been a few recent sightings of individuals on passage and on former breeding grounds.

The most striking physical feature of the **avocets and stilts** is the proportions of their bills and legs. The long, slender bills may either be straight or curve upward. Their legs, too, are long, and in the case of stilts extremely long. Avocets and stilts are thus adapted for feeding in deep water; the three species of stilts usually feed in slightly deeper water than the avocets.

The ibisbill is found only in mountainous river valleys between 5,250 and 14,450ft (1,600–4,400m) above sea level in parts of Asia, while the Andean avocet is restricted to lakes and marshes above 11,800ft (3,600m) in the Andes. The five other species are largely found in a variety of lowland wetlands which include freshwater marshes, brackish and coastal salt marshes and coastal and inland salt lakes. The stilt is the most widespread, with six subspecies found

over six continents. Some populations of the most widespread species migrate over considerable distances. Up to 30,000 Eurasian avocets have been counted wintering in the Great Rift Valley of East Africa.

Stilts have characteristic black bills and bright pink legs and feet, while avocets have black bills and blue-gray legs and feet. The ibisbill, however, has a red bill and legs. The front toes are well webbed in avocets and the South Australian Banded stilt, but only partly so in the other species.

The variation in the amount of webbing on the feet is related to the importance of the swimming habit in each species. Avocets and stilts fly with quick wingbeats and the legs trail behind the body.

All species take a wide range of aquatic invertebrates and small vertebrates in relatively deep water. Important prey include mollusks, crustaceans including brine shrimps, insect larvae, annelid worms, tadpoles and small fish. Stilts seize their prey from above or below the water surface with their long needle-like beaks. Avocets either seize their prey directly in the water or with a scything motion of the bill. With this last method the curved part of the submerged bill locates the prey by touch as it moves from side to side in the water or soft mud. Ibisbills wade breast deep in the mountain rivers and can probe for prey under stones and boulders.

Avocets appear to prefer nesting on islands, where predation may be reduced. In all species incubation is done by both sexes. Most birds first breed when they are two years old. The Banded stilt is highly colonial: colonies of up to 27,000 pairs have been recorded, with the nests only about

◄ **Stilts and Eurasian avocet** ABOVE at Masai Mara nature reserve, Kenya. The avocet is an immature, tinged with brown.

◄ **A female stilt tends her nest** BELOW atop a tussock by the water's edge.

▼ **Mating ceremony of the stilt.** The female solicits the male by adopting, usually in shallow water, the rigid posture (1) which she maintains for most of the ceremony. The male responds by dipping his bill in the water (1), shaking it, and preening himself, a procedure repeated several times (2,3). Then the male mounts the female (4). The male mates (5) and dismounts almost in one movement, the two birds crossing bills, and the male's wing across the female's back breaking the descent (6). After mating, in the "leaning" ceremony (7), the two may stand apart then lean toward one another several times.

6.6ft (2m) apart. Stilts usually nest in loose colonies of 20–40 pairs, American avocets in loose colonies of 15–20 pairs and Eurasian avocets in colonies of 20–70 pairs. Ibisbills defend linear territories of about 0.6mi (1km) along rivers. All species seem highly territorial, have fairly aggressive displays, defend nesting territories and noisily mob intruders and potential predators. The young leave the nest within 24 hours of hatching and the brood-rearing areas, which may change during the one-month fledging period, may be vigorously defended by the adults.

The habitats of most species, although sometimes specialized, do not appear to be universally threatened. In 1969 there were about 10,000 pairs of Eurasian avocets in northwest Europe. Breeding numbers had increased in a few countries, including Britain, Denmark and Sweden, but had decreased in a few countries in southeast Europe, probably due to changes in land use. The Hawaiian race of the stilt may be endangered: in 1944 there were only about 200, but these had increased to 1,500 in 1969 as a result of protection measures.

Small and graceful, the **phalaropes** are the most specialized swimmers among the shorebirds. The three species have lobed, partially webbed toes, laterally flattened tarsi (lower legs) that reduce underwater drag and plumage like that of a duck on their underparts. This provides a layer of trapped air on which they float—as lightly as corks. Indeed, phalaropes are so buoyant that they cannot remain waterborne in strong gales. Outside the breeding season vagrant individuals may appear almost anywhere in the world, as they get blown

before strong gales. In fact, in Newfoundland they are known as "gale birds."

Wilson's phalarope breeds inland in the southern parts of North America. The breeding distribution of the other two species is circumpolar, the Gray (or Red) phalarope in the high arctic tundra and boreal zone and the Red-necked phalarope in the subarctic tundra. All three species select shallow waters, ponds and lakes near to marshy and grassy areas. The Red-necked phalarope favors permanent bodies of fresh water, Wilson's phalarope fresh to salt semi-permanent waters, and the Gray (Red) phalarope temporary ponds of the tundra. Wilson's phalarope winters at inland and coastal waters in South America, while the other two species winter in the open oceans.

Phalaropes have relatively long necks and beautiful breeding (nuptial) plumages, acquired in late spring but quickly lost. All have some white parts on the head, and red and black markings. The amount of red is variable. The "Gray phalarope" is actually the reddest: the description "gray" refers to the predominant color of the upperparts of the winter plumage; in the United States, "Red" phalarope is the more usual name for this species. The female birds are markedly different from the males, both larger (10 percent in the Red-necked, 20 percent in the Gray or Red, and 35 percent in Wilson's phalarope) and gaudier in their breeding plumage. This reflects the initiating role of the female in many aspects of breeding behavior (see text, right).

The bill is straight and needle-like in Red-necked and Wilson's phalaropes, thicker in the Gray (Red) species. All are active feeders, scarcely stopping as they peck at their prey. All can feed while spinning—swimming in tight circles. This may be a technique for stirring up invertebrate foods, making them more obvious and causing them to rise to the water surface, where they can be picked off. All phalaropes forage in shallow water, along the shoreline or among wracks of seaweed. The fine bills and large eyes help in catching the prey, which is chiefly insects (all lifestages), especially midges and gnats. The range of prey taken is large, and includes water snails, water beetles, caddis flies and large plankton. Phalaropes are highly opportunistic feeders at their breeding grounds—Red-necked phalaropes will quickly change from swimming and pecking at newly emerged midges to walking along the shoreline and pecking at emerging caddis flies as they dry off on partly submerged stones. The oceanic plankton taken includes tiny fishes, crustaceans and small jellyfish. Gray (Red) phalaropes sometimes pick parasites off the backs of whales.

Adult females are known to live at least five years, and probably breed first when they are one year old. The breeding season

▲ **Long legs trailing,** and upcurved bills to the fore, a group of American avocets takes flight.

▶ **Male Northern or Red-necked phalarope on nest.** The larger and more brightly colored females choose the nest site, secure mates by display flights, then after mating and egg-laying may mate with other males. The males do all the incubation of the eggs and care for the chicks.

The Fall and Rise of Avocets in Britain

Avocets bred regularly in eastern England until the early 19th century, before they were wiped out by wetland reclamation followed by persistent egg collecting and shooting. For over a hundred years there was no regular breeding, until in 1947 Havergate Island and Minsmere in Suffolk were colonized. During the 1939–45 World War, the cattle-grazed fields of the Minsmere level had been deliberately flooded as a defense measure, and, as a result of damage to a main sluice caused by a stray shell from a nearby firing range, the pastures on Havergate became inundated.

Breeding numbers at Havergate steadily increased to almost 100 pairs over the next 10 years, with an average 1.5 chicks successfully fledging for each pair of breeding adults. This success coincided with a steady increase in numbers of breeding Black-headed gulls in the same area to about 6,000 pairs. There was intense competition for nest sites. Gulls took over avocet nests within hours of their completion, and also killed newly hatched avocets as they were being led through the densely packed gulleries. Over a period of eight years from 1957, the fledging success of avocets averaged about 0.5 per breeding pair, and breeding numbers dropped to 48 pairs. Constant removal of Black-headed gulls' nests and eggs by conservationists caused the larger birds' breeding numbers to drop to 1,000–1,500 pairs by 1965—a level at which they have since been maintained. The effect on avocets was marked. Over the next five years from 1965 to 1969, their breeding population recovered (118 pairs in 1969), fledged chicks averaging 1.7 per pair.

By the late 1970s breeding success at Havergate had again dropped, this time to 0.1 per breeding pair. This decline was a result of a fall in numbers of prey species, which were adversely affected by hyper-salinity in the lagoons caused by a shortage of fresh water from the island's artesian wells. New sluices were built, and the island's ditches cleared, so that a regular flow of tidal brackish water could circulate throughout the lagoons. A new range of invertebrate food species is now developing, and the breeding performance of the 100 pairs of avocets is again improving.

At Minsmere the 1947 breeding attempt was not repeated until 1963. Since then avocets have built up to over 50 pairs.

Havergate and Minsmere are now nature reserves. The avocet is now the emblem of the Royal Society for the Protection of Birds.

is very short. Generally females arrive at the breeding grounds in June, ahead of the males, but the sexes sometimes arrive together, apparently paired. Otherwise, pairing takes place in a few days. The females may participate in nest-site searches and both sexes make nest scrapes. It appears that the female selects the chosen site and the male prepares the final nest, hidden in a dry grass or a sedge tussock near to water. Some roles are sex-reversed. The female takes the initiative in courtship and with display flights. She pays the male constant attention until a pair bond is formed. Incubation of the eggs and care of the young are exclusively carried out by the male.

The two birds are seldom far apart for the duration (often brief) of the pair bond, and keep in touch with repeated short calls. Nesting can be solitary or loosely colonial. The two arctic-nesting species often nest in or near colonies of Arctic terns, which may help in providing an increase in vigilance against predators. Gray (Red) phalaropes copulate on land, Red-necked while swimming, and Wilson's phalaropes while either standing in water or swimming.

Normally one egg is laid each day for four days. The male begins to incubate some time between the production of the first and third eggs. After the initial egg laying, female Red-necked and Gray (Red) phalaropes may mate with other males if there are enough males around. A female will start to lay a clutch of eggs for a new male some 7–10 days after completing her first. She will remain at the breeding ground and provide second clutches for the original or second male should the first ones be destroyed.

The incubating male rarely leaves the nest. The small eggs, the brief courtships and polyandrous habit (one female mating with several males) all seem to be adaptations for the short breeding season. The chicks of one clutch hatch more or less at the same time. The hatchlings are well developed and leave the nest when some 3–6 hours old. They are cared for by the male only. He broods them frequently in the day and night during the first few days, and also at times of bad weather. They swim and feed like ducklings under his supervision, before he abandons them at 11–14 days.

All three phalaropes are relatively common throughout most of their breeding range which, in the case of the Red-necked and Gray (Red) phalaropes, is usually well beyond any damaging human activities. However, in the case of the Wilson's phalarope some of its prairie marsh habitat is being drained.   GJT

Going Out with the Tide

Conservation of shorebirds

The streamlined shape, strong flight and often spectacular flock aerobatics of shorebirds are features related to their long-distance migrations and occupancy of wilderness areas such as coastlands and arctic tundra.

But the highly migratory nature of shorebirds (waders) poses its own problems for their survival. A single population of a species may depend, for example, on summer breeding areas in the Soviet Union, sites for feeding to deposit fat as fuel for migration in, say, Sweden or Poland, a molting area on the German or Dutch coast, and several sites used at different stages of the winter, in Britain and France. Arctic-breeding populations tend to suffer naturally from very variable breeding success, and it can therefore be difficult to estimate the quality of habitat they require in the non-breeding areas. The concentration of shorebirds from their widespread breeding areas to relatively small coastal and wetland sites at other times of the year makes them particularly vulnerable.

Drainage of wetlands and reclamation of coastal salt marshes has been a traditional activity around the coasts of Europe probably for 2,000 years, but modern technology has caused a drastic increase in the rate and nature of this change. Today reductions in intertidal habitat result from the increasing need for deepwater ports, and land for related industry, especially the development of North Sea oil, areas for waste disposal, tidal power projects, and water storage. Such developments, of course, occur throughout the world.

Paradoxically, the international scale of the problem has its advantages, in that international conventions encourage national governments to conserve sites. By 1983, for example, 34 countries had complied with the 1971 "Ramsar" Convention on Wetlands of International Importance especially as Waterfowl Habitat, which requires governments to conserve at least one designated site of international importance. The European Economic Community Directive on Conservation of Birds (1979) requires the designation of areas of habitat, especially wetlands, and recognizes the need for both further research and for updating, in the light of the findings, of its own provisions.

International protection measures came earlier in North America, and from different causes. The Treaty on Migratory Birds in 1916, between the USA and Canada (extended in 1936 to Mexico), was a response to excessive commercial hunting—some species (notably the Hudsonian godwit, *Limosa haemastica*) have still not recovered from its effects. Some species of waders can still be legally shot in Europe; restrictions vary between (and even within) countries. The pattern is similarly mixed in the areas of Africa used by some of these same populations: in parts of West Africa, important for waders, there is no local tradition of killing birds, while elsewhere in Africa, birds have long been an important food source. In the Far East, there are bilateral agreements on bird protection between two or more of the USA, the USSR, Japan and Australia, but uncontrolled hunting occurs in other areas.

When all the appropriate habitat at a site disappears then so do all the waders. However, sometimes only part of the habitat is lost to the birds (or "reclaimed" by man for industry, etc). When 60 percent of intertidal land was lost at Seal Sands, in the Tees estuary, northeast England, the resulting decreases in numbers of different shorebird species varied between 0 and 95 percent. This variation is related to the resulting changes in duration of tidal exposure and the differing feeding times required by various species, the adaptability of different species to using alternative feeding areas, especially at high water, the effects of the changes on numbers and sites of prey species, and alterations to the competitive balance between different bird species.

What happens to birds that are displaced—do they survive elsewhere, or die? In recent decades, snipe populations have been displaced by extensive drainage of the wet agricultural "polder" land in the Netherlands. Information on the numbers of snipes ringed and recovered reveals a shift of a main fall molting area from the Netherlands to Britain between the 1950s and the 1970s. However, corresponding numbers of birds may have been displaced from the new winter grounds, and it is possible that any reprieve was relatively short lived—a 1982–83 survey revealed a major and continuing loss of wet meadowland in Britain, again due to drainage.

The loss of wet meadowland and other pasture, often to the plow, is encouraged by agricultural policies in Europe, even where it is not by itself economically viable. This change is serious also for some breeding populations. For example, snipe, which were formerly widespread and common in the English and Welsh lowlands, were restricted by 1982–83 to about 2,000 pairs, half of them on only five sites. Similarly, afforestation of moorland areas is becoming a threat for upland-breeding shorebirds in

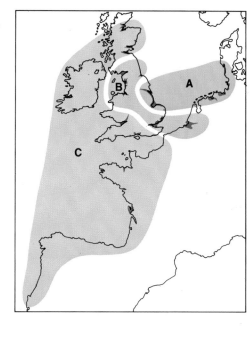

▲ **A flock of Marbled godwits** on their coastal wintering ground. Marbled godwits breed in west central Canada and winter along coasts south to Peru. Birds with white wing-bars and tails are willets (*Catoptrophorus semipalmatus*).

◄ **Uses and abuses of intertidal areas.** Coastal sites in northwestern Europe marked in red have been subject to major losses of the shorebirds' intertidal habitat induced by the activities of man, or are currently under threat.

Areas within broken lines illustrate the way in which one shorebird species, the dunlin, uses northwestern Europe as its major non-breeding area. Sites in area (**A**) are used in the fall, while the birds replace their summer plumage, before moving further east for the winter. The birds may return to use these sites in spring before moving on to their more northerly, or arctic, breeding areas. Sites in area (**C**) are mainly used in winter. Sites in area (**B**) are used extensively in both fall and winter, often by different birds. Individual birds depend on a sequence of sites. Loss of one site may affect populations at others.

some areas, including Britain. Recreational use of beaches, another principal breeding habitat in temperate regions, causes problems for species in Europe, North America and for some Southern Hemisphere species.

In arctic breeding areas, waders tend to be dispersed thinly over wide areas and damage from localized development is less likely. However, protected sites, where required, have to be extensive. Few major threats are known to breeding areas in the Arctic of the Old World or Greenland, though little information is available from the USSR. However, as oil-related developments increase in coastal areas of Alaska and arctic Canada, waders may face problems, as the tundra breeding habitat is very sensitive to any disturbance.

One recent conservation success has been in the Netherlands, where the delta of the Rhine, Meuse and Scheldt rivers has been progressively closed by barrages since the disastrous floods of 1953. Because of pressure from environmentalists and fisheries groups, the final closure was changed from a permanent dam to a closable tidal-surge barrier, allowing the Oosterscheldt estuary to remain tidal, albeit with a reduced tidal range and area.

On estuaries, at least, public demand can help mitigate adverse effects, and even enhance the areas for shorebirds. However, this requires the involvement of shorebird biologists early in the feasibility and planning stages of such projects—which is all too rare. Biologists can also assess, using counts and studies of shorebird movements, the areas where such developments can cause least damage to shorebird populations. MWP

JACANAS AND OTHER WADERS

Families: Jacanidae, Rostratulidae, Haematopodidae, Burhinidae, Glareolidae, Thinocoridae, Chionididae, Dromadidae
Order: Charadriiformes (suborder: Charadrii, part).
Forty-eight species in 19 genera.
Distribution: see maps and table.

Jacanas   **Crab plover**   **Oyster-catchers**

Seed snipes   **Sheathbills**   **Pratincoles**

Stone curlews   **Painted snipes**

ᴀ ʟᴏɴɢꜱɪᴅᴇ the more easily recognized shorebirds and waders of the order Charadriiformes (see preceding pages) are eight small families that are more wader- than duck- or tern-like, yet sufficiently different to be put in families separate from the sandpipers and plovers. Some, like the oystercatchers and painted snipes, are obviously shorebirds, with their long legs and long slender bills. But others, such as the seed snipes and sheathbills, are so different in appearance that their inclusion in the order (mainly on the basis of skull characters) comes at first as a surprise.

Jacanas are a small group of waterbirds characterized by their striking plumage and extremely long toes and claws, which enable them to walk with ease on floating vegetation and on the leaves of waterlilies (they are sometimes called "lily-trotters"). The seven species occur widely throughout the marshlands, rice fields and freshwater margins of the tropics. Though often quite abundant, they are often inconspicuous in the reedy vegetation despite their generally bold disposition and bright colors. Most have a fleshy shield above the bill, which is bright blue in the African jacana, pearly gray in the Madagascar jacana, livid red in the Bronze-winged jacana and lobed red or yellow in the American jacana; on the Comb-crested jacana it is yellow or red and developed into a vertical comb. All have short tails except for the Pheasant-tailed jacana, which in breeding plumage sports long central tail feathers which add 10in (25cm) to its normal 12in (30cm) length. All have a short spur, sharp or blunt, on the carpal joint of the wing.

All records indicate that jacanas have a mixed diet of predominantly aquatic insects, mollusks, and the occasional small fish and the seeds of aquatic plants. These are found as the birds stalk nimbly from leaf to leaf, occasionally jumping a patch of open water with the help of a flick of the wings.

In most species the breeding season is protracted and coincides with the local wet season, when insect food is more abundant. In all but the Smaller jacana the female is

◄▼► **Representative species of jacanas and other waders.** (1) Territorial "piping" display of Black oystercatchers (*Haematopus bachmani*). (2) Territorial display of female Painted snipe (*Rostratula benghalensis*). (3) Greeting posture of Stone curlew or thick-knee (*Burhinus oedicnemus*) in courtship. (4) An American jacana (*Jacana spinosa*) or "lily-trotter." (5) A Crab plover (*Dromas ardeola*) teaches its single young to hunt crabs; IN BACKGROUND, ABOVE Crab plovers return along an Indian Ocean coastline to their communal roosting site.

the larger and polyandry (females mating with more than one male) is commonplace. In the Pheasant-tailed and Bronze-winged jacanas polyandry appears to be the rule: in the African and American jacanas the type of habitat seems to influence whether mating is monogamous or polyandrous. For example, American jacanas breeding in uniform marshy habitats are monogamous, each pair inhabiting a relatively large territory. In areas containing scattered ponds in Mexico and Puerto Rico, females have 1–4 mates and while they take no part in incubating or rearing young they help defend the males' territories against intruders.

Even in the monogamous species the male performs all the duties of nest building, incubation and the care of the chicks. The exceptions are the Smaller jacana, in which both male and female bear brood patches, and the Comb-crested jacana in which both sexes tend the young.

Adaptations to a life in watery places include the Pheasant-tailed jacana's reported habit of incubating the eggs two under each wing, away from the water, and the ability of both adults and chicks of the African jacana to hide from predators by submerging, leaving only the bill and nostrils above water. Several species have been observed, when disturbed, to carry small young to safety under their wings or attempting to lure predators away with a "broken wing" display.

The intricate plumage of **painted snipes** is both extremely beautiful and a wonderful disruptive camouflage. The plumage of the South American bird is basically alike in the two sexes, while in the Old World species the slightly larger female is the gaudier. Both have broad, round wings, a characteristic rail-like flight and long bills, down-curved at the tip, with the nostrils set in deep narrow grooves that extend over half the bill's length.

Both species feed in typical wader fashion, probing soft soils and mud for insects and seeds, and they forage mostly at dawn and dusk, when they may leave the thicker vegetation to exploit open grassland and pasture.

So far as is known, the South American painted snipe is monogamous and territorial in its breeding habits. The better-studied Eurasian species is, however, generally polyandrous. Toward the beginning of the breeding season, females start their evening displays, calling from the ground or from a low display flight. The display call is a succession of low hooting notes which, thanks

▲▲ **Eurasian oystercatcher on its nest** LEFT and probing in sand for food ABOVE. Pied or black plumage and a blunt-ended, straight red bill are characteristic of all oystercatchers.

◄ **Long toes take the weight** of the African jacana, enabling it to "lily-trot" on floating vegetation.

to the birds' long, convoluted, resonating trachea, are audible from well over half a mile (1km) away. In this way the female claims a territory for herself and attracts male birds. Intruding females are repelled with a display in which the wings are outstretched and turned forward to show the spotted flight feathers. Later on, when competition for males intensifies, females may actually fight to defend their mates from the advances of rivals. Females take the initiative in courting, circling the male in the spread-wing posture and giving a melodious "boo" call, reminiscent of the sound made by blowing across the neck of a bottle. After mating, the male builds a nest into which the female lays her eggs before leaving to court other males. Her progress is rapid and the next clutch is usually laid before the first hatches.

The males are not territorial and those mated to a single female usually nest quite close together. The chicks can run as soon as they are dry and are fed and brooded solely by the male, who may give the spread-wing threat display to distract or deter predators or human intruders. After breeding, small flocks comprising two or more males and their broods may form before the birds finally disperse.

The **oystercatchers** are a very uniform family characterized by their long, straight, blunt-ended red bills, pied or black plumage and relatively short legs. Their taxonomy is

rather confused and up to 11 species and 21 subspecies are recognized by some authorities. All are coastal, though the wholly black species (Sooty, Black and Blackish) generally prefer rocky shorelines to the sandy or muddy ones favored by the others. Though not at all well studied, they all appear similar in their habits. The following details, based mainly on the Eurasian species, are probably typical.

Oystercatchers are gregarious and flock throughout the year, except while breeding, when pairs take up territories on beaches, on fields near the coast or occasionally inland by lakes and rivers. They do not breed until between three and five years of age but usually form pairs earlier than this, non-breeding birds roosting in flocks during the breeding season. Territories are proclaimed and boundaries contested by means of a ritualized "piping display" in which a bird stands at its territory boundary, neck arched and bill pointed downward, and gives a succession of piping notes. The display normally attracts the owners of adjacent territories and up to 10 pairs may gather and display either standing or rushing up and down. A version of this display may also be given on the wing and is perhaps the most familiar sight for a casual intruder in oystercatcher territory.

Usually, three eggs are laid in a scrape and are brooded by both parents. Predation rates are often high and several replacement clutches in a season are common. The chicks can run within a short while of hatching, but due to the oystercatcher's specialized diet they are unable to feed themselves and must follow the parents who forage for them. The first chick to hatch is fed first and soon a size hierarchy develops in which the largest chick has first refusal of any food the parents offer.

Adult oystercatchers feed mainly on various types of bivalve mollusks, both surface-dwelling species such as mussels and those, such as cockles, which live buried in the sand. Two main methods of opening these prey are used. Should the bird be able to surprise an open shell, either by stalking it on the surface or probing in the sand, the bill is driven in between the shell halves. The adductor muscle which holds together the shell halves is cut with a scissor-like bill action and the flesh is chiselled or shaken out of the defenseless mollusk. If the shell halves are closed, one side may be broken into by hammering with the bill, and the flesh removed. Individual birds tend to specialize on one particular type of prey and develop their own technique for consuming

Female Casanovas—Polyandry in Waders

In several of the shorebird and wader families, notably among the jacanas, painted snipes, and phalaropes, the roles of male and female are reversed. One female takes a number of mates and leaves them to incubate the eggs and rear the young. This breeding system, called polyandry, is very rare in birds and has been reported regularly or occasionally in only thirteen families comprising less than one percent of all bird species. The rarity of polyandry attests to the rarity of the pressures required for its evolution, and much about it remains a mystery.

The young of many bird species stay in the nest and require the efforts of both parents to feed them. However, in more primitive species, whose precocious young leave the nest and feed themselves, it is possible for just one parent to guard them. One parent may thus have the opportunity to desert its mate and breed again without fear of its first brood dying. The deserted partner must of course remain with its young or lose all of its offspring. Since natural selection tends to favor individuals with the ability to produce large numbers of offspring that survive to

breeding age, desertion will be beneficial only if the deserter gets more matings and if its original mate assumes entire responsibility for the young it is left with. Since the female lays the eggs and in most birds is the partner required for most of the incubation, most species show little possibility for the development of polyandry. What factors might act to result in the female playing the Casanova?

One factor that facilitates polyandry is that the male should spend more time incubating than the female. It may be that poor food supply obliges the female to continue feeding in order to recoup the reserves of energy lost in egg laying, or heavy predation on eggs and chicks may force females to feed to gather reserves for repeat clutches. A further requirement is a surplus of males in the population for females to mate with. Certainly among shorebirds and waders, whose eggs are laid in the open, predation pressures are often very high. Once the polyandrous system starts, females may evolve conventional "male" characters, such as gaudy plumage and large size in order to compete better with other females for males.

it. Young oystercatchers may rely on their parents for food for months before learning the basic techniques and may eventually acquire their parents' own peculiar methods and prey preferences. It may be as long as two years after independence before they are sufficiently skilled to survive on mussels alone and during this period they feed extensively on ragworms and other invertebrates found on mudflats and fields by the coast.

The sole representative of its family, the **Crab plover** is instantly recognizable by its massive bill and pied plumage. Like a cross between an avocet and an oversized plover, this curious, little-studied bird inhabits sandy beaches and mudflats of the African and Asian coasts of the Indian Ocean. When walking, the long neck is often carried hunched between the shoulders, giving a silhouette that is somewhat gull-like but made distinctive by the long wader legs with their short toes and partial webs.

Crab plovers are highly gregarious at all seasons and usually feed in flocks of 20 or more searching the intertidal zone for the crabs which are their staple food. Once captured, a crab is easily broken by the powerful bill and swallowed. Crab plovers tend to be nocturnal, as they feed on tropical fiddler crabs which emerge in numbers at dusk to feed and find mates.

Crab plovers breed colonially and thousands may congregate in an area of just a few thousand square yards (up to about 0.6 ha). Colonies are confined to areas of sand and dunes in which the nesting burrows may be excavated. The birds dig a tunnel up to 6.6ft (2m) long, using both bill and feet, and enlarge a chamber at the end in which the single egg is laid. This feature is surprising in a long-legged bird, and unique among shorebirds. Unusually for a shorebird, the chicks remain in the nest until well after they are full grown, possibly as a precaution against predation by the crabs that will later be their prey. Food is brought to them by both parents. After leaving the nest, young birds apparently take some time to acquire the skills necessary to successfully tackle an angry crab. They accompany their parents, begging for food and often standing by, watching them capture a crab, as though unsure of which is the predator and which the prey.

Outside the breeding season the gregarious habit persists, large flocks forming to fly to and from the traditional roosting sites. On several occasions flocks have been observed to gather to mob a human hunter who has shot one of their number.

Stone curlews' alternative name of thickknees derives from their especially knobbly leg joints, but the most striking feature about their appearance is their large, piercing yellow, hawkish eyes which stare out from under pronounced eyebrows and fit them well for evening and night-time activity.

▼► **Representative species of waders**
CONTINUED. (1) Least seed snipe (*Thinocorus rumicivorus*) performing "butterfly" display flight. (2) A Cream-colored courser (*Cursorius cursor*) at the run. (3) Collared pratincole (*Glareola pratincola*) in "broken wing" display. (4) Egyptian plover (*Pluvianus aegyptius*) performing wing-raising display used to greet mate. (5) Snowy or Yellow-billed sheathbills (*Chionis alba*) harassing Chinstrap penguin for the krill it is bringing to its young.

Stone curlews are a fairly uniform family, all having cryptic brown plumage heavily streaked with brown and black above, pale underparts and pronounced white wing-bars shown in flight. The two *Esacus* species are plainer above and pale below and have prominent black markings about the eye and crown. All have stout to massive bills, well able to cope with their varied diet of insects, crustaceans, mollusks and small vertebrates. They are terrestrial birds and run swiftly, flying low only when necessary, with their long legs trailing behind. Typically they inhabit dry open country and semi-desert, though the Water thick-knee and Senegal thick-knee favor lake and river margins, and the Great and Beach stone curlews frequent coasts. Out of the breeding season they often gather in small groups.

When breeding, pairs of most species take up territories in open areas that are free of vegetation and afford a good view in all directions. The European species defends its territory with an aggressive display in which the bird draws itself into as upright a position as possible, body almost vertical, fanned tail pointing downwards and folded wings held away from the body. Pairs collaborate in territorial defense and the period

during which a territory is established may be prolonged. The courtship posture is quite the opposite, the pair standing together with necks arched and bills pointed downward.

The eggs are laid in a scrape in the ground and incubated by both birds in turn, the off-duty parent usually standing guard nearby, watching out behind its sitting partner. The chicks can stand and walk by the second day and disperse from the nest soon thereafter. The parents feed them for the first few days and they gradually learn to feed themselves. If danger threatens, the parents may pick up small chicks in their bill and carry them to a hiding place. Distraction displays are not common but when they are given are very strenuous, the bird jumping and falling fluttering to the ground to roll with extended wings and hissing cries.

In Europe, the Stone curlew is now much reduced in numbers due to loss of suitable habitat and increasing disturbance. Stone curlews require open ground and absolute freedom from human activity, and such places are becoming increasingly rare.

The **pratincoles and coursers** are distinct groups within the family Glareolidae, which also contains the rather anomalous Egyptian plover and Australian dotterel. The Egyptian plover is usually considered to be a closer relative of the coursers, while some include the Australian dotterel with the pratincoles and others place it in another family altogether, the true plovers (Charadriidae).

Pratincoles are wonderful flyers, their long pointed wings, forked tails and agile flight in pursuit of winged insects being reminiscent of swifts. However, they also feed on insects on the ground and are fast runners. The Long-legged pratincole is the odd one out and is mainly terrestrial in its habits. Pratincoles favor flat open country, both near water and in more arid areas, where there is an abundant supply of insect food. They are gregarious, forming flocks both inside and outside the breeding season, and nest in small, loose colonies within which each pair maintains its own territory. The chicks stay in or near the nest for 2–3 days, fed by both parents, after which they gradually learn to feed themselves. As in other waders, elaborate "broken wing" displays are commonly given by the parent to lure predators from their chicks.

The coursers, with their longer legs, short tails and characteristic upright stance, are running birds which take flight only if forced. Their cryptic sandy plumage is plainer than the pratincoles', though many sport conspicuous black-and-white eye stripes. They favor arid and desert areas and are also gregarious, gathering in flocks and family parties after breeding. Poorly known, they appear to be monogamous and territorial, both parents tending the young which stay with them until well after fledging.

The Egyptian plover is a beautiful and striking bird with blue-gray wings, orange belly and bold black-and-white marking on the head. It prefers the margins of inland lakes and rivers and neighboring fields and grasslands, feeding on insects and invertebrates taken on the ground, particularly at the water's edge. They are extremely tame and often frequent the vicinity of human habitations. Old stories that they feed on the scraps left between the teeth of basking crocodiles make good telling, but have never been properly authenticated! Though they may flock outside the breeding season they are basically solitary, nesting in pairs in territories. Members of a pair greet each other on landing with an elaborate wing-raising display in which the beautiful wing markings are shown to advantage. When leaving the nest, the incubating bird buries its eggs in the sand, smoothing over the side so that the nest is completely invisible. This is still done if the bird is surprised, though haste makes for a less than perfect job. Newly hatched chicks receive the same treatment and are covered totally with sand. Should the eggs become too hot, they are cooled with water gathered in the adult's belly feathers. Very young chicks are cooled in the same way and may also drink from the soaked feathers. Distraction displays are not common but adults may feign a broken wing on occasion. The chicks feed themselves from the outset but must be shown food to start with.

The squat, short-legged, short-billed **seed snipes** are, with the sheathbills, perhaps the least wader-like of the shorebird-related families. The two *Thinocorus* species are more like larks or buntings, while the *Attagis* species most resemble small partridges. The Least seed snipe prefers the arid coastal and dune areas and inland dry plains of lower altitudes. The White-bellied and Gray-breasted seed snipes range further into the higher, dry slopes of the Andes, and the Rufous-bellied species favors wetter moorland in the high mountain pastures. They are all fast-running, ground-dwelling birds, and tend to be gregarious, often gathering in coveys like partridges. Their short, stout bills are an adaptation to their mainly seed diet, though cactus buds and the succulent parts of growing plants are also eaten. Their plumage is generally cryptic, with brown feathers edged with black and buff above, but the Gray-breasted and Least seed snipes have a gray forehead and black and buff markings on the sides of the head and neck which are more pronounced in the male than the female.

Males of the two *Thinocorus* species take up territories and perform a display flight reminiscent of a lark, flying up then gliding down on stiff wings giving a rapid staccato song. The ascent of the Least seed snipe is higher than that of the Gray-breasted and the display lasts rather longer. Both species may also sing from a perch and the Least seed snipe has been observed performing a "butterfly" flight, beating its wings in a stiff, exaggerated manner.

In all but one species the buff or cream eggs with darker markings blend with the dry stony soil by the scrape. The dark olive

▲ **A Water thick-knee** (or dikkop) confronts a monitor lizard.

◄ **A Long-legged or Australian pratincole** broods its young on the simple scrape that is its nest.

and black eggs of the White-bellied seed snipe are better camouflaged for the mossy soils of its heathland habitat. In the *Thinocorus* species, and probably the others also, the female alone incubates, kicking loose material over the eggs to hide them if she wants to leave the nest or is disturbed. In the latter case she may use a distraction display, fluttering low over the ground or trailing a wing. The young are very precocious and feed themselves soon after hatching. Both parents guard them and the male, too, may use distraction displays, running to and fro with hunched back and drooping wings to lure intruders away.

For some European people, the first time they heard of the strange Antarctic **sheathbills** was the discovery of a lone stowaway on a British troopship returning from the Falkland Islands in 1982. The two species are closely similar in appearance and habits but geographically separated. The slightly larger Black-faced sheathbill is resident on some of the remotest sub-antarctic islands, while the Snowy sheathbill breeds in the Antarctic but migrates, in rather random fashion, to the Falklands and coasts of Argentina during the southern winter.

These are indeed peculiar birds, forming a possible evolutionary link between the shorebirds and the gulls. They share certain anatomical features with both groups and have a rudimentary spur on the carpal joint of the wing—a typical plover feature. They have a bald patch around the eye and naked carbuncled skin above the pale yellow (Snowy sheathbill) or black (Black-faced species) bill. The bill is broad and strong with a horny sheath which partially covers the nostrils. The plumage is white, the flight pigeon-like, the gait like that of a rail and the general behavior like a crow or gull. They are terrestrial by preference but will fly if forced or when on migration.

Sheathbills are opportunistic feeders and their diet is very varied. In winter they boldly frequent the rubbish heaps of whaling stations and antarctic survey bases, scavenging offal and household scraps as well as feeding among seaweed for intertidal invertebrates. When the seals come to breed, like crows at lambing they grow fat on stillborn pups and the afterbirths. In their own breeding season they turn for food to the large colonies of breeding penguins. Pairs of sheathbills take up territories, containing a number of penguins, which they defend vigorously from other sheathbills, and harass the penguins in order to steal the krill they bring for their chicks. Pairs often join forces to surprise the adult penguin, drive off the chick and scoop up the krill as it is regurgitated. This rich food is ideally suited for the rapidly growing sheathbill chicks, which wait at the nest to be fed. Penguin eggs are also stolen, and adult sheathbills feed extensively on penguin droppings. The penguins clearly resent these depredations and may lunge out with their bills. However, they generally make little impression on the bold and agile sheathbills.

After fledging, the young disperse to the shoreline to scavenge for scraps of fish, limpets and kelp. Because of their messy feeding habits, sheathbills take great pains to keep clean, and they spend a considerable proportion of their time in bathing and preening. They have no obvious predators, except for the odd egg lost to other sheathbills, and share with skuas the easy life afforded to scavengers in an area so rich in food resources.   ASR

FAMILIES OF JACANAS AND OTHER WADERS

Jacanas

Family: Jacanidae
Seven species in 6 genera.

Africa S of Sahara, India, SE Asia, New Guinea, N Australia, C and S America. Marshes, still and slow-moving water covered in floating vegetation. Size: length 6–12in (15–30cm), except Pheasant-tailed jacana (see text); weight 1.4–8.1oz (40–230g); female larger than male in most species. Plumage: striking; mostly black and white on head and neck; upperparts various chestnut browns, often darker below and with white on flight feathers; sexes similar. Voice: generally noisy, with variety of high, staccato, squawking calls. Nests: simple, of aquatic leaves, usually on floating vegetation or raised platforms; occasionally, partially submerged. Eggs: normally 3–4, highly polished with dark spots, streaks and lines; incubation about 21–26 days; fledging period several weeks at least. Diet: insects and seeds of aquatic plants.

Species: **African jacana** or **lily-trotter** (*Actophilornis africana*), **American jacana** (*Jacana spinosa*), **Bronze-winged jacana** (*Metopidius indicus*), **Comb-crested jacana** (*Irediparra gallinacea*), **Madagascar jacana** (*Actophilornis albinucha*), **Pheasant-tailed jacana** (*Hydrophasianus chirurgus*), **Smaller jacana** (*Microparra capensis*).

Painted snipes

Family: Rostratulidae
Two species in 2 genera.

Africa, India, SE Asia, Australia, southern S America. Swamps, marshes, rice paddies. Size: length 8–10in (20–26cm), weight 2.7–5.8oz 76–165g), females slightly larger than males. Plumage: brown and chestnut, marked with black and buff above and white or cream below. Prominent buff stripes on head and across shoulders. Striking round yellow spots on wing feathers. Voice: soft booming notes, growls and hisses. Nest: simple cup of stems and leaves hidden on ground in tall vegetation. Eggs: 2–4, cream to yellow-buff, heavily spotted with black and brown; 0.5oz (13g); incubation 19 days. Young are nidifugous. Diet: insects, earthworms, snails and seeds.

Species: **Painted snipe** (*Rostratula benghalensis*), **South American painted snipe** (*Nycticryphes semicollaris*).

Oystercatchers

Family: Haematopodidae
Six species of the genus *Haematopus*.

Europe, Asia, Africa, Australia, N and S America except in high latitudes. All types of coast and fresh and brackish waters and marshlands. Size: length 14.6–17.7in (37–45cm), weight 15–27.2oz (425–770g). Plumage; pied or uniform black; sexes alike. Voice: wide variety of simple and complex piping calls. Nest: shallow scrape in sand or shingle, generally unlined. Eggs: 2–3 (range 1–5), brown or gray with black, gray and brown spots and streaks; generally 1.4–1.8oz (40–50g); incubation 24–27 days; fledging period 28–32 days (Eurasian oystercatcher). Diet: chiefly bivalve mollusks; also limpets, crabs, worms, echinoderms (starfishes, sea urchins).

Species: **American oystercatcher** (*Haematopus palliatus*), **Blackish oystercatcher** (*H. ater*), **Black oystercatcher** (*H. bachmani*), **Eurasian oystercatcher** (*H. ostralegus*), **Magellanic oystercatcher** (*H. leucopodus*), **Sooty oystercatcher** (*H. fuliginosus*). Total threatened species: 1.

Crab plover

Family: Dromadidae
Sole species *Dromas ardeola*.

Africa, Madagascar, Middle East, India, Sri Lanka. Tropical coastlines of sand dunes, mudflats, coral reefs and estuaries. Size: length 13–14in (33–36cm); weight about 8.8–11.5oz (250–325g). Plumage: white with black back and primary feathers; sexes alike. Voice: noisy with variety of harsh, barking calls and sharp whistles. Nest: unlined hollow at end of tunnel in the sand. Eggs: 1, occasionally 2, white; about 1.6oz (45g); incubation and fledging periods not known. Diet: chiefly crabs, also mollusks, worms and other invertebrates.

Stone curlews

Family: Burhinidae
Nine species in 2 genera.
Stone curlews, thick-knees, stone plovers or dikkops

Europe, Africa, Asia, Australasia, S America. Sparsely vegetated open country, near water or in more arid regions, steppe, deserts, mudflats, savanna and open coastlines and estuaries. Size: length 12.6–21.7in (32–55cm); weight up to 2.2lb (1kg). Plumage: pale sandy browns above, streaked black; pale streaked breast and whitish underparts; sexes alike. Voice: wailing bi-syllabic whistles given communally at dusk, and variety of other hoarse, rasping calls, hissing and creaking sounds. Nests: shallow scrape in soil, shingle or sand, unlined or lined with debris. Eggs: generally 2, creamy white, ocher, buff, pale brown or brownish-gray marked with brown, black and purplish-gray spots and blotches; in Stone curlew, average 1.3oz (38g), incubation 24–27 days, fledging 36–42 days. Diet: terrestrial invertebrates, small vertebrates (frogs, rodents), crabs and mollusks in coastal species.

Species: **Beach stone curlew** (*Esacus magnirostris*), **Double-striped thick-knee** (*Burhinus bistriatus*), **Great stone curlew** (*E. recurvirostris*), **Peruvian thick-knee** (*B. superciliaris*), **Senegal thick-knee** (*B. senegalensis*), **Southern stone curlew** (*B. magnirostris*), **Spotted thick-knee** or **Cape dikkop** (*B. capensis*), **Stone curlew** (*B. oedicnemus*), **Water thick-knee** or **dikkop** (*B. vermiculatus*).

Pratincoles and coursers

Family: Glareolidae
Seventeen species in 4 genera.

Europe, Asia, Africa, Australasia. Open or scrub country, generally in arid regions. Plumage: pratincoles generally brown above with white rump and belly; many have colored throats bordered with black. Coursers generally cryptic buffs and sandy browns; many have bold black markings on head and breast; sexes alike. Nest: unlined or sparsely lined scrape in sand or gravel. Eggs: 2–3 (occasionally 1, 4 or 5), yellow-brown, cream or buff, speckled with black, brown and gray; generally about 0.5oz (15g) where known; incubation 17–31 days; fledging period 25–35 days where known. Diet: chiefly insects, occasionally other invertebrates.

Species: **Australian dotterel** (*Peltohyas australis*), **Black-winged pratincole** (*Glareola nordmanni*), **Collared pratincole** (*G. pratincola*), **Cream-colored courser** (*Cursorius cursor*), **Eastern collared pratincole** (*Glareola maldivarum*), **Egyptian plover** (*Pluvianus aegyptius*), **Gray pratincole** (*Glareola cinerea*), **Heuglin's courser** (*Cursorius cinctus*), **Indian courser** (*C. coromandelicus*), **Jerdon's courser** (*C. bitorquatus*, possibly extinct); **Little pratincole** (*Glareola lactea*), **Long-legged pratincole** (*G. isabella*), **Madagascar pratincole** (*G. ocularis*), **Temminck's courser** (*Cursorius temminkii*), **Two-banded courser** (*C. africanus*), **Violet-tipped courser** (*C. chalcopterus*), **White-collared pratincole** (*Glareola nuchalis*).

Seed snipes

Family: Thinocoridae
Four species in 2 genera.

Montane western S America. Open country (except Least seed snipe). Size: length 7.5–12in (19–30cm); weight 2.1–8.8oz (60–250g). Plumage: generally various browns above, marked with black, gray and cinnamon; females like males but less strongly marked. Voice: song a series of rapid tri-syllabic notes, also short, rasping and peeping alarm calls. Nests: scrape in the ground lined with any available loose material. Eggs: 4, buff or cream, speckled dark brown and lilac or olive, blotched with black; incubation about 25 days; young nidifugous; fledging 49–55 days (in Least seed snipe). Diet: seeds and succulent vegetation.

Species: **Gray-breasted seed snipe** (*Thinocorus orbignyianus*), and **Least seed snipe** (*T. rumicivorus*); **Rufous-bellied seed snipe** (*Attagis gayi*), **White-bellied seed snipe** (*A. malouinus*).

Sheathbills

Family: Chionididae
Two species of the genus *Chionis*.

Antarctic and sub-Antarctic islands. Coasts. Size: length 15–16in (38–41cm); weight 10.3–19.4oz (290–550g). Plumage: entirely white; sexes alike. Voice: harsh crow-like calls and guttural, rattling croaks. Nests: in crevice in rocks or in former petrel burrow; may be lined with stones, debris, seaweed or lichen. Eggs: 2, sometimes 3 or 4, white or grayish with dark brown blotches; incubation 28–32 days, fledging 50–60 days. Diet: omnivorous, opportunist feeders and scavengers.

Species: **Black-faced sheathbill** (*Chionis minor*), **Snowy sheathbill** (*C. alba*).

► **Wet and bedraggled,** a recently hatched American jacana chick drying out on leaves of waterlilies in a Brazilian rain forest.

GULLS, TERNS AND SKUAS

Families: Laridae, Sternidae, Stercorariidae, Rynchopidae
Order: Charadriiformes (suborder: Lari).
Ninety-five species in 15 genera.
Distribution: see maps and table.

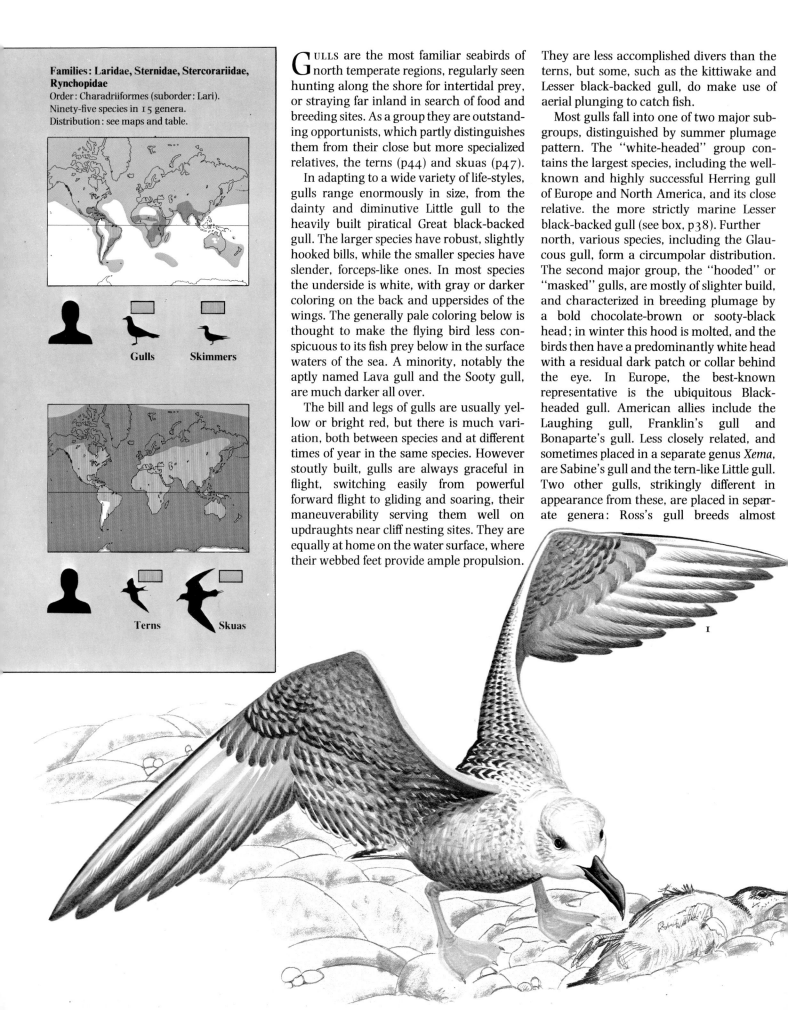

Gulls   **Skimmers**

Terns   **Skuas**

Gulls are the most familiar seabirds of north temperate regions, regularly seen hunting along the shore for intertidal prey, or straying far inland in search of food and breeding sites. As a group they are outstanding opportunists, which partly distinguishes them from their close but more specialized relatives, the terns (p44) and skuas (p47).

In adapting to a wide variety of life-styles, gulls range enormously in size, from the dainty and diminutive Little gull to the heavily built piratical Great black-backed gull. The larger species have robust, slightly hooked bills, while the smaller species have slender, forceps-like ones. In most species the underside is white, with gray or darker coloring on the back and uppersides of the wings. The generally pale coloring below is thought to make the flying bird less conspicuous to its fish prey below in the surface waters of the sea. A minority, notably the aptly named Lava gull and the Sooty gull, are much darker all over.

The bill and legs of gulls are usually yellow or bright red, but there is much variation, both between species and at different times of year in the same species. However stoutly built, gulls are always graceful in flight, switching easily from powerful forward flight to gliding and soaring, their maneuverability serving them well on updraughts near cliff nesting sites. They are equally at home on the water surface, where their webbed feet provide ample propulsion.

They are less accomplished divers than the terns, but some, such as the kittiwake and Lesser black-backed gull, do make use of aerial plunging to catch fish.

Most gulls fall into one of two major subgroups, distinguished by summer plumage pattern. The "white-headed" group contains the largest species, including the well-known and highly successful Herring gull of Europe and North America, and its close relative. the more strictly marine Lesser black-backed gull (see box, p38). Further north, various species, including the Glaucous gull, form a circumpolar distribution. The second major group, the "hooded" or "masked" gulls, are mostly of slighter build, and characterized in breeding plumage by a bold chocolate-brown or sooty-black head; in winter this hood is molted, and the birds then have a predominantly white head with a residual dark patch or collar behind the eye. In Europe, the best-known representative is the ubiquitous Black-headed gull. American allies include the Laughing gull, Franklin's gull and Bonaparte's gull. Less closely related, and sometimes placed in a separate genus *Xema*, are Sabine's gull and the tern-like Little gull. Two other gulls, strikingly different in appearance from these, are placed in separate genera: Ross's gull breeds almost

exclusively in northeast Siberia and is unique in having rosy-pink plumage on the head and underparts, as well as a black collar instead of a complete hood; also confined to the high Arctic is the Ivory gull, resplendent in its all-over pure white plumage.

Although the gulls enjoy a worldwide distribution, the largest concentrations occur in the Northern Hemisphere, where they have succeeded in colonizing the harshest of marine environments. The Ivory gull, for example, breeds in the presence of pack ice and snow where none but the hardiest vegetation survives. Although gulls are well represented in temperate and subtemperate latitudes, they are more sparsely distributed in the tropics; this has been attributed to a relative lack of shore food. Although most gulls live on or near the coast throughout much of the year, others live deep in the heart of the continents. The Great black-headed gull and the rare Relict gull thus breed on islands in the inland seas and lakes of the central Asian steppes, many hundreds of miles from the nearest ocean.

At the end of the breeding season, when adherence to a colony on land is no longer required, many gulls disperse into offshore waters and some, like the kittiwake, then lead a truly open-sea (pelagic) existence, British-bred birds journeying as far as the coasts of Canada. While there may be a strong random element in such dispersal, birds often congregate at food-rich cold-water upwellings at the edge of continental shelves. Compared with the terns and skuas, however, rather few gull species are true migrants. A notable exception is Sabine's gull, which has a circumpolar breeding distribution but at the end of summer migrates

◄▲► **Representative species of gulls.**
(1) Great black-backed gull (*Larus marinus*), largest of all gulls, in first-winter plumage, scavenging on a dead razorbill. (2) Kittiwake or Black-legged kittiwake juvenile (*Rissa tridactyla*). (3) Ivory gull (*Pagophila eburnea*) in first-winter plumage. (4) Little gull (*Larus minutus*) juvenile, world's smallest gull. (5) Sabine's gull (*L. sabini*) on nest. (6) Ross's gull (*Rhodostethia rosea*). (7) Swallow-tailed gull (*Creagrus furcatus*) of the Galapagos and La Plata Islands (Ecuador), said by some to be world's most beautiful gull.

south through the Atlantic and Pacific to winter off Africa and South America; the bulk of the Atlantic migrants cross the Equator and make for the productive Benguela Current off Namibia and South Africa. Gales in the fall not uncommonly blow Sabine's gulls towards the British coast, where enthusiastic bird-watchers delight in identifying these rare and elegant visitors. Some species regularly migrate overland, like Franklin's gull, which passes in the spring and fall over the Great Plains of North America.

Outside the breeding season, gulls typically continue to be highly gregarious, often assembling in massive flocks for feeding, roosting and bathing. The favored roosting sites are extensive open areas that offer a good all-round view for early detection of ground predators. Gulls often loaf on the flat expanses of airfields, where they can present a serious obstacle to low-flying aircraft.

All gulls can store substantial quantities of food in their crops, from which they regurgitate when feeding mates or young. Birds usually settle at their night roosts with full crops, and leisurely digestion follows. Indigestible parts of the meal are periodically disgorged in the form of pellets. Analysis of these gives a good idea of the diet.

Gulls have a range of feeding habits unparalleled in almost any other group of birds. In the Arctic, for example, where there is a limited variety of prey, Glaucous and Ivory gulls regularly eat the feces of marine mammals, and also associate with whales to exploit the invertebrates they force to the surface. Swallow-tailed gulls are exceptional among gulls in feeding entirely at night, their large eyes apparently helping them to detect and capture fish or squid. In temperate latitudes, the flexibility and ingenuity of foraging habits is just as striking. Herring gulls and their kin smash open shellfish by carrying them to a height and dropping them onto the rocks below.

Many Herring gulls have, during the course of this century, cashed in on the abundance of food offal on garbage dumps, and in consequence have increased remarkably in numbers during recent years. Gulls which breed inland also enjoy a wide variety of natural foodstuffs, the smaller species such as Little and Franklin's gulls dipping tern-like to pluck insects as small as midges from the water or land. Many species follow the plow for earthworms and other soil creatures. The Lesser black-backed gull, which is essentially a fish-eating species, in some places includes large numbers of

worms in its diet. In the fall, stubble grain provides a valuable bonus on agricultural land.

The larger gulls often prey on birds and mammals that share their breeding stations. The Glaucous gull is an important predator of Little auks, while the Great black-backed gull plunders a wide variety of seabirds, notably puffins, and can dispatch a good-sized rabbit. Gulls have also learned, skua-like, to harry other seabirds, forcing them to disgorge their food; terns which share colony space with, for example, Black-headed or Silver gulls, regularly suffer from such piracy. Sometimes gulls shadow foraging ducks, cormorants or pelicans, and rob them as soon as they surface with prey. In the same way, Black-headed and Common gulls are frequently found in fields among flocks of lapwings, which are greatly superior in the art of locating and extracting earthworms; the gulls are quick to pounce on a successful lapwing to relieve it of its worm. In Australia, the Silver gull has begun to forage on plowed fields far inland, repeating a pattern found in other parts of the world where man has developed arable farming on a significant scale.

In most regions, gulls breed once a year during a well-defined season that corresponds with the summer flush of food in the environment. In the tropics, where the food supply is less seasonal, more complex patterns may occur. The Swallow-tailed gull, for example, is known to breed in every month of the year; pairs that raise young successfully will mount another breeding attempt 9–10 months later, unsuccessful

▲ **A Dolphin gull** (*Larus scoresbii*) feeds on mussels on the shores of the Falkland Islands.

▶ **Loud and clear,** the call of the abundant Herring gull can be heard along the coasts, in the harbors, and on the garbage dumps, lakes and rivers of North America and Eurasia and into North Africa and Arabia. Its large gape enables it to swallow surprisingly large prey such as mackerel and herring.

"Nature" *and* "Nurture" Set Species Apart

The Herring gull and the Lesser black-backed gull are two distinct species: they are dissimilar and they do not normally interbreed when they occur together. However, the two do illustrate how closely related species may be induced to interbreed if the recogniton barriers which separate them are broken down.

During the ice ages of the Pleistocene epoch, 2 million to 10,000 years ago, the ancestors of today's Herring gull diversified, as a result of being isolated into a number of refuges separated by extensive ice sheets. A yellow-legged form confined to Central Asia later gave rise to the Lesser black-backed gull, while a pink-legged form spread from northwest Asia via North America to Europe, where it came into contact with Lesser black-backed gulls. By this time, however, the Herring gull had diverged in ecology and behavior to such an extent that the two did not readily interbreed.

Today, Lesser black-backed gulls differ from Herring gulls in Britain not only in appearance but also in being more migratory, and, to a lesser extent, in diet. How influential is nature as opposed to nurture in maintaining these differences and keeping the species distinct? In an experiment designed to explore this question, eggs in a mixed colony were interchanged between nests of the two species. On hatching, the resulting Herring gull chicks were raised by Lesser black-backed parents, and vice versa. There was not much change in the migratory tendencies of the cross-fostered gulls. However, their breeding habits were markedly affected. On reaching adulthood, many of the fostered young, especially females, mated up with a member of the "wrong" species, and successfully raised hybrid young. Thus the isolating mechanisms between the two species may fail if the young of each are brought up to "think" that they belong to the other species. EKD

birds sooner still. In southwest Australia, the Silver gull may breed twice a year, in spring and fall, an apparently unique pattern.

Gulls are generally monogamous and usually pair for as long as both members survive. However, in species such as the kittiwake, divorce is not uncommon, especially among inexperienced birds, and individuals will seek a new mate if the existing pair-bond proves unfruitful. As the breeding season approaches, gulls typically assemble in large, dense colonies, frequently reclaiming their nest site of the previous year. Many species breed on cliff ledges or atop coastal islands, while inland species often seek the safety of a marsh. Common gulls may build their nests on the stump or fork of a tree up to 33ft (10m) above the ground, also not uncommonly on stone walls and buildings. In keeping with their growing use of man's domain, Herring gulls are also favoring rooftops, chimney stacks, etc. The kittiwake, a gull of the open seas for much of the year, also sometimes adopts a window ledge as a substitute for its usual cliff-nesting habitat. The Gray gull breeds in one of the most inhospitable habitats chosen by any bird— the hot, arid deserts of Peru and Chile— while Ivory gulls sometimes nest on stony patches on ice floes.

The density of nesting depends partly on the local food supply. In temperate regions, where fish stocks are high in summer, many gull species breed in huge colonies, siting their nests only 3 feet or so from one another, and defending a territory little larger than the nest itself. Such gulls are notably successful in ousting smaller competitors from their nesting space, and populations on the increase often completely expel less competitive seabirds from

islands. On the Isle of May, in Scotland, where Herring gulls increased from a solitary pair in 1907 to over 14,000 pairs in the space of 60 years, terns were forced to abandon the island as a breeding site. Where the food supply is less plentiful, gulls may nest much more sparsely. In an extreme case, Lava gulls, which number about 300–400 pairs and occur only on the Galapagos Islands, typically nest over 1.9mi (3km) from each other.

In species which nest densely, there is much rivalry as the pairs stake out territories at the start of the breeding season; males are the main aggressors, but the females also join in. Gulls command an impressive repertoire of aggressive and appeasement displays and calls during these contests. Although prolonged fights sometimes take place, most of this behavior is ritualized and injuries are avoided. Black-headed gulls, for example, regularly avert their heads ("head-flagging") when squaring up to one another, so hiding the provocative black mask and bill. Rival Herring gull males may symbolically tug and tear at the vegetation along a contested territorial boundary, then each may claim victory by throwing their heads back and "long-calling" vociferously, before resuming hostilities. Such shows of strength also attract females, which typically approach bachelor males tentatively in a submissive cowed posture. Once accepted by the male, the female is fed by the male as a prelude to egg-laying.

The clutch is typically 2–3; the tropical Swallow-tailed gull is unique in laying only one egg. Both sexes share incubation, changing over several times each day until the eggs hatch, usually after about four weeks. The emerging young are mobile as

► **Black-legged kittiwakes** ABOVE share a cliff-ledge colony site with Common guillemots or murres.

At these sites, the nests are safe from predators. The kittiwake shows a number of behavioral differences from ground-nesting gulls. For example, when they fish they dart the head horizontally and try to grasp the bill of the opponent. Then they twist the head from side to side until the opponent is unbalanced and thrown off the nest ledge. The ground-nesting species usually try either to get above their opponent and peck down, or to pull the opponent.

► **A Great black-backed gull** BELOW coping with success. This species takes a wide variety of prey, killing fish, seabirds and rabbits, as well as taking carrion. It can be a ferocious killer in seabird colonies, gulping down nestlings in a single mouthful.

▼ **Ritualized aggression** and appeasement displays in gulls (see text, RIGHT). (1) Long call. (2) Begging for food. (3) Tugging at grass on territory border. (4) "Head-flagging." (5) Threat.

soon as their down dries, but remain in or near the nest for a week or so where their parents can brood and tend them closely. When small, they jostle for food by pecking at the parent's bill; in some species a brightly colored spot near the parent's bill-tip serves as a target and stimulus for this begging action. Once liberated from the need for brooding, the young may seek refuge in vegetation, etc near the nest. If they trespass onto neighboring territories they are often fiercely attacked by the owners. Injury and even death may result.

In the larger gulls, some adults specialize in killing the young of other broods and feeding them to their own offspring. At one Herring gull colony it was observed that almost a quarter of all hatchlings were cannibalized in this way and many eggs were also pirated. In species which lay three eggs, the last laid egg is typically the smallest. Gull clutches hatch over a few days, so that the last chick has to compete with larger siblings. This third "runt" chick is therefore prone to succumb if food is short, and more likely to fall victim to adult cannibals. Occasionally, a cannibal Herring gull has difficulty in distinguishing the instinct to nurture its own offspring from the urge to kill and eat the young of other pairs. One such adult ate over 40 chicks while sharing incubation of its own clutch. When its own brood hatched, it continued to bring live chicks to its nest site, but failed to kill them. Over a week, it added eight live healthy young to its own brood. The task of raising this extended family proved insurmountable in the end, but one of the adopted young was successfully raised to fledging.

By the time the young leave the nest at 3–7 weeks (depending on species), they are fully feathered, but in a mottled brown garb quite different from their parents. This dress is lost by degrees, until breeding age is reached. The parents usually continue to feed their offspring for some time after fledging, up until $1\frac{1}{2}$ months afterwards in some of the larger gulls.

Like other seabirds, gulls that survive the rigors of juvenile life can, on average, look forward to a relatively long life. Ringing studies show that Black-headed gulls and Herring gulls can live over 30 years. Presumably because breeding is a hazardous venture, requiring considerable experience, gulls generally do not breed until they are several years old—two years in Little and Black-headed gulls, usually five in Herring and Lesser black-backed gulls. When they approach breeding age, some birds may return to the colony where they

THE 4 FAMILIES OF GULLS AND THEIR RELATIVES

Gulls
Family: Laridae
Forty-five species in 5 genera.

Worldwide, but few in tropics. Chiefly coastal waters. Size: 10–30in (25–78cm) long and 3oz–4.4lb (90g–2kg); males somewhat larger than females. Plumage: chiefly white, gray and black in adult, streaked or mottled brown when immature. Sexes similar. Voice: wide repertoire includes ringing, laughing sounds, yelping, mewing, and whining notes. Nests: typically a cup of vegetation, seaweed, etc, sometimes substantial, often on a cliff ledge or on the ground, some on marshes, bushes or trees. Eggs: usually 2–3, olive, brownish or greenish, heavily mottled; weight ranges from 0.7oz (19g) in the Little gull to 4.1oz (117g) in the Great black-backed gull; incubation 3–5 weeks; young fledge after 3–7 weeks. Diet: fish, crustaceans, mollusks, worms and, in smaller species, insects; also vegetable food, refuse and carrion, some preying on birds and mammals.

Species include, in arctic latitudes: **Glaucous gull** (*Larus hyperboreus*), **Iceland gull** (*L. glaucoides*), **Ivory gull** (*Pagophila eburnea*), **Ross's gull** (*Rhodostethia rosea*), **Sabine's gull** (*L. sabini*); in temperate latitudes: **Black-headed gull** (*L. ridibundus*), **Bonaparte's gull** (*L. philadelphia*), **Common** or **Mew gull** (*L. canus*), **Franklin's gull** (*L. pipixcan*), **Great black-backed gull** (*L. marinus*), **Great black-headed gull** (*L. ichthyaetus*), **Herring gull** (*L. argentatus*), **kittiwake** or **Black-legged kittiwake** (*Rissa tridactyla*), **Laughing gull** (*L. atricilla*), **Lesser black-backed gull** (*L. fuscus*), **Little gull** (*L. minutus*), **Relict gull** R (*L. relictus*), **Ring-billed gull** (*L. delawarensis*), **Western gull** (*L. occidentalis*); in Mediterranean latitudes: **Audouin's gull** R (*L. audouinii*), **Mediterranean gull** (*L. melanocephalus*), **Slender-billed gull** (*L. genei*); in comparable, or warmer, climate, S Hemisphere: **Gray gull** (*L. modestus*), **Silver** or **Hartlaub's gull** (*L. novaehollandiae*); in the tropics: **Gray-headed gull** (*L. cirrocephalus*), **Lava gull** (*L. fuliginosus*), **Sooty gull** (*L. hemprichii*), **Swallow-tailed gull** (*Creagrus furcatus*), **White-eyed gull** (*L. leucophthalmus*).

Terns
Family: Sternidae
Forty-one species in 7 genera.

Worldwide. Chiefly coastal and offshore waters, some up rivers and in marshes. Size: 8–22in (20–56cm) long and 1.8oz–1.5lb (50–700g, males somewhat larger than females. Plumage: chiefly white, gray and black. Voice: most varied repertoire from shrill to hoarse, penetrating calls

to soft crooning notes. Nests: usually a simple scrape, occasionally well lined; some make floating rafts (marsh terns); others in trees and on cliff ledges (White tern and noddies), in holes in cliffs (Inca tern), sometimes under boulders or down burrows. Eggs: 1–3, pale cream to brown or greenish, with darker blotches; most weigh about 0.7oz (20g), but range 0.4oz (Little tern) to 2.3oz (Caspian tern) 10–65g; incubation 18–30 days; fledging mostly at 1–2 months. Diet: chiefly fish, squid and crustaceans; in marsh terns insects, amphibians and leeches.

Species include, in temperate latitudes: **Aleutian tern** (*Sterna aleutica*), **Arctic tern** (*S. paradisaea*), **Black tern** (*Chlidonias nigra*), **Caspian tern** (*Sterna caspia*), **Common tern** (*S. hirundo*), **Gull-billed tern** (*S. nilotica*), **Little** or **Least tern** (*S. albifrons*), **Roseate tern** (*S. dougallii*), **Sandwich tern** (*S. sandvicensis*), **Whiskered tern** (*Chlidonias hybrida*), **White-winged black tern** (*C. leucoptera*); in the tropics: **Black noddy** (*Anous tenuirostris*), **Bridled tern** (*Sterna anaethetus*), **Brown noddy** (*Anous stolidus*), **Damara tern** R (*Sterna balaenarum*), **Inca tern** (*Larosterna inca*), **Sooty tern** (*Sterna fuscata*), **White tern** (*Gygis alba*). Total threatened species: 2.

Skuas or jaegers
Family: Stercorariidae
Six species in 2 genera.

Large skuas
Three species of the genus *Catharacta*. Antarctic, sub-Antarctic, southern S

America, Iceland, Faroes, N Britain. Coastal heaths. Size 2.4–4.2lb (1.1–1.9kg); females slightly larger than males. Plumage: brown, with white wing flashes. Elongated central tail feathers in adults. Voice: limited range of yelps. Nests: scraped depression on ground. Eggs: normally 2; olive with brown blotches; weight 2.5–3.9oz (70–110g); incubation 30 days; nestling period 45–55 days. Diet: catholic, particularly fish, krill, seabird eggs and chicks, adult seabirds.

Species: **Great skua** (*Catharacta skua*), **South polar skua** (*C. maccormicki*), **Chilean skua** (*C. chilensis*).

Small skuas or jaegers
Three species of the genus *Stercorarius*. Arctic and boreal regions. Tundra and coastal heaths. Size: 8.8oz–1.8lb (250–800g); females slightly larger than males. Plumage: dimorphic; all brown, or brown above and creamy white below. Voice: mewing cries. Nests: scrape on ground. Eggs: normally 2; olive with brown blotches; incubation 23–27 days; nestling period 24–32 days. Diet: small mammals, insects, berries, birds, eggs, fish (often stolen from other seabirds).

Species: **Parasitic jaeger** or **Arctic skua** (*Stercorarius parasiticus*), **Long-tailed jaeger** or **skua** (*S. longicaudus*), **Pomarine jaeger** or **skua** (*S. pomarinus*).

▲▶ **Terns.** (1) Blue-gray noddy (*Procelsterna cerulea*). (2) Lesser noddy (*Anous tenuirostris*). (3) White tern (*Gygis alba*). (4) Inca tern (*Larosterna inca*). (5) Arctic tern (*Sterna paradisaea*). (6) Large-billed tern (*Phaetusa simplex*). (7) Black tern (*Chlidonias nigra*) juvenile. (8) Sooty tern (*Sterna fuscata*). (9) Caspian terns (*S. caspia*) adult and RIGHT first-winter plumage.

Skimmers
Family: Rynchopidae
Three species of the genus *Rynchops*.

Tropical Africa, S Asia, southeastern N, C, and S America. Major river systems and ocean coasts. Size: length 14–18in (35–45cm); to 14.1oz (400g) (males), about 10.6oz (300g) (females); Plumage: chiefly black or dark brown above, white or light gray below; sexes similar. Voice: simple barks (Black skimmer) or shrill, chattering calls (others). Nests: simple scrape in sand or on shell bank. Eggs: usually 3–4 (range 2–5), whitish or beige with dark brown or black blotches and irregular spots; about 1.6 × 1.2in (4 × 3cm); incubation 22–24 days; nestling period 25–30 days. Diet: primarily small fish, also small invertebrates such as shrimps, prawns, and other small crustaceans.

Species: **African skimmer** (*Rynchops flavirostris*), **Black skimmer** (*R. niger*), **Indian skimmer** (*R. albicollis*).

were born in order to establish a territory, and they sometimes settle remarkably close to their natal nest site. However, other gulls may travel considerable distances to join other colonies, a dispersal that probably helps to mitigate the possible adverse effects of inbreeding.

Many, but not all, gull species have probably never been as numerous as they are now, given the new food supplies made available by man. Foremost among scarce gulls is the Relict gull, of which no more than 1,500–1,800 pairs are known from Lake Alakul and Lake Barun-Torey deep in the interior of the USSR.   EKD

Terns are among the most graceful and appealing inhabitants of shorelines and marshes. Many are familiar summer visitors to north temperate coasts, catching the eye with their winnowing flight and spectacular plunge-diving for fish. Some, like the massive Caspian tern, show the close kinship of terns with the gulls (p36), while the resemblance of other members to the skimmers (p50) is also evident.

Most terns (22 species) belong to the "black-capped" group of species of *Sterna*. These sea terns or "sea swallows" have a slender form, long tapering wings, a deeply forked tail, and are agile in flight. The typical plumage pattern is white below and gray above, with a black crown which in some species is crested. Juveniles are often mottled brown, especially on the back, and may take 2–3 years to assume adult appearance. In the marsh terns (three species of *Chlidonias*) and noddies (three species of *Anous*), the plumage is generally darker or even black. Conspicuously different is the slate-blue Inca tern, with its yellow gape wattles and white moustache. Among the terns, the bill—often bright yellow, red, or black— varies in shape from pincer- to dagger-like, depending partly on the size of the prey taken. The flight, though buoyant, is strong, often allowing a sustained hover. Although the feet are webbed, most terns seldom settle on water for long.

The terns are to be found worldwide, extending to all but the highest, ice-fast latitudes. Habitat preference divides the species broadly into two groups, sea terns and marsh terns. Some sea terns, such as the Roseate tern and Caspian tern, are among the most cosmopolitan of all birds. While the majority prefer warm tropical and subtropical waters, others favor colder latitudes for breeding, and the sea terns thus range from the Arctic to the Antarctic. By contrast, the marsh terns have adopted a largely inland

existence, on freshwater marshes, lakes and rivers, often deep in the heart of continents.

Terns undertake prodigious migrations, many journeying in summer to the food-rich waters of higher latitudes to breed, and resorting to tropical climes for the winter. The Arctic tern undertakes possibly the longest migration of any bird species. Many breed north of the Arctic Circle and move south to the Antarctic for the northern winter, an each-way journey of some 9,300mi (15,000km) "as the crow flies." By doing so, they exploit the long daylight for prolonged feeding time in both hemispheres. The ringing of terns and plotting their movements has done much to unravel the routes taken; many Canadian Arctic terns, for instance, cross the Atlantic on westerlies to the European coast on their way south. While most travel by sea, feeding as they go, overland routes are not uncommon, and many marsh terns, for example, cross the Sahara *en route* from their breeding grounds to their African winter quarters.

The sea terns are primarily fish-eaters, though squid and crustaceans are also relished. The black-capped terns are bold plungers, spotting their prey as they hover into the wind, before diving headlong (see box). In general, the bigger the tern, the higher and deeper it dives; the Caspian tern may plunge from 50ft (15m). Unlike gannets, terns do not swim underwater, and prey is seized near the surface. Noddies typically dip to the surface and may use their feet for pattering like storm petrels. They often catch flying fish in mid-air. Noddies and some other tropical terns range far

▲ **The only tern with all-white plumage,** the White tern ranges widely throughout the tropical and subtropical oceans. It lays its single egg directly on a tree branch.

◄ **Elaborate courtship of terns.** (1) Female Arctic tern pursues male upward in "high flight." (2) Male Sandwich tern feeding his mate. (3) Common terns mating. (4) Erect or "pole" stance of Sandwich tern pair, seen after copulation and also after high-flight.

Apprentice Plunge-divers

Plunge-diving for fish is the hallmark of many terns. A typical plunge-diver in European waters is the Sandwich tern. The bird flies upwind, usually 16–20ft (5–6m) above the surface, and, on spying its prey just below the surface, hovers briefly before diving headlong into the water. The prey is seized in the vice-like grip of the bill, just behind the gills, and quickly eaten. When young are being fed, the fish is held cross-wise in the bill and carried back to the colony.

As a technique for obtaining food, plunge-diving is remarkably successful. An adult tern often secures a fish in one dive out of three. But it is a difficult technique and many factors can make the task more so. Fishing success is greatly reduced in strong winds, partly because the shoaling prey, often sprats or sand eels, sink deeper to avoid the turbulent wave action. Very calm seas also appear to pose problems, possibly because the fish can see the tern overhead and take evasive action.

It is also possible that in calm conditions the fish can sense the tern's splash on entry just soon enough to veer off.

The young Sandwich tern not only has to learn the best places to fish, but also needs to develop skills over time. Its first efforts are often shallow, unrewarded belly flops, but it gains practice by picking up bits of seaweed and other flotsam. Faced with the additional hazards of migrating south, the young bird continues to be fed by its parents for perhaps 3–4 months after fledging. Meanwhile, it gradually learns to dive from greater heights, and gains access to prey at greater depths, down to a maximum of about 3.3ft (1m) below the surface. However, even at 7–9 months old, in their West African winter quarters, some juveniles are still noticeably less adept than their parents at catching fish.

This long apprenticeship probably helps to explain why most young Sandwich terns stay in the winter quarters for two years.   EKD

offshore to feed, swallowing their prey for later regurgitation to the young. Though most terns are daytime feeders, some, such as Sooty terns, have been recorded feeding at night. The dainty marsh terns are well adapted for hawking insects or hovering to pluck them off vegetation. They also make shallow plunges for frogs and other aquatic animals. The Gull-billed tern is the most terrestrial of all, and swoops to seize large insects, lizards, and even small rodents from the ground. The rate of feeding visits to the young varies according to the distance the parents must travel to hunt. While a marsh tern may feed its young every few minutes, the Sooty tern, which ranges hundreds of miles to forage, many only deliver a meal once a day.

In common with many other seabirds, most terns are long-lived, if they survive to adulthood. Arctic terns have been shown by ringing to live 33 years or more, and a life span of 20 years is probably not unusual. Breeding may begin as early as two years, but more often at three or four in temperate breeding species, generally later in tropical species. Most Sooty terns, for example, do not reach sexual maturity until at least six years old.

In higher latitudes, terns usually have a well-defined breeding season once a year, in Europe from about May to July. In the tropics, breeding is generally not synchronized to a particular time of year. In a few populations, however, terns breed both at intervals of less than a year and synchronously. On Cousin Island in the Indian Ocean, Bridled terns breed every $7\frac{1}{2}$ months, while the highly adaptable Sooty tern breeds, depending on location, at intervals varying from six to 12 months; in some cases it seems likely that food is more or less equally abundant at all times of year.

Terns generally pair for life. Even though the pair bond breaks down outside the breeding season, there is a strong tendency to return to a previously successful breeding site, which enables former mates to rendezvous at the start of each new breeding season. Courtship is an elaborate ritual, especially in birds seeking a mate for the first time. In many terns, the first stage of pairing is the "high flight," in which the male ascends at speed, as if to demonstrate his prowess, to often several hundred feet while the female pursues him. At the end of the climb the prospective pair glide and zigzag earthwards. With growing familiarity, the male increasingly courtship-feeds his mate; this has more than just symbolic value—it helps the female to form eggs

and perhaps allows her to gauge the fishing skill of her partner. Ground courtship often occurs near the male's chosen nest site, and involves much elegant strutting and pirouetting with raised tail and drooped wings. This is usually the prelude to copulation.

Most terns breed in bustling colonies, often at high density. They also roost *en masse* and may join together to mob predators at the colony. The colony site is usually on flat open ground, often on an island or reef. Noddies, however, crowd on trees, bushes and cliff ledges, while Inca terns seek crevices in rock. The White tern is celebrated for building no nest, opting to lay its single egg directly on to, usually, the branch of a tree. Most ground nesters are scarcely more constructive, merely fashioning a shallow scrape, at the best thinly lined. Noddies and marsh terns, however, build a more substantial platform of vegetation, the latter anchoring a raft of reeds, etc to submerged plants. Both sexes defend the nest territory, often only 10 square feet or so in extent, while the "crested" terns, which nest most densely of all, may be within jabbing distance of neighbors.

▶ **Pirates' shoreline squabble** OVERLEAF. The Great skua will harass other birds, forcing them to disgorge their food, which it eats, or occasionally killing and eating them. These birds, photographed on the Auckland Islands south of New Zealand, belong to the sub-Antarctic population.

▼▶ **Skuas and jaegers.** (1) Great skua (*Catharacta skua*) long-calling. (2) Pomarine skua or jaeger (*Stercorarius pomarinus*) in adult breeding (pale) plumage. (3) Arctic skua (*S. parasiticus*) in adult breeding (pale) plumage, harrying Atlantic puffins.

The normal clutch varies from one egg in tropical species to 2–3 in higher latitudes; incubation, shared by the sexes, lasts 3–4 weeks. On hatching, the downy chicks are soon actively exploring their surroundings, but seldom stray far unless disturbed. Then they take refuge in vegetation, or under stones, driftwood and the like, while the well-grown young of "crested" terns may seek safety in numbers, forming a mobile crèche. Parents returning with food recognize their own young in the crèche by voice, and feed only them. After the young fledge, they have much to learn about catching prey for themselves (see p45) and are fed by their parents for some time, before gradually being weaned off.

The isolation sought by terns for breeding purposes is an increasingly scarce resource as man turns more to the coast and sea for leisure, commercial fishing, and other activities. Pressure on land use in South Africa has reduced the Damara tern to a precarious 1,500 pairs, while snaring for food and sport in its West African winter quarters is believed to have contributed to the decline of the European Roseate tern to around 1,000 pairs. By contrast, many populations continue to flourish in remoter regions, and on Pacific Christmas Island alone, the Sooty tern is numbered in millions.   EKD

During their breeding season, **skuas and jaegers** are the pirates and predators of the skies in high latitudes. They have been seen closer to the South Pole than any other vertebrate apart from man. One individual ringed as a chick at Anvers Island, Antarctica, was shot five months later in Godthabsfjord, Greenland—the longest journey of any bird ever recorded by ringing. Skuas will harry other seabirds until they disgorge their last meal, which they then catch in mid air. In North America and elsewhere the small skuas are called "jaegers," after the German word meaning hunter. The Great skua has been seen to kill prey many times heavier than itself, such as the Gray heron, Graylag goose, shelduck and Mountain hare.

Outside the breeding season, skuas migrate over all the world's oceans, the jaegers also traveling in some numbers directly overland. Records of Arctic skuas in Austria and Switzerland in the fall are not uncommon. The large species, on the other hand, tend to remain some distance offshore, but a few storm-tossed young Great skuas have been picked up, exhausted, in central Europe. One, ringed as a chick in Shetland, was rescued from the central reservation of a motorway in West Germany only to be shot a week later as it attacked chickens on an east Austrian farm.

Skuas are closely related to, and presumably evolved from, the gulls, which clearly originated in the Northern Hemisphere. However, early in the evolution of the skuas, one form must have colonized the Antarctic, where it has given rise to the three very similar large skua species. The small populations of the Great skua in the North Atlantic are almost certainly recently derived from birds blown north from the South Atlantic, as measurement and plumage of the two subspecies are very similar. The Great skua is thus unique among seabirds in that it breeds in both the sub-Antarctic and the Northern Hemisphere.

The three species of large skua are generally brown. The Chilean skua has conspicuous rufous underwing feathers, while the South polar skua has both dark and light phases (dimorphic plumage)—light-phase birds increase in frequency towards the Pole. It is not known why skuas should benefit from having plumage that is paler on the upperparts in regions with more snow and ice.

All three jaegers display two color phases. The dark phase is extremely rare in the Long-tailed jaeger. In the Arctic and Pomarine jaegers the proportions of birds of each phase within the population vary geographically. In Shetland less than 25 percent of Arctic jaegers are light; the proportion tends to increase northwards, with nearly 100 percent light in Spitzbergen and arctic Canada. The elongation of the two central tail feathers, characteristic of adult skuas, is prominent in the Arctic jaeger and extreme in the Long-tailed jaeger. The Pomarine jaeger has twisted club-shaped central tail feathers. All juvenile jaegers are barred below.

The skuas have feet that are gull-like, but with prominent sharp claws. The bill is hard and strongly hooked at the tip, adapted for tearing flesh. In gulls, as in many other bird families, males are slightly larger than females, but the opposite is true for skuas, as for birds of prey. In both these groups the male does most of the hunting and the female remains in the territory to guard the nest or young.

Skuas take many types of food. Pomarine jaegers feed largely on lemmings in summer and on small seabirds in winter, less regularly by fishing or by harassing other birds (piracy). Long-tailed jaegers feed on lemmings, insects, berries, small birds and eggs in summer and by piracy, chiefly by

harrying terns, in winter. In arctic tundra areas, Arctic jaegers feed on insects, berries, small birds and eggs, and some rodents; in coastal areas they feed almost exclusively by piracy of terns, kittiwakes and auks.

Skuas are normally monogamous and pair for life. In New Zealand and on Marion Island, Great skua trios comprising one female and two males occur regularly, a social system not yet found in any other skua. Distances between skua nests vary enormously, from often 1.2mi (2km) apart on arctic tundra, down to just 16–33ft (5–10m) within the largest Great skua colonies in Shetland. On Foula, Shetland, 306 pairs of Arctic jaegers breed in a colony occupying 0.7sq mi (1.7sq km), approximately the area defended by a single pair breeding on arctic tundra. Part of the explanation for this difference is that skuas nesting in Shetland do not obtain food within their territory, but feed at sea. Skuas defend their nests by dive-bombing intruders, including humans. Jaegers have a "broken wing" distraction display.

Skuas have only two brood patches, and birds with three eggs usually fail to hatch any. Most pairs with two eggs manage to hatch both, but if food is short, the older chick, which hatches 1–3 days before the second, will attack and kill its smaller sibling. In Shetland, Arctic jaegers begin breeding when 3–6 years old, while Great skuas first breed when between five and 10 years old. Presumably this long period of immaturity helps the skua to learn the many skills needed to be an effective hunter and parasite of other seabirds.   RWF

Skimmers are among our better-named birds, for they skim the surface of lakes, rivers and lagoons, deftly snapping up fish with their uniquely adapted bills. They crowd by the hundreds into nesting colonies on sand bars, where the contrast between their brilliant bills and legs, and their stark plumage, make them a prized "target" of wildlife photographers and artists.

Even though the skimmer family is represented by only three species in the world, it is widely distributed. Three subspecies (or races) of the Black skimmer are found in the New World: the North American subspecies inhabits the ocean coasts and the Salton Sea in the western USA. The two South American subspecies are almost exclusively riverine, using coastal areas out of the breeding season. African skimmers are most abundant in East and Central Africa on the larger river systems. Indian skimmers range from Pakistan across India to the Malay Peninsula, mostly in close association with large rivers.

The Indian and Black skimmers have orange-red bills (but the Black skimmer's is black toward the tip) and vermilion legs and feet in the breeding season (duller at other times), while the African skimmer has yellow legs and feet and a yellow-orange bill. The young of all species are lighter brown above and less white below, and the tail is mottled, unlike the mostly white tail of the adults. The wings are very long, with a span $2\frac{1}{2}$ times the length of the bird.

But the most striking feature in all species is the large, scissor-like bill with its flattened "blades," the upper mandible fitting into a notch between the edges of the lower mandible, which is $\frac{1}{4}-\frac{1}{3}$ as long again as the upper. It was once thought that the lower mandible had great touch sensitivity, but recently this has been found not to be the case. When feeding, skimmers hold the bill open in such a position that the tip of the lower mandible slices the water. When the lower mandible touches a prey item, usually a small fish, the head flexes downward rapidly, trapping the prey sideways between the "scissors" (hence the popular name "scissorbill"). The musculature of the head and neck is well developed and acts as a shock absorber. Skimmers often feed at dusk and throughout the night, especially in the non-breeding season. The skimmer eye has a vertical pupil, much like that of a cat, which may enhance its light-gathering properties. Skimmers prefer to feed in waters with little surface turbulence, such as lakes, pools, marsh and river edges. After "cutting a trail" in the water, birds often double back and retrace their course. snapping up prey

▲ **"Cutting a trail"** a Black skimmer slices the surface with its long lower mandible as it skims shallow water foraging for fish.

◀ **The bill of a skimmer** (again the Black species of the New World). The lower part may be one-third as long again as the upper. Bill and strengthened neck muscles are adaptations for a method of fishing that is without parallel among birds. This is a young bird.

families, only skimmers have a shorebird-like "broken wing" distraction display.

Skimmers are highly social birds in all seasons of the year. When they reach breeding age (probably at 3–4 years), they gather on open, sandy bars and small islands where courtship begins. Vertical flights and aerial chases by courting birds are common at this time. The breeding colonies, established on these sites after a few weeks, range in size from a few pairs up to 1,000 or more. Skimmers often form mixed colonies with terns and they probably benefit from some terns' greater display of aggression in driving off predators.

Skimmers have small nesting territories, with nests spaced 3.3–13ft (1–4m) apart, depending on vegetation and terrain. The degree to which birds nest at the same time (synchrony) can be very high in certain areas in the colony. Aggression is high during the period of territory establishment and egg-laying, and both sexes engage in disputes over space and mates. The males are more aggressive toward other skimmers, while females more frequently interact with other species nesting nearby. Males incubate and brood more than females, at least during the day. Males and females switch incubation duties frequently, especially in the hottest part of the day. Foot and belly-wetting by adults helps to regulate the temperature of the incubated egg. After the young hatch, the females feed the young more than the males do. Parents feed the young beyond the four-week nestling period, and the fledged young accompany adults on feeding forays, perhaps learning where and how to fish.

The nesting period at a skimmer colony is often considerably longer than that of most of their gull and tern relatives—along the eastern USA the Black skimmer may nest from May to October. After the nesting season, skimmers gather in loose flocks at certain "staging areas." They follow major river systems and coastal routes when migrating to distant wintering areas. Some populations of skimmers are non-migratory.

Skimmers are not presently considered threatened. However, damming of rivers in India, Africa and South America continues to reduce the nesting habitat. This, coupled with destruction of tropical forest, diminishes water quality and productivity which, in turn, affects skimmers' diet. In North America, many coastal habitats have been disturbed, forcing Black skimmers (and other species) to nest on small saltmarsh islands and even roofs of buildings in some areas.   RME

in their wake. They usually feed alone or in pairs, but on occasion groups of 10–15 birds may engage in brief bouts of intense feeding in a particular spot. In coastal areas, feeding increases at low or ebbing tides.

Male Black skimmers are much larger than females. Measurements of wing-span, bill, tail, and weight show males ranging from about 10 percent (wing, tail) to 25 percent (weight, bill length) larger than females. Such dimorphism is not confirmed for African and Indian skimmers.

Skimmers used to be considered more closely related to terns than gulls—unlike gulls, neither skimmers nor terns use their wings during aggressive encounters. However, further analysis of breeding behavior suggests that the skimmers split from the ancestral stock before the divergence between terns and gulls. Of the three

AUKS

Family: Alcidae
Order: Charadriiformes (suborder: Alcae).
Twenty-two species in 13 genera.
Distribution: N Pacific, N Atlantic and Arctic
oceans and coastal regions.

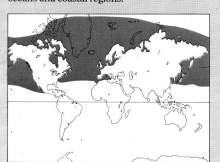

Habitat: breeding, mainly along coasts on
islands and headlands; non-breeding, mainly in
coastal waters.

Size: from 6.5in (16cm) long and 3.2oz (90g)
in the Least auklet to 18in (45cm) long and
2.2lb (1kg) in the Common guillemot (extinct
Great auk up to 11–17.6lb/5–8kg); males of
most species only slightly larger than females.

Plumage: most species dark above, pale below;
some have colored (red, yellow) bill or feet.

Voice: growls and yelps; some species almost
silent.

Nests: breed on open ledges (no nest), in
crevices or burrows, with very simple nest;
Marbled murrelet on large branches of conifers.

Eggs: 1–2; 0.7–3.9oz (16–110g); pear-shaped
and variable in color and markings (razorbills
and guillemots) to ovoid and plain; incubation
29–42 days; chick stays at nest site for very
variable period, 2–50 days.

Diet: fish or crustaceans caught by diving from
the surface.

Species include: **Ancient murrelet**
(*Synthliboramphus antiquus*), **Atlantic** or
common puffin or **puffin** (*Fratercula arctica*), **Black
guillemot** or **tystie** (*Cepphus grylle*), **Cassin's
auklet** (*Ptychoramphus aleuticus*), **Common
murre** or **guillemot** (*Uria aalge*), **Craveri's
murrelet** (*Brachyramphus craveri*), **Great auk** Ex
(*Pinguinus impennis*), **Japanese murrelet**
(*Synthliboramphus wumizusume*), **Kittlitz's
murrelet** (*Brachyramphus brevirostris*), **Least
auklet** (*Aethia pusilla*), **Little auk** or **dovekie**
(*Plautus alle*), **Marbled murrelet** (*Brachyramphus
marmoratus*), **Parakeet auklet** (*Cyclorrhynchus
psittacula*), **Pigeon guillemot** (*Cepphus columba*),
razorbill (*Alca torda*), **Thick-billed murre** or
Brünnich's guillemot (*Uria lomvia*), **Whiskered
auklet** (*Aethia pygmaea*), **Xantus's murrelet**
(*Brachyramphus hypoleuca*).

Ex Extinct.

THEIR upright posture and their "human
expressions" give some auks a comical
appearance. Humans have eaten the birds
and their eggs for thousands of years, yet it
is only in the last 10 years or so that many
features of auks' bizarre and varied biology
have been discovered. For example, most
auks breed in colonies on rocky coasts, but
the nest of one species, the Marbled murrelet, occurs up to 100ft (30m) above
ground level in the branches of coniferous
trees in remote areas up to 6mi (10km) or
more inland. Fewer than five nests of this
common seabird have been found.

In many respects, the auks are the ecological counterparts of the Southern Hemisphere's penguins—both groups have much
reduced wings which they use to swim
underwater in pursuit of prey. Most auk species breed in temperate, boreal or arctic
waters. Outside the breeding season, auks
may move further south. Some British puffins and razorbills winter as far south as the
Mediterranean, and in the Pacific several
auks which breed in Alaska winter as far
south as California. Auks spend most of their
lives at sea, coming ashore only to breed.
Eighteen of the 22 species breed in the
Pacific, and six in the North Atlantic—the
Common and Thick-billed murres are common to both oceans. The large number of
species in the Pacific, particularly the Bering
Sea, suggests that the family might have
originally evolved there.

When Young Auks Leave Home

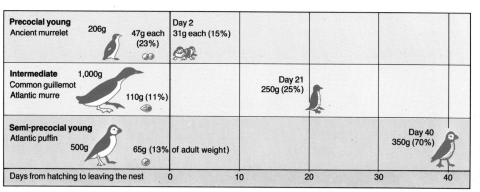

In most bird families, the newly hatched
young are either naked and helpless,
remaining in the nest for days (nidicolous), as
in blackbirds and sparrows, or they may be
covered with down, with their eyes open and
able to feed themselves (precocial), as in
chickens and ducks. The auks are unique in
the range of precocity and developmental
patterns shown by the young.

Most auks (eg puffins, auklets and Black
guillemots) hatch semi-precocial young
(down-covered with open eyes, but dependent
upon their parents for food), which remain at
the nest site for 27–50 days until they have
grown to almost full size. They then leave the
nest site independently of their parents. (The
Little auk may be exceptional among the
semi-precocial species, as the chick may be
accompanied by its father in the same way as
in the murres—see below.)

At the other extreme are four Pacific
murrelets (Xantus's, Craveri's, Ancient and
Japanese murrelets). They all produce a clutch
of two eggs and hatch precocial young which
leave the nest site when only two days old and
are accompanied by their parents. The eggs of
these species are large—even for auks—and
the chicks are well developed on hatching,
with feet almost adult size!

The third pattern, shown only by Common
murres, Thick-billed murres and the razorbill,
is intermediate. Young birds leave the colony
after 18–23 days, one-quarter grown and still
flightless. They are cared for by their father,
at sea, for several weeks.

The early life-histories have evolved in
relation to the amount of food the parents can
bring to their chicks. In the species which
hatch semi-precocial young, parents can find
sufficient food to rear the chick to full size at
the breeding site. For the species with
precocial young, their plankton food supplies
are either difficult for the parents to locate, or
a long way from the colony. By taking their
young to sea soon after hatching, the parents
avoid the energetic expense of commuting
between feeding and breeding areas. This also
allows them to rear two chicks, rather than
one as in most other auks. The intermediate
pattern is a compromise between the other
two.

It may be that the evolution of truly
precocial young has not been possible in
murres and the razorbill because of the size of
the eggs of these species. Relative egg size in
auks (as in other birds) is inversely
proportional to body size: large auks produce
relatively smaller eggs than small auks. The
precocial murrelets are among the smallest
auks and produce relatively enormous eggs,
from which it is possible for the young to
hatch at a sufficiently advanced stage of
development to become independent early on.
The guillemots and razorbill are the largest
auks, and therefore unlikely to lay an egg
large enough to produce a precocial chick.

▲ **Bill-full of fish** for the Atlantic puffin's single chick. Specialized spines on the tongue and upper mandible of the bill make it possible to carry up to 50 or more larval fish back crosswise in the bill to the nest burrow.

The auks feed in both inshore and offshore waters. They are not, however, such lovers of the open oceans as some other seabirds, including shearwaters and petrels. Auks feed by diving and pursuing prey underwater, and all species feed on fish or plankton (invertebrates and larval fish). Some species, like the auklets of the Pacific, and the Atlantic Little auk (or dovekie), feed almost entirely on plankton; others, like the Common murre, eat mainly fish.

Auks are small to medium-sized birds with short tails and small wings. Unlike penguins, all auks can fly (though the much larger Great auk couldn't). In fact the size of their wings is a compromise: large enough for flying but small enough to use in the denser medium of water—hence their rapid wingbeats and whirring flight.

The legs of most auks are positioned toward the rear of the body, which accounts for their upright posture. Some species, including the puffins, walk on their toes, as do most birds, but the murres and razorbill walk on their tarsal bones. The legs of auks are slightly compressed laterally, an adaptation for swimming, although less so than in grebes and shearwaters. The three toes are connected by webs, and in species such as the Atlantic puffin and Black guillemot the legs and feet are bright orange or red. The mouth is also brightly colored in some species, red in the Black guillemot, yellow in the razorbill. The shape of the bill varies

markedly between species, partly reflecting differences in diet and feeding methods. In all auks the bill is relatively short, and in the razorbill and puffins it is laterally compressed. The large, colorful bill of the Atlantic puffin plays an important role in pair formation and courtship. The bill comprises nine distinct plates which are shed each year during the molt. Outside the breeding season, the puffin's bill is much reduced in size and is less brightly colored.

All auks have distinct winter plumages, and in some species the change in appearance between summer and winter can be quite dramatic. The Black and Pigeon guillemots are black with a white wing patch in the summer, but during the winter they are mainly white and gray. The Marbled murrelet and Kittlitz's murrelet have cryptic brown summer plumage, but outside the breeding season are mainly black or gray above and white below. In some of the auklets, such as the Whiskered auklet, long head plumes and "whiskers" are lost during the winter. During the molt, which in most species occurs soon after breeding is over,

Close Neighbors in the Colony

Common murres characteristically breed in bodily contact with their neighbors, at densities greater than any other bird species— Up to 7.5 pairs per sq ft (70/sq m) have been recorded! Like several other auks, murres make no nest, but lay their single egg directly onto bare rock. The eggs or chicks of solitary pairs, or of pairs in low-density groups, often fall prey to marauding gulls or crows. The high-density groups present an impenetrable barrier to such predators, and in these colonies most pairs successfully rear young.

However, breeding in large, dense colonies is not without its own problems. Despite such high-density breeding, each pair vigorously defends a tiny territory: the close proximity of neighbors results in almost continuous social interaction.

Common murres have evolved a large repertoire of calls and displays that enable them to live together with some degree of harmony. Sometimes a threat (1) is employed to warn off an intruder. Fights, although common, are usually very brief, because they are cut short by one of several appeasement displays. These include: (2) side-preening; (3)

stretching away or turning away; and (4) a ritualized walk when passing other birds in the colony.

With breeding so close together, and in the absence of distinct nests, the chances of the eggs and chicks of different broods becoming mixed up are fairly high. Since it would not be to any bird's advantage to rear an unrelated chick, Common (and Thick-billed) murres have evolved to a marked extent the ability to pick out and retrieve both their egg and their chick. Egg color and markings are extraordinarily variable between individuals

▲ **Common murre (guillemot) with its single egg.** Color and patterning of the eggs are more varied than within perhaps any other bird species, the different base colors (turquoise to white) and markings (red, brown, or black) helping the parent to recognize its own egg.

▷ **Densely packed nests** OVERLEAF of the Common murre or guillemot give protection against gull and crow raiders. Guillemots nest closer to one another than almost any other bird.

◀ **Atlantic or Common puffins** leave their summer nesting colonies to spend the winter on the open seas.

the larger auks are flightless, probably for some 45 days, as the flight feathers are dropped simultaneously. The wing-loadings (ratio of body weight to wing size) of the murres, razorbill and other large species are so high that the sequential loss of feathers (one after another at intervals, as in most birds) would merely preserve a reduced ability to fly that was grossly expensive in terms of energy required. The wing-loading of the smallest species is lower; they can molt their flight feathers one at a time and still retain the ability to fly. The flightless Great auk also molted in this way.

Auks obtain all their food from the sea, by diving from the surface and pursuing prey underwater. Most of what we know about auk diets has been learned from what the chicks are fed while at the colony. It is interesting that in the North Atlantic only one species, the Little auk, feeds almost exclusively on plankton, whereas in the North Pacific there are at least six plankton-feeding auk species, among them the Least auklet, Cassin's auklet and Parakeet auklet. This difference may be due to a greater total biomass and diversity of plankton in the North Pacific. Certainly there are also more individuals and species of plankton-feeding whales in the North Pacific than in the North Atlantic.

Auks are long-lived birds and there are several records of Common murres and Thick-billed murres that were ringed as

adults and found still breeding 20 years later! Like many other seabirds, auks show a number of features associated with great longevity. They characteristically have a low reproductive rate, laying only one or, in some species, two eggs each year. Young birds disperse away from the breeding colony and may spend two or three years at sea before they start breeding activities. The young of most auks do not breed until they are at least three years old. The Atlantic puffin provides a typical example of the sequence of events after the chick leaves the colony. It remains at sea away from the breeding area until its second summer, when it may visit its natal colony for a few weeks. Usually such two-year-old birds spend very little time on land. In its third summer the young puffin will return a little earlier and attempt (probably unsuccessfully) to find a mate and a suitable burrow to breed in. Egg-laying may occur for the first time in the fourth or fifth summer. Although auks generally breed with the same partner each year, the pair does not remain together over the winter. In all auk species, individual pairs use the same site year after year, whether it is a tiny rock ledge (eg Thick-billed murre) or an earth burrow (eg puffins and auklets). One advantage of such nest-site fidelity is that it enables pair members to meet up again each spring.

In ice-free areas, auks may return to their breeding colonies several weeks or months before breeding. This is particularly true of Common murres – at some British colonies, the birds may be present for four or five months before any eggs are laid. Even in more northerly regions, auks may spend several weeks at the colony prior to breeding. This time is spent re-establishing pair bonds, mating and, for puffins and auklets, cleaning out the nesting burrow. Copulation takes place at, or near, the breeding site (razorbills) or, in a few species (puffins), on the sea. Mating is frequent and, in some species, a noisy affair. In Common murres mating may occur 3–4 times a day in the 2–3 weeks prior to egg-laying, and each copulation lasts 20 seconds on average. In most songbirds, by comparison, copulation lasts only 1–2 seconds. Monogamy is the rule in all species, the male and female cooperating to rear the chick(s). Despite the monogamous mating system, male Common murres also attempt to mate with any unattended female in the colony. The arrival of a female can result in a frenzy of mating activity, with up to 10 males simultaneously trying to mount the female. These attempts may sometimes succeed, since the female is

of the same species. If the egg rolls away, as frequently occurs, the adult will retrieve it, ignoring the eggs of its neighbors.

It is just as important for chicks not to get mixed up, and chicks are also individually recognizable—by their voice. Common murre chicks take between one and five days to hatch after making the first hole in the eggshell. During this time the chick and parents call to each other, learning each other's voice. Once hatched, adults and chick can recognize one other; the parents care for and feed only their own chick.

often pinned to the ground and even if her partner is present he is unable adequately to defend her against such odds.

The eggs of auks are relatively large, and constitute between 10 and 23 percent of the female's body weight. Among burrow-nesting auks, the eggs are mainly white with a few darker markings. The eggs of Kittlitz's murrelet and the Marbled murrelet are cryptically colored olive green with dark blotches. These two species nest alone and in the open—Kittlitz's murrelet on the ground in the tundra vegetation or on rocky mountain slopes, and the Marbled murrelet on the ground or, probably more often, on the moss- and lichen-covered branches of large coniferous trees. The eggs of the Common murre and Thick-billed murre are among the most striking of any bird species, being very pointed and ranging in color from bright blue or green to white (see box, pp 54—55).

Most auk species, in common with most other seabirds, breed a considerable distance from their food supply, and can only provide enough food for a single chick. However, two-egg clutches do occur, typically in species which either feed close inshore (Black and Pigeon guillemots) or have chicks that are well developed on hatching (see p52). These two eggs are laid several days apart—three days in the Black guillemot and seven days in the Ancient murrelet. Incubation starts when the second egg is laid, so the chicks hatch at about the same time.

The male and female change places on the nest at intervals varying from just a few hours in the Black and Pigeon murres, to 12–24 hours in Common and Thick-billed murres, up to 72 hours in the Ancient murrelet. The duration of these incubation shifts also reflects the time required by the off-duty birds to find food.

In most species which have been studied, breeding success is generally high, with 50–80 percent of pairs successfully rearing young. Failures usually occur because of predation and infertility or, in cliff-nesting species, by eggs rolling off the breeding ledges. The pointed (pyriform) shape of guillemot eggs is commonly thought to prevent eggs from rolling off the breeding ledges. However, experiments have indicated that the shape is more likely to be an adaptation to the semi-upright posture of guillemots as they incubate. The shape maximizes the area of the egg touching the adult's brood patch.

The young of most species are fed by their parents at the colony. Among those species which breed on open ledges, such as the Common murre, Thick-billed murre and the razorbill, only one adult can forage for the chick at a time. The other parent must remain to brood the chick and protect it from predators such as gulls.

The Little auk feeds its young on crustaceans, such as shrimps, which range in size from 2–16mm (0.08–0.6in) in length. As in other plankton-feeding auks, food is carried back to the chick in a throat pouch, as a "plankton soup." Little auks feed their young 5–8 times a day and each meal contains on average 600 items, with a total weight of 0.1oz (3.5g). In contrast, the Common murre feeds its young mainly on fish that school at medium depths, such as capelin, sand eels or sprats. A single fish, weighing 0.4–0.5oz (10–15g), is carried back lengthwise in the bill; the chick is fed 2–5 times a day. The Black and Pigeon guillemots specialize in bottom-dwelling fish of similar size, such as blennies and sculpins. A single fish is carried crosswise in the bill to the chicks about nine times a day. Puffins usually carry several larval fish (up to 60 have been recorded) crosswise in their bill.

The process of young auks leaving the colony, conveniently but inaccurately referred to as "fledging," varies between species. Until relatively recently the details were poorly known, and obscured by strange myths and legends. For several species the truth is indeed quite remarkable, and seeing young auks leave the colony can be an unforgettable experience.

It was previously thought that young Atlantic puffins were deserted by their parents and starved into leaving the colony. In fact the parents continue to feed the chick up until the day it leaves the colony. Young puffins, Black guillemots and auklets fledge alone, at night, unaccompanied by their parents. They probably fly several hundred feet before alighting on the sea and dispersing away from the colony. By contrast, the young of the two other murres and the razorbill are still flightless when they leave the colony, accompanied by their father. Where they breed on 1,000ft (300m) cliffs, fledging can be spectacular. For several hours before leaving, the chicks become more and more excited, jumping up and down as they exercise their tiny wings, and uttering shrill "weeloo, weeloo" cries. Chicks may deliberate for several minutes before launching themselves into the air, and fluttering down onto the sea, closely followed by the father. In some areas, razorbills and murres do not have direct access to the sea; the chick may land on another ledge during its descent and may have to scramble

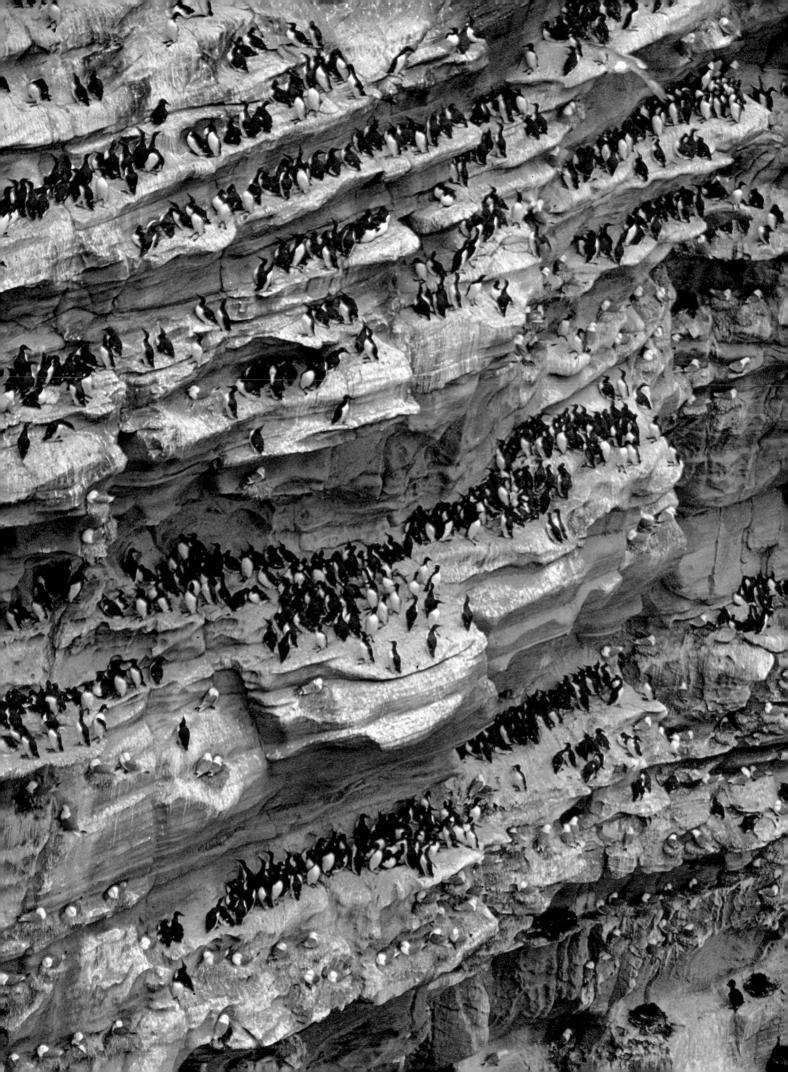

over boulders to reach the sea. Father and chick recognize each other's calls and the adult may find the chick and guide it to the sea. In a third variation on the fledging theme the young leave the nest when only about two days old. Among the four species of precocial murrelets (Ancient, Craveri's Japanese and Xantus's), both parents accompany the two tiny young to the sea. It is not known how long these auk chicks are cared for at sea by their parents.

Some colonies, like those of the Little auk, may be enormous and contain over a million birds. Only two species breed in solitary pairs, Kittlitz's murrelet and the Marbled murrelet. The Black and Pigeon guillemots breed in small, loose colonies. Solitary or loosely colonial species feed inshore on a predictable food supply. In contrast, colonial species typically feed further offshore and exploit patchily distributed, unpredictable prey, such as shoaling fish or plankton. The mobility of such prey makes it difficult to locate. It may be advantageous to be part of a colony so that information on the whereabouts of food can be obtained from other colony members. At large colonies the "traffic" between feeding areas and the colony may be sufficiently dense to enable birds to locate feeding areas simply by following the flight line of incoming birds.

Auks are especially vulnerable to any factor which reduces their numbers, because of their slow reproductive rate. Whereas a small songbird species might recover from

▲ **Razorbills,** stouter in build than murres (guillemots), and with a heavier bill bearing a white stripe. All auks use their wings to "fly" underwater in pursuit of their prey—fish or, in smaller species, plankton and crustaceans such as shrimps.

▲ **Black guillemot with sand eel prey** ABOVE RIGHT. Guillemots take fish from medium depths.

◄ **Whiskered and "horned,"** a Rhinoceros auklet (*Cerorhinca monocerata*) of the North Pacific.

▶ **The Least auklet,** smallest of the North Pacific plankton feeders, is half the size of the Rhinoceros auklet.

▶ **The Tufted puffin** FAR RIGHT (*Lunda cirrhata*) like other auks has a summer plumage with more white feathers; many auks also have heavier and more brightly colored bills, and some have whiskers or tufts, in the breeding season.

a 50 percent population reduction in one or two years, most auks might take 20 years to recoup such losses. In most parts of their range auks are thought to be much lower in numbers than they were previously.

Auks themselves, and their eggs, are highly palatable. Traditional hunting, using nets, snares etc on a local scale, probably had little effect on auk numbers, but the use of firearms and commercial egg-collecting have caused the extinction of many colonies and one entire species. Excessive egg-collecting of Common murre eggs at the Farallon Islands off California caused the murre population to fall from about 400,000 birds in 1850 to just a few hundred in the 1920s. The Thick-billed murre has suffered a similar fate in Novaya Zemlya, USSR, where both adults and eggs have been overexploited. Large numbers of the Great auk once bred on Funk Island, Newfoundland, but in the 17th century this became a regular stopping-off place for sailors and fishermen, who took many adult birds for food. Towards the end of the 17th century, the Greak auks were systematically killed for their feathers and, by 1800, the colony was extinct. The last Great auks were killed in 1844 on Eldey, a small island off Iceland.

Auks are particularly vulnerable to oiling, because they spend so much of their time on the sea. Fuel oil released onto the sea, either deliberately when cleaning tanks or as a result of accident, coats the birds' plumage and destroys their waterproofing. In some cases, oil is ingested as the birds attempt to clean themselves, and this may be toxic. During the past 40 years oil pollution has been a major cause of deaths in most auk populations.

Commercial fishing activities have also taken their toll. The Danish salmon gill-net fishery, for example, destroyed one-half to three-quarters of a million Thick-billed murres each year between 1968 and 1973. In recent years the number of auks drowned in gill nets may have fallen somewhat. A more widespread phenomenon is competition for the same species of fish. Up until the last 10 years or so, fish such as capelin, sand eel and sprat were important to the birds but of no commercial significance to man. However, now that the stocks of larger commercial fish, like cod, have been fished-out, man has turned his attention to those small fish upon which many species of auks depend for their food. If such fisheries are allowed to develop extensively in an unrestricted way, the consequences for the auks may be very grave.   TRB

SANDGROUSE

Order: Pteroclidiformes
Family: Pteroclididae.
Sixteen species in 2 genera.
Distribution: Africa, S Iberia and France,
Middle East to India and China.

Habitat: desert, semi-desert, dry grasslands,
arid savanna and bushveld.

Size: 10.6–19in (27–48cm) long, weighing
5.3–14.1oz (150–400g).

Plumage: mainly dull tones of buff, ocher,
rufous, olive, brown, black and white. Males
usually spotted or barred; most have black,
white or chestnut chest bands. Females usually
ocher or buff with black streaking and barring.
This sexual dimorphism is marked and
invariable. Central tail feathers very long in
several species.

Eggs: almost always 3, sometimes 2; elongated,
equally rounded at each end; light cream,
grayish, greenish or pink, blotched, smeared
and spotted with brown, red-brown, olive-
brown and gray; incubation 21–31 days;
fledging period about 4 weeks.

Diet: almost exclusively small dry seeds; some
other plant material, insects, small mollusks
and grit.

Voice: mellow whistled or chuckling calls in set
phrases of 2 or more syllables, usually given in
flight, and highly characteristic for each
species.

Nest: simple scrape in open or by a bush, stone
or grass tuft; sometimes scantily lined with dry
plant fragments or small stones.

Species: **Black-bellied sandgrouse** (*Pterocles
orientalis*), **Black-faced sandgrouse**
(*P. decoratus*), **Burchell's** or **Variegated
sandgrouse** (*P. burchelli*), **Chestnut-bellied
sandgrouse** (*P. exustus*), **Crowned** or **Coroneted
sandgrouse** (*P. coronatus*), **Double-
banded sandgrouse** (*P. bicinctus*), **Four-
banded sandgrouse** (*P. quadricinctus*),
Lichtenstein's sandgrouse (*P. lichtensteinii*),
Madagascar sandgrouse (*P. personatus*),
Namaqua sandgrouse (*P. namaqua*), **Painted
sandgrouse** (*P. indicus*), **Pallas's sandgrouse**
(*Syrrhaptes paradoxus*), **Pin-tailed sandgrouse**
(*Pterocles alchata*), **Spotted sandgrouse**
(*P. senegallus*), **Tibetan sandgrouse** (*Syrrhaptes
tibetanus*), **Yellow-throated sandgrouse** (*Pterocles
gutturalis*).

WITH their robust bodies, small heads
and short legs, sandgrouse can be mis-
taken for pigeons in silhouette, but their
markings are very different—beautifully
colored and patterned for camouflage in
their open, usually arid, habitat.

Most sandgrouse species are cryptically
spotted, barred or streaked; they crouch on
the ground to avoid detection, but their
long, pointed wings also enable them to
make a quick getaway in swift, direct flight,
rather like that of a plover. Their plumage
is dense; the entire body is covered with a
thick undercoat of dark down, and even the
base of the bill and the legs are feathered
(only in front in *Pterocles*, all round and
down to the toes in *Syrrhaptes*). This insu-
lates the bird against the temperature
extremes of night and midday, winter and
summer, and protects the nostrils against
windblown sand and dust. The hind toe is
lost (*Syrrhaptes*) or reduced (*Pterocles*) and

the three short front toes are stout and fairly
broad for walking on loose sand.

To judge from their feather structure,
general biology, behavior and chick
plumage patterns, the sandgrouse appear to
have arisen from a wader (shorebird)
ancestor, probably from the coursers
(p31). By contrast, the skeleton resembles
very closely that of the doves to which they
are undoubtedly related, but which arose
earlier from the same evolutionary line.

Sandgrouse eat mainly small seeds with
a relatively high protein content (in particular those of legumes) and a low water content (less than 10 percent water as a rule).
These they pick up by walking with small
steps, pecking frequently with their short
bills. The crop of an adult Black-bellied sandgrouse was found to contain about 8,700
indigo plant seeds, while that of a Namaqua
sandgrouse chick just a few days old con-
tained 1,400 tiny seeds. Sandgrouse take up

▷ **Water hole gathering** OVERLEAF of Namaqua sandgrouse in southwestern Africa. Large flocks of hundreds or thousands of birds gather daily at set times to drink at water holes. Males also soak their belly feathers in the water which they then take back to feed the chicks.

◀ **Chicks drink** from the belly feathers of a male Namaqua sandgrouse on his return from the water hole.

◀ **The Pin-tailed sandgrouse,** BELOW from southwestern Europe and North Africa to Central Asia and India.

grit to help break down the seeds in the gizzard. They feed for most of the daylight hours, resting only in the extreme heat of midday in summer, usually in the shade of a bush.

Sandgrouse need to drink every 2–3 days, possibly every day in hot weather. Large flocks of hundreds or thousands of birds gather daily at set times (depending on the species) at water holes. Most species drink in the morning only, but four are exclusively night-time drinkers (Painted, Lichtenstein's, Four-banded and Double-banded sandgrouse) and form a subgenus *Nyctiperdix*, characterized also by barred plumage in both sexes, and bold black-and-white frontal patches in the males.

Sandgrouse may fly up to 50mi (80km) one way to water, though seldom more than 12–20mi (20–30km). They assemble in ever-increasing numbers near the water, then fly or run to drink quickly, taking about 10 gulps of water, raising the head to swallow between each gulp. Some species, like Burchell's sandgrouse of the Kalahari, land

Flying Water Carriers

Young sandgrouse have a diet of dry seeds and are unable to fly or walk to the nearest isolated water hole. They must have water, however, and it is the male parent that is uniquely adapted to provide it. From the day they hatch, until at least two months later, young sandgrouse are brought drinking water in the soaked belly feathers of the adult male.

When the chicks are very small, the female flies off first to drink. On her return the male takes his turn while she takes over brooding. Before walking into the water, he rubs his belly in dry sand or soil to remove waterproofing preen oil; then he wades in belly-deep, keeping wings and tail well clear of the water, intermittently rocking his body up and down to work the water deeply into the belly feathers; this may take a few seconds or as much as 20 minutes. The returning male stands erect and the chicks run to drink from the central groove in his belly plumage. The chicks having drunk their fill, the male walks away, rubs his belly on a patch of sand to dry the feathers, and the family moves off to feed for the rest of the day.

The male's belly feathers have a unique structure which allows them to hold relatively large amounts of water on their inner surfaces, where evaporation is kept to a minimum. The barbules of the central portion of each belly feather are spirally coiled when dry, and they lie flat on the feather vane, tightly coiled together to give the feather structural cohesion. When wet, the barbules uncoil and stand at right angles to the feather vance, forming a dense bed of hairs about

0.004in deep, which holds water like a sponge.

With one exception, all sandgrouse species so far studied employ this water-carrying mechanism. (The Tibetan sandgrouse does not need to, as snow melt is always close by in the Central Asian mountains that are its home.) It certainly prevents the male parent from depleting his own internal water supply, as would happen if he were to regurgitate water from his crop in the same way as the doves. Furthermore, although the parents start with three young, usually only one survives to fly, so the demand for water transport by the male is limited.

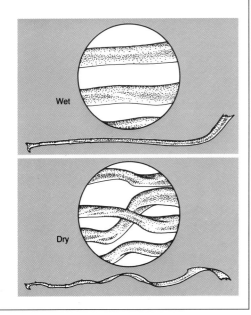

right at the water or even on the surface, floating like ducks while drinking, and taking off without effort. Sandgrouse will not normally drink water with a salt content higher than about 40 percent of that of sea water, since their kidneys are poorly adapted to excreting high salt concentrations. Furthermore they lack a salt gland, unlike most shorebirds, with which to excrete excess salt. In high temperatures (above about 99°F/37°C) sandgrouse tend to become inactive, seek shade and cease feeding, drooping their wings and holding their wrists well away from the body to increase heat loss.

Courtship involves head-down, tail-up chasing displays, similar to some threat displays. All species so far studied are monogamous, but are not very territorial. Northern Hemisphere species breed in spring and summer, Southern Hemisphere species mainly in winter; but in the Namib and Kalahari deserts of southern Africa times may vary depending at least partly on rainfall. The female usually incubates by day and the male at night, though this pattern may be somewhat different in the four members of the subgenus *Nyctiperdix* .

The chicks begin to feed on small seeds within a few hours of hatching. Seeds are shown to them by the pecking movements of the female parent. The young can fly a little at about four weeks, but are provided with water by the male (see box, p61) for at least another month, when they can fly well enough to accompany the parents to the water hole. They attain sexual maturity at about a year.

Non-breeding flocks of thousands of birds are known (such as in Namaqua sandgrouse), but these are exceptional other than at water holes. Flocks usually number 10–100 birds on their feeding grounds.

Sandgrouse are among the favorite prey of raptors, especially the Lanner falcon which hunts mainly at the water holes, as well as of such carnivores as foxes, jackals and mongooses, to which they are particularly vulnerable when nesting.

Sandgrouse are no longer in great demand for the pot and for sport, as they once were (attempts to introduce them from India and Pakistan into arid regions of the USA for sporting purposes have failed). Poor agricultural practices, exacerbated by drought, may be increasing the extent of suitable habitat. Combined with the provision of watering places fed by bore holes, conditions for most sandgrouse species have undoubtedly been improved by man's activities.   GLM

PIGEONS

Order: Columbiformes
Family: Columbidae.
About 300 species in 42 genera.
Distribution: widespread except Antarctica and high northern latitudes; members of the family have reached many isolated islands.

Habitat: most in woodland or forest; some in open country or on cliffs.

Size: 6–33in (15–82cm) long, weight 1–85oz (30–2,400g).

Plumage: the majority of species quietly colored in grays and browns; some more brightly colored; birds of the large tropical genus *Treron* mainly bright green. Some with crests. Sexes usually similar.

Voice: a wide range of soft calls and coos; song usually simple, consisting of only a few notes.

Nests: the large majority build simple twig nests on the branches of trees, a few nest in holes or on the ground.

Eggs: almost always either one or two, white; weight 0.1–1.8oz (2.5–50g). Many species have several broods. Incubation period 13–18 days in most species but 28 days in the largest; nestling period not well known for many species, but up to 35 days, possibly longer in some. However, in many species the young leave the nest before they are fully grown and complete their growth later.

Diet: primarily vegetable matter: fresh green leaves, fruit or seeds; several are serious pests of crops as a result.

Species include: **Collared dove** (*Streptopelia decaocto*), **Diamond dove** (*Geopelia cuneata*), **Eared dove** (*Zenaida auriculata*), **imperial pigeons** (*Ducula* species), **Mauritius pink pigeon** [E] (*Columba mayeri*), **Orange dove** (*Ptilinopus victor*), **Passenger pigeon** [Ex] (*Ectopistes migratorius*), **Plain-breasted ground dove** (*Columbina minuta*), **Purple-crowned pigeon** (*Ptilinopus superbus*), **Rock dove, Feral pigeon** or **Racing pigeon** (*Columba livia*), **Scaly-breasted ground dove** (*Columbina passerina*), **Stock dove** (*Columba oenas*), **Turtle dove** (*Streptopelia turtur*), **Victoria crowned pigeon** (*Goura victoria*).
Threatened species: 16.

[E] Endangered. [Ex] Extinct.

THAT pigeons are successful is evident to anyone who has seen the huge populations of feral birds (all descended from domesticated Rock doves) dwelling in the cities of Europe, Asia and America. These pigeons have benefited from the decline of their predators, the birds of prey, the presence of suitable nest-sites on buildings, and the human habit of feeding them. Pigeons, being mainly seed-eaters, have also benefited from the spread of agriculture. In both city and country, this success has brought them into conflict with people.

The family is found almost worldwide, with members in all regions except Antarctica. Some species, such as the Rock dove and Collared dove are even found north of the Arctic Circle. Pigeons are good dispersers, judging from their wide distribution on islands of the Indian and South Pacific Oceans, although they failed to reach a few isolated groups, such as the Hawaiian archipelago. Throughout their range, pigeons occur in a wide variety of terrestrial habitats, from tropical rain forests to deserts, and from above the snowline in the Himalayas to the centers of the largest cities.

Pigeons generally have plump stocky bodies with a small head and bill, and short legs. The plumage is soft and dense, and some tropical species are brilliantly colored or have ornamental crests, but most pigeons are dressed in neutral browns, grays and pinks, although often with small bright, or iridescent, patches on the wings or neck. In most species the sexes look similar, with the female slightly duller, but in some, for example the Orange dove, the sexes are very different in color. Juvenile plumage generally differs from that of adults, but molt into adult plumage occurs within months of leaving the nest.

Pigeons are typically tree-dwelling, but some cliff-dwelling and ground-dwelling species occur too. Tropical fruit-pigeons spend the most time in trees, feeding, roosting and nesting there, whereas many other species nest in trees but feed on the ground. Pigeons and doves feed on a wide variety of vegetable matter, with seeds, fruits, leaves, buds and flowers forming most of the diet, but many species take a limited amount of small snails and other invertebrates, particularly during the breeding season. Most species have a strong muscular gizzard and a long narrow intestine. Grit is often taken to help break down hard seeds in the gizzard. Some fruit-eating species, such as the imperial pigeons, have a strong stomach and a short wide gut. They digest only the pulp of the fruit they eat, voiding the stones

▲ **The Spotted dove** (*Streptopelia chinensis*), one of the turtle doves, and a species that has been successfully introduced to Mauritius, Hawaii, Reunion, Celebes, Moluccas and islands of the Flores Sea in Indonesia.

▶ **Peacock of the pigeon family** is the Victoria crowned pigeon. It is the largest pigeon, and the male uses the crest in a bowing display during courtship.

▼ **A flurry of white** from doves outside a mosque in Afghanistan. These are feral birds derived from white breeds of the Rock dove.

intact. Because the seeds are undamaged, pigeons can be important in the dispersal of fruiting plants, and many examples of the coevolution of fruiting plants and pigeons are known.

Unlike most birds, pigeons drink actively by immersing their bill in water up to their nostrils and sucking without raising their heads. Some species may fly considerable distances to water, where they gather in large flocks at dawn and dusk.

As a family, pigeons have a very limited range of vocalizations, most of which are recognizable as modifications of a "cooing" call. Some species additionally utter muted cries in certain circumstances. Normal flight is often noisy and in some situations this may be used as a social signal; during display and escape flights a wide range of species apparently attract attention by the loud noise made by clapping their wings together.

Pigeons are strong fliers and some migrate thousands of miles, for example the Turtle dove. Wing muscles make up as much as 32 percent of the body-weight of Rock doves which have been specially bred for their speed and homing abilities. Good "racing pigeons" can achieve mean flight speeds of around 44mph (70km/h).

Pigeons are often gregarious, gathering in large flocks at good feeding or roosting sites, and some species, such as the Eared dove, even breed colonially. The extinct Passenger pigeon of North America nested in enormous colonies: in the late 18th century there were thought to be as many as 3,000 million of them. Some of the colonies occupied several square miles and it was so easy to shoot them in large numbers that the bird was hunted commercially even

Pigeon Milk

Pigeons are very unusual among birds in that they produce a milk which has a chemical composition similar to that produced by mammals; flamingos are the only other birds to share this feature.

Pigeon or crop milk is a secretion of the adult crop which forms the complete diet of nestlings for the first few days of life. Thereafter, nestlings are fed an increasing percentage of food items obtained by the parents, but the actual quantity of milk in the mixture remains fairly constant until the young are well grown.

Crop milk is produced by both sexes in response to secretion of the pituitary hormone, prolactin (the same hormone is responsible for milk production in mammals). From about the midpoint of incubation the tissue of part of the crop begins to thicken and blood vessels grow into this region. Growth of the crop wall can more than triple the weight of the crop over the last half of incubation, and so by the time the young hatch, reddish folds with a honeycomb texture are visible in the crop. From this region, cells containing the "milk" are successively detached into the crop, and these are then regurgitated to the young. Milk cells are initially sloughed off only when the crop is empty, thus ensuring that it is not contaminated by other foods. Later, crop milk production is confined to periods when adults tend the young, but the milk is mixed with other foods.

Crop milk is a thick solution (19–35 percent dry matter) with a consistency and appearance of cottage cheese. It contains 65–81 percent water, 13–19 percent protein, 7–13 percent fat, 1–2 percent mineral matter and vitamins A, B and B_2, but no carbohydrates. The dry matter is mostly protein, which is composed of a large variety of amino acids. Crop milk compares well with mammalian milks as a source of essential fatty acids: it is low in calcium and phosphorus, but is high in sodium. Because of the high water content, milk production puts a relatively heavy drain on the adult body water reserves.

Milk production seems to be an adaptation to ensure that nestlings receive the adequate and predictable supply of energy and nutrients that are required for the high growth-rates that are characteristic of pigeons.

when it was greatly reduced in numbers. The species was exterminated in the wild in about 1900 and the last specimen died in Cincinnati Zoo in 1914.

Most pigeons and doves build a fragile-looking nest of interwoven twigs, usually in the branches of a tree, but sometimes on man-made structures. Some species nest in open situations on the ground, but others such as the Rock dove naturally nest in crevices or caves and, exceptionally, a few species such as the Stock dove nest in a true hole in a tree or in a burrow. The female

On the other hand, breeding seasons are often very long and many species have multiple broods, with up to eight in a year in some cases. This is helped by having short incubation and fledging periods compared with other birds of similar size, and by having successive clutches overlapped; that is, a new clutch is laid (sometimes in the same nest) while the parents are still tending young from the previous brood. Both sexes share in incubation and the care of young, and both produce pigeon milk (see box), which is rich in energy and nutrients and helps the nestlings to grow exceptionally rapidly. Chicks of all open-nesting pigeons studied to date fledge when still not adult size, and when still well below adult weight (usually about 65 percent, but as little as 26 percent in the case of the Purple-crowned pigeon). However, chicks of hole-nesting Stock doves fledge at about adult size and weight.

Some pigeons can breed at an exceptionally early age—five months in the case of Scaly-breasted ground doves—and many species are relatively long-lived, especially when kept in captivity.

The creation of large areas of agricultural land has greatly benefited a number of species. Many species were adapted to feed on grains and fruits before these were developed for human use, and in certain areas they have become a serious agricultural pest, for example the Eared dove in South America. Pigeons have the ability to fly into an area, quickly fill their crop with food, and return to the safety of woodland to digest their meal. Some species are potential carriers of agricultural diseases and even pose a health hazard to humans, especially the feral pigeons found in towns.

In recent years, the Collared dove has shown a dramatic spread. Originally it bred in Europe only in the extreme southwest. About the turn of the century, it started to spread slowly through the Balkans. From about 1930 it spread very rapidly northwestwards through Europe. It first bred in England in 1955 and within 15 years it has spread to almost all of the British Isles. Since then it has continued to increase very rapidly and is now virtually uncountable.

At the other end of the spectrum, many pigeons have very limited distributions, especially some of the island species, and many are seriously threatened by habitat destruction. Attempts are being made to increase the numbers of the Mauritius pink pigeon by reintroducing into the wild birds that have been raised in captivity.

generally builds the nest, but the male brings most of the material. All species lay only one or two white, or near-white eggs. The majority of species lay two eggs, but tropical, fruit-eating, or large species generally lay one-egg clutches. Pigeon eggs are exceptionally small in relation to adult body-size when compared with those of other birds and this, combined with the small clutch size, means that the pigeons have the smallest total clutch weights in relation to adult weight (about 9 percent) of all the families of nest-reared land birds.

▲ **Protected by prickles** of a cactus, a Mourning dove (*Zenaida macroura*) on its nest. This is the common dove of North America.

◄ **Young Turtle doves** begging food from parent. Even when nearly fledged, the regurgitated food will contain some milk secreted from the crop.

HR

PARROTS, LORIES AND COCKATOOS

Order: Psittaciformes
Family: Psittacidae.
Three hundred and twenty-eight species in 77 genera.
Distribution: S and C America, Africa and Madagascar, southern and SE Asia, Australasia and Polynesia.

► **The strikingly demarcated** colors of the male Australian king parrot, one of the most vivid of all parrots, seen here in heavily wooded country in eastern Australia.

▼ **Green-rumped parrotlets** (*Forpus passerinus*). Despite their reputation for gaudy coloring, most parrots are predominantly green.

PARROTS have been valued as cage-birds and pets since ancient times. Our earliest written account of a pet parrot is a Greek description of a Plum-headed parakeet dating from about 400BC. The author, a physician, was clearly captivated by the bird's ability to speak the language of its homeland, India, and also observed that it could be taught to speak Greek. From then on, it seems, exotically colored talking parrots became favorite status symbols among the ruling classes of Greece, Rome and Europe. Later, 15th- and 16th-century explorations in the New World brought to light many new parrot species, and these and subsequent discoveries in the East Indies and Australia helped to fuel the interest of European collectors.

Nowadays, a huge range of species is kept in captivity and, unfortunately, the aviculturist's obsession with novel or exotic forms is undoubtedly accelerating the extinction of some species. The budgerigar of Australia is the only species of parrot which has been truly domesticated. After the dog and cat it is probably the most common household pet in western countries.

The parrots form a distinctive and fairly uniform order of birds comprising the single family Psittacidae. Because of their many unique and specialized features it is difficult to determine the relationship between parrots and other groups of birds. They are usually, however, classified somewhere between pigeons and cuckoos, although their affinity with either of these orders is, at best, tenuous and indistinct. This suggests that parrots diverged from other lineages at a comparatively early stage in bird evolution. The earliest known fossil remains of a parrot is a single leg bone from *Achaeopsittacus verreauxi*, a lower Miocene species, some 30 million years old.

Parrots are widely distributed within the tropics and the Southern Hemisphere. The Carolina parakeet of North America was at one time the most northerly representative of the family. However, the species was wiped out in the early 20th century, and this title now belongs to the Slatey-headed parakeet of eastern Afghanistan although there are more northerly populations of introduced species such as the Monk parakeet in the eastern USA. Tierra del Fuego, the home of the Austral conure, marks the southern limit of parrot distribution. The Rose-ringed parakeet has the widest geographical distribution of any parrot. Its range extends from North Africa to the Far East and, recently, it has been introduced accidentally to parts of Europe. The parrot with the most restricted world distribution is probably Stephen's lory, a small species confined to the 13.5sq mi (35sq km) Henderson Island in the South Pacific. By far the largest number of different species of parrot is found in South America and Australasia, whereas relatively few species occur in Africa and Asia.

All parrots share a number of distinctive features in common. The most obvious of these is the characteristic parrot bill which consists of a downward-curving and somewhat hooked upper mandible which fits neatly over a smaller, upward-curving lower mandible. The upper half of the bill is attached to the skull by a special kind of hinge and this gives it greater mobility and leverage. The parrot bill is a highly adaptable structure. It can be used to perform delicate tasks such as preening, but at the same time is powerful enough to crush the hardest nuts and seeds. The bill also serves as a third "foot"—a kind of grappling-hook which the bird uses in conjunction with its feet when clambering about among the treetops. In the Great-billed parrot of Indonesia, the bill is abnormally large and bright red in color. This conspicuous structure presumably serves as some kind of visual display.

The feet of parrots are also unusual: the two outer toes of the foot point backwards and grip in opposition to the two forward-pointing inner toes. This arrangement

The Parrot Family (Psittacidae)

Ex Extinct. E Endangered. R Rare. V Vulnerable. I Threatened, but status indeterminate.

Three hundred and twenty-eight species in 77 genera.
S and C America, southern N America, Africa and Madagascar, southern and SE Asia, Australasia and Polynesia. Principally lowland tropical and subtropical forest and woodland; occasionally in mountain forest and open grassland. Size: length from 3.5–39in (9–100cm). Plumage: exceptionally variable: many species brilliantly colored, others predominantly greenish or brownish. Males and females usually similar or identical in appearance and coloration, with some notable exceptions. Voice: typically noisy and unmusical, involving enormous variety of calls. In captivity, some species become accomplished vocal mimics. Nests: usually in holes in trees; rarely in burrows in cliffs, soil or termitaria. A few species nest communally in large grass or twig

nests. Eggs: generally 2–8, depending on species; invariably white and relatively small; length from 0.5–2in; incubation period 17–35 days; nestling period 21–70 days. Diet: chiefly vegetable material: fruit, seeds, buds, nectar and pollen. Small insects occasionally ingested.

Species include: **African gray parrot** (*Psittacus erithacus*), **Austral conure** (*Enicognathus ferrugineus*), **Australian king parrot** (*Alisterus scapularis*), **Black lory** (*Chalcopsitta atra*), **Blue-crowned hanging parrot** (*Loriculus galgulus*), **Blue-and-yellow macaw** (*Ara ararauna*), **Blue-winged parrot** (*Neophema chrysostoma*), **Brown-throated conure** (*Aratinga pertinax*), **budgerigar** (*Melopsittacus undulatus*), **Buff-faced pygmy parrot** (*Micropsitta pusio*), **Carolina parakeet** Ex (*Conuropsis carolinensis*), **Crimson rosella** (*Platycercus elegans*), **Derbyan**

parakeet (*Psittacula derbiana*), **Eclectus parrot** (*Eclectus roratus*), **galah** (*Cacatua roseicapilla*), **Glaucous macaw** E (*Anodorhynchus glaucus*), **Golden-shouldered parrot** R (*Psephotus chrysopterygius*), **Great-billed parrot** (*Tanygnathus megalorhynchus*), **Ground parrot** V (*Pezoporus wallicus*), **Hispaniolan parrot** (*Amazona ventralis*), **Hyacinth macaw** (*Anodorhynchus hyacinthus*), **Imperial parrot** E (*Amazona imperialis*), **kakapo** E (*Strigops habroptilus*), **kea** (*Nestor notabilis*), **Monk parakeet** (*Myihopsitta monachus*), **Night parrot** I (*Geopsittacus occidentalis*), **Papuan lory** (*Charmosyna papou*), **Patagonian conure** (*Cyanoliseus patagonus*), **Peach-faced lovebird** (*Agapornis roseicollis*), **Plum-headed parakeet** (*Psittacula cyanocephala*), **Puerto Rican parrot** E (*Amazona vittata*), **Purple-crowned lorikeet** (*Glossopsitta*

porphyrocephala), **Rainbow lorikeet** (*Trichoglossus haematodus*), **Red-capped parrot** (*Purpureicephalus spurius*), **Red-rumped parrot** (*Psephotus haematonotus*), **Red-tailed amazon** E (*Amazona brasiliensis*), **Rock parrot** (*Neophema petrophila*), **Rose-ringed parakeet** (*Psittacula krameri*), **Scaly-breasted lorikeet** (*Trichoglossus chlorolepidotus*), **Sierra parakeet** (*Bolborhynchus aymara*), **Slatey-headed parakeet** (*Psittacula himalayana*), **Stephen's lory** (*Vini stepheni*), **Sulfur-crested cockatoo** (*Cacatua galerita*), **Swift parrot** (*Lathamus discolor*), **Varied lorikeet** (*Trichoglossus versicolor*), **Wilhelmina's lorikeet** (*Charmosyna wilhelminae*), **Yellow-faced parrot** (*Poicephalus flavifrons*). Total threatened species: 30.

(zygodactyly) not only provides parrots with an extremely powerful grasp, but also enables them to use their feet like hands for holding and manipulating objects close to the bill. In terms of manual dexterity, parrots are unsurpassed by any other group of birds. However, this ability is absent in species which feed habitually on the ground. Like humans, parrots also display both right- and left-handedness, or rather, footedness. In one study it was found that out of a flock of 56 Brown-throated conures, 28 consistently used the right foot to hold food while the other 28 used the left. When walking along a perch or on the ground, most parrots are noticeably pigeon-toed, and have a characteristic and somewhat comical swaggering gait.

Parrots are variable in their powers of flight. In general, flight is swift and direct in small species and relatively slow and laborious in larger ones. There are, however, some notable exceptions. The South American macaws, for instance, are fast fliers despite their size. Species such as the budgerigar and many of the lories are highly nomadic and are capable of flying considerable distances in search of food. The Swift parrot and Blue-winged parrot, both from southeastern Australia, are migratory and every year fly across Bass Strait—a distance of 124mi (200km)—in order to breed in Tasmania. As its name implies, the Swift parrot flies with exceptional speed and directness.

Differences in flying ability in parrots are linked with differences in wing structure. Generally speaking, species which fly rapidly have comparatively narrow, tapering wings, while the wings of slow-flying forms are correspondingly broad and blunt. The kakapo of New Zealand has very short wings and is the only parrot which is entirely flightless. The structure of the tail in parrots is highly variable. In macaws and in the Papuan lory, tails are especially long and elegant and may comprise almost two-thirds of the bird's total length. Long tails like this probably serve an important signalling function. At the other extreme, the tail of the Blue-crowned hanging parrot is so short and blunt that it is almost concealed by the tail coverts. The racket-tailed parrots of Indonesia and the Philippines have distinctive elongated central tail feathers which consist of long, bare shafts with flattened spoon-shaped tips. The function of these unusual tail structures is unknown. The tail feathers of the New Guinea pygmy parrots also terminate in short bare shafts. These are stiffened and help to support these tiny birds when they are climbing about and feeding on tree-trunks.

Parrots are renowned for their gaudy plumage, and some of the larger, tropical species such as the South American macaws

▲◀ **Representative species of parrots.**
(1) Hyacinth macaw (*Anodorhynchus hyacinthinus*) using zygodactylous claws to grip Brazil nut. (2) Rainbow lorikeet (*Trichoglossus haematodus*). (3) Fischer's lovebird (*Agapornis fischeri*). (4) Female Eclectus parrot (*Eclectus roratus*). (5) Sulfur-crested cockatoo (*Cacatua galerita*). (6) Black-capped lory (*Lorius lory*) showing the adaptation of the tongue for feeding on nectar. (7) Crimson rosella (*Platycercus elegans*). (8) Red-capped parrot (*Purpureicephalus spurius*). (9) Blue-crowned hanging parrot (*Loriculus galgulus*). (10) Kea (*Nestor notabilis*).

are undoubtedly among the most brilliantly colored of all birds. Despite this, the majority of species are predominantly green and are well camouflaged among the foliage in which they live. The large cockatoos of Australia are highly conspicuous. Most of them have prominent erectile crests on their heads, and they are generally either white, salmon-pink or black in color. Males and females in the majority of parrots are either very similar or identical in appearance. However, there are some notable exceptions to this rule. For example, males of the Australian king parrot have brilliant scarlet plumage, whereas females and juveniles are almost entirely green. In the Eclectus parrot of New Guinea and Australia, males and females are so different in coloration that for many years they were thought to belong to different species. Males are bright emerald green with scarlet underwings and flanks, while the female is a rich crimson red with a violet-blue belly and lower breast. This species is also unique among parrots in that the female is gaudier and more conspicuous than the male.

The vast majority of parrots are very much tree-dwellers, and they tend to be most plentiful in and around lowland tropical forests. A number, such as the budgerigar of Australia and Fischer's lovebird of East Africa, inhabit more open, grassy habitats, but even these species are generally never seen very far from the cover of trees. Two exceptions are the completely terrestrial Ground and Night parrots of Australia. The former inhabits coastal heaths and sand dunes; and the latter, which until very recently was thought to be extinct, is confined to arid desert grassland. Although parrots are generally less common at high altitudes, several distinctive species are restricted to mountains. These include the Papuan lory from New Guinea, the Derbyan parakeet from the Himalayas, the Yellow-faced parrot from Ethiopia, and the Sierra parakeet from the South American Andes.

The kea of the Southern Alps of New Zealand is perhaps the most unusual of all highland forms. These large bronze birds live among snow-covered mountains between 2,000 and 6,500ft (600–2,000m), and appear to enjoy rolling and frollicking in the snow. Around ski resorts and human habitations they are bold and inquisitive and have been known to enter buildings through chimneys in order to steal food. In addition to their normal vegetarian diet, keas have also taken to feeding on rubbish tips and carrion, and they have even

acquired a widespread though exaggerated reputation for killing sheep.

Seeds and fruits of various kinds make up the diet of the majority of parrots, although the lories and lorikeets of Australasia specialize in feeding on tree pollen and nectar (see pp76–77). Most parrots procure their food in the treetops, where their zygodactylous feet and hooked bills enable them to climb about with extraordinary skill and agility. However, some of the smaller parakeets, parrotlets and lovebirds feed extensively on grass seeds on or near the ground.

Parrots have a reputation for extreme longevity. In captivity, some of the larger species live from 30–50 years, and 80 years has even been reported in some cases. Generally speaking, the smaller species have much shorter life spans. Most parrots attain sexual maturity between their second and fourth years.

The timing and duration of the breeding season in parrots depends very much on their geographic location and on the principal types of food on which they depend. In general, species living outside the tropics, where food availability tends to be

► **Yellow blaze in the sky** of a Blue-and-yellow macaw, a large species often kept in captivity. Distribution of macaws, largest of all parrots, is centered on the Amazon Basin. Like all macaws, collectings birds in the wild is threatening populations. However, captive breeding is successful and may stop this drain.

▼ **A flock of galahs.** These elegant pink and gray birds are the commonest parrots in Australia. They feed in large numbers on crops, often causing considerable damage.

seasonal, have more regular and better defined breeding seasons than those in tropical regions. For instance, the Purple-crowned lorikeet of southern Australia breeds from August to December, whereas the Varied lorikeet from Australia's northern tropics will breed at any time of the year. Most parrots are monogamous, and males and females often pair for life. Pairs remain together constantly and the bond between them is reinforced by mutual feeding and preening. The details of courtship have only been described for a few species. Prior to copulation, the males of most species display to the females with a variety of relatively simple movements and postures, including bowing, hopping, wing-flicking and flapping, tail-wagging and strutting. Areas of conspicuous plumage are often incorporated in these movements and, in many species, the brightly colored irises of the eye are expanded—a phenomenon known appropriately as "eye-blazing." When the female is ready to mate she adopts a characteristic crouching position and allows the male to mount. The male's attempts at copulation are often interspersed with curious treading movements performed on the female's back. The function of these movements is unknown.

The two New Zealand species, the kea and the kakapo or Owl parrot, are both polygamous. In the former, males sometimes mate and share parental duties with several different females at the same time. The mating system of the nocturnal kakapo is highly unusual. The males congregate at night in specific areas, known as leks, and advertise their location with loud booming calls. Females then visit these sites and mate with the male of their choice. As far as is known, male kakapos play no part in parental care. Because it is flightless and therefore highly vulnerable to introduced domestic cats, the kakapo has vanished from the North Island of New Zealand and is almost extinct on the South Island, where a few individuals are known to survive still in Fjordland. A small population of kakapos still exists on Stewart Island, and some of these have recently been transferred to Little Barrier Island.

The majority of parrots—large and small—nest in holes in the limbs or trunks of trees, often at a considerable height above the ground. These they either excavate themselves or steal from other hole-nesting species such as woodpeckers. The nest cavity is generally lined with a layer of decayed wood-dust, although the African lovebirds and the hanging parrots of Asia line their nests with grasses, leaves and strips of bark which the female collects and carries to the nest tucked under the feathers of her rump. Termite colonies are also exploited as nest-sites by a number of parrot species. The Golden-shouldered parrot of Australia excavates its nest burrow in terrestrial termite mounds, while the Buff-faced pygmy parrot of New Guinea makes its nest in tree-borne termitaria. The termites presumably provide a certain amount of protection from predators.

Talking Parrots

The talking abilities of captive parrots have attracted human interest since ancient times. Most people assume that parrots merely mimic sounds at random and are incapable of using speech in appropriate contexts—hence the phrase: to learn something "parrot-fashion," meaning to memorize things without understanding them. Recent research in the USA, however, suggests that some parrots can be trained to use human language as a means of communicating intelligently with people.

After months of careful instruction, researchers at Purdue University have succeeded in training Alex—a young male African gray parrot—to learn verbal labels for 23 different objects or materials such as paper, cork, nut, rock and water. He also knows five different colors, four different shapes, numbers up to five, and commands such as "want," "come here" and "you tickle me." More to the point, Alex is able to combine these vocalizations to identify, request or refuse more than 50 different items, even items which were not included as part of his original training schedule. During his second year of training, and without any formal instruction, Alex also began using the word "no" when he didn't want to be handled. This was a particularly interesting development, since linguists regard negation as a relatively advanced conceptual achievement. Alex is a long way from being able to hold a conversation with his trainers, but he is less than three years old and his verbal abilities already far exceed any previous expectations.

Unlike many other avian mimics, parrots have never been observed to imitate calls of other species in the wild. It is therefore something of a mystery why this ability appears so well developed in captive birds. The calls of wild parrots are often enormously diverse and variable, and it has been suggested that parrots need their extraordinary imitative powers in order to learn to communicate effectively with each other. However, in the abnormal social conditions of captivity this desire to imitate members of the same species is transferred to humans and human vocalizations.

The Rock parrot nests only under rocks just above the high-tide mark on the coast of southern Australia, while the Patagonian conure excavates nesting burrows up to 10ft (3m) long in the cliffs and river banks of Patagonia. The Ground parrot of Australia makes its nest in a shallow depression under a bush or grass tussock. Several species of parrot nest colonially. The Peach-faced love-bird either constructs its own nesting colonies from grasses and leaves or, more often, invades and takes over the existing colonies of weaver-finches. Perhaps the most advanced nesting behavior among parrots is found in the South American Monk parakeet. This species nests communally in immense structures which they build from twigs in the tops of trees. Within the main structure, each pair has its own separate nest-chamber.

In all but a few species of parrot, the eggs are incubated exclusively by the female. The male, however, keeps her supplied with food during this critical period. The young are blind and helpless when they hatch, and develop rather slowly. In small species such as the budgerigar they leave the nest 3–4 weeks after hatching, but in the much larger Blue-and-yellow macaw the nestling period may be as long as 3½ months. As a rule, both parents play an equal role in feeding the young. Juvenile parrots are generally noticeably smaller than the adults of either sex and they also tend to have duller plumage colors.

Although a few atypical species, such as the Australian Ground parrot, seem to be largely solitary, the vast majority of parrots are sociable and gregarious birds which are usually observed in pairs, family parties or small flocks. Occasionally, when conditions are appropriate, some of the smaller species aggregate in very large numbers. Observers in Australia, for example, sometimes report flocks of wild budgerigars so vast that they darken the sky. When wild populations of parrots reach these proportions they sometimes cause serious damage to crops. Fortunately, population explosions of this kind are comparatively rare, and are usually brought under control by natural mortality due to starvation and diseases such as ornithosis (psittacosis), to which parrots are particularly susceptible.

Apart from man, the most important predators of parrots are various hawks and falcons, although monkeys and other tree-dwelling mammals are also responsible for taking a significant number of eggs and nestlings. When feeding in flocks, parrots are often noisy and quarrelsome and appear to be oblivious to potential predators. However, when danger threatens, these flocks fall perfectly silent before exploding suddenly from the treetops accompanied by harsh screams. Most predators find the ensuing chaos and confusion disconcerting.

On the principle that there is safety in numbers, many species of parrot also roost communally at night. Communal roosts are often in traditional locations and tend to be used year after year. Favored sites often consist of exceptionally tall or isolated trees where the birds can get a good view of approaching predators. Asian hanging parrots have the distinction of roosting suspended upside-down like bats. At a distance, it is difficult to distinguish a dead tree full of roosting hanging parrots from a tree with normal foliage.

Parrots are among the noisiest of all birds and, in general, their voices are harsh and unmelodic. Calls include a range of chatters, squeaks, shrieks, clicks, squawks and screams, many of them loud, discordant and thoroughly disagreeable. The Crimson rosella of Australia has a pleasant whistle-like call and another Australian species, the Red-rumped parrot, produces a melodious trilled whistle which is about the nearest any parrot has come to a song. In some species, pair-mates perform vocal duets—rapidly alternating sequences of calls which are exchanged between partners. Parrots are notorious vocal mimics, although this ability is only apparent in captive birds (see box). Parrots, particularly the larger species, are playful and inquisitive and are thought to be relatively intelligent. Like primates, they are easily bored by captivity and may become destructive and belligerent as a result.

Although as a group parrots are comparatively successful, many species have become extinct within the last few centuries and many more are seriously endangered. One of the most mysterious disappearances was that of the Carolina parakeet of the southeastern USA. During the early part of the 19th century this species was common throughout its range, but by 1831 it was already on the decline and the last known specimen died in Cincinnati Zoo on the 21st February 1918. It is not known what caused the extinction of the Carolina parakeet. However, the species was regarded as an agricultural pest and there is little doubt that human persecution played a major part in its initial decline.

Nowadays, the most serious threat to parrots is the continued uncontrolled destruction of the world's tropical and subtropical

▲ **Rainbow rockface.** The Green-winged (or Red-and-green) macaw (*Ara chloroptera*) and the Scarlet (or Red-and-yellow) macaw (*A. macao*) belie their names in having most of the other colors of the rainbow as well.

▶ **A budgerigar** leaving its nest-hole in a tree. In the Australian outback all but a very few (yellow) budgerigars are green. Budgerigars have been bred in captivity for 100 years for their colorful plumage, lively disposition and ability to mimic or "talk." Captive breeds may have blue, gray, violet, red-eyed, clearwing or pied plumage.

forests, since these are the preferred habitat for the majority of parrot species. In southeastern Brazil, for example, forest cover has been so reduced by felling that species such as the Glaucous macaw and the Red-tailed amazon are now seriously threatened and, in the case of the macaw, may already be extinct. The other major threat to rare parrots is the voracious demand of the pet-trade.

Island species of parrot are especially vulnerable to human activities. Most have small populations and relatively slow breeding rates and, because they have evolved in isolation, they tend to be more sensitive to habitat destruction and less able to cope with introduced competitors, predators and diseases. In 1975 there were only 13 Puerto Rican parrots left in the wild and it looked as though the species was doomed. However, an emergency conservation program involving strict control of hunting and trapping, artificially increasing the number of suitable nest-sites, and cross-fostering of eggs and nestlings between the Puerto Rican parrot and the closely related and non-endangered Hispaniolan parrot, has had dramatic success. In October 1982 the wild population had more than doubled and there were also 15 birds carefully maintained in captivity. This recovery clearly shows what can be done when sufficient manpower and resources are available.

JAS

Lotus-eaters

Nectar-feeding lories and lorikeets

Lories and lorikeets are flamboyant, almost theatrical birds. The Rainbow lorikeet possesses up to 30 different ritualized gestures, including a variety of stylized hopping, walking, flying and preening movements, which it incorporates into elaborate "dances." Most of these performances are aggressive and are used to intimidate rivals of the same species, but males also use similar displays to impress females during courtship.

The lories and lorikeets form a distinct subgroup within the parrot family. They occur throughout much of Indonesia, New Guinea, Australia and the Pacific, and they differ from other parrots in their habit of feeding mainly on pollen and nectar from flowering trees and shrubs.

Typically, lories and lorikeets have sleek, glossy plumage, and the group includes some of the most brilliantly colored of all parrots. In the wild, they are mostly gregarious and their behavior is generally noisy and conspicuous. The most widespread of the lories is the Rainbow lorikeet which is distributed throughout eastern Indonesia, New Guinea, northern and eastern Australia, and the western Pacific islands. The species is divided up into 22 distinct island races or subspecies. The mountainous island of New Guinea has by far the highest diversity of different species and is also close to the geographic center of their distribution.

In order to cope with their specialized diet, these birds have evolved structural modifications of the bill, tongue and alimentary canal. The bills of lories are narrower, more elongate and less powerful than those of other parrots, and the gizzard—the muscular organ used by most other species to pulverize hard or fibrous foods—is relatively thin-walled and weak. Their most striking adaptation is the tongue, which is rather long for a parrot and equipped with a tuft of thread-like papillae at its tip. These papillae are normally enclosed within a protective cup-like sheath when the bird is at rest or feeding on fairly substantial foods such as fruit or seeds, but they can be expanded like the tentacles of a sea-anemone when the tongue is extended to feed on flowers. In this state, the tongue is an effective instrument for mopping up pollen and nectar. Fringe- or brush-tipped tongues are also found in several other families of nectar-feeding birds (the same adaptations are found in some species of nectar-feeding bats).

Few of the tree and shrub species exploited by lories for food have distinct flowering seasons. Individual flowering trees of the same species are often highly dispersed, and pollen and nectar production can vary considerably from year to year, as can the length of the flowering period. The locally abundant but highly erratic nature of this food resource has a number of important consequences for the birds. For example, most species of lory and lorikeet are highly nomadic and cover considerable distances in search of food. In the Pacific region, Rainbow lorikeets have been observed flying up to 50mi (80km) between neighboring islands. Lories also tend to be opportunist breeders. In other words, instead of confining themselves to a fixed breeding season, pairs generally start to breed whenever sufficient pollen and nectar is available. In practice, breeding tends to peak during the rainiest part of the year, since this also corresponds to the period when most trees come into flower. Lories are monogamous and, as far as is known, males and females pair for life. As in many other parrots, enduring pair-bonds have probably evolved in response to ecological factors. The absence of a well-defined breeding season favors a continuous, year-round association between pair-mates so that their reproductive cycles are always synchronized, as they

▲ **Pugnacious lorikeets** have a large repertoire of displays which they incorporate into "dances" performed in the face of rivals and, by males, in courtship. Among the gestures employed are: (1) the "hiss-up," (2) "strong fluttering," (3) "ritualized scratching," (4) "bobbing," (5) "bouncing."

► **A Rainbow lorikeet** feeding on a silk oak, *Grevillea dryandrii*. The tongues of lorikeets have a tuft of thread-like papillae at the tip which they use to mop up pollen and nectar from flowers.

▼ **Lorikeets all in a row.** The four birds lower down the branch are Rainbow lorikeets; that at the top of the branch is a Scaly-breasted lorikeet.

5

can commence breeding whenever conditions are suitable.

Lories are exceptionally pugnacious birds and many have evolved unusually elaborate threat displays. This behavior may also be an adaptation to feeding on flowers. When trees come into flower within the tropics they tend to attract considerable numbers of birds of different species, all eager to exploit the temporary abundance of pollen and nectar. Within this highly competitive environment, the more aggressive species such as lories seem to be at an advantage. In Australia, lories have also become exceptionally bold and opportunistic in their rela-

tionships with people. Rainbow and Scaly-breasted lorikeets inhabit city suburbs and are easily persuaded to visit bird-tables. In parts of Queensland, huge flocks of these two species are fed publicly for the entertainment of tourists.

The group includes a number of very rare and endangered species. Stephen's lory, the most easterly representative of the group, is confined to Henderson Island in the Pitcairn Archipelago. Several members of the eastern Polynesian genus *Vini* are currently threatened by habitat destruction, illegal trapping and the effects of introduced avian malaria.   JAS

CUCKOOS, TURACOS AND HOATZIN

Order: Cuculiformes
Families: Cuculidae, Musophagidae,
Opisthocomidae.
One hundred and fifty species in 34 genera.
Distribution: see map and table.

Turacos   Hoatzin   Cuckoos

▶ **The Great spotted cuckoo** ABOVE, an African and southern European species, and one of the most elegant cuckoos. Its main hosts are small crows such as magpies.

▶ **The Blue-headed coucal** BELOW (*Centropus monachus*) of Africa builds its own, domed nest and cares for its young.

IN ENGLAND, spring begins in a curious way: buyers of the London *Times* eagerly turn to the letters page, hoping that nature's own confirmation of springtime—the cuckoo's *cuck-coo, cuck-coo* call—has been duly reported. The irony is that many of these keen correspondents and readers will never have laid eyes on a cuckoo, having detected its presence only by the call. The European cuckoo thus has the distinction—to add to its notorious parasitism—that its annual cycle impinges on human habits in this peculiar way.

The **cuckoos** are a very diverse family: the sturdy roadrunner of arid North American deserts bears precious little resemblance to the delicate Klaas's cuckoo of the African bush. Details of internal anatomy, as well as the possession of a foot having two toes pointing forwards and two back (zygodactyly), distinguish cuckoos from the superficially similar songbirds and relate them to the parrots and nightjars. This unusual foot structure gives the cuckoos the ability to climb stealthily among slender reed stems or run swiftly over the ground with almost equal poise.

Many species are reminiscent of small hawks, having a distinctly downcurved bill and long tail, and share with these birds the discomfort of "mobbing" attacks by small songbirds. The reason for these unwelcome attentions is, of course, that many cuckoos reproductively parasitize the smaller birds.

The 3 Families of Cuckoos, Turacos and Hoatzin

Cuckoos
Family: Cuculidae
One hundred and twenty-seven species in 28 genera.
Europe, Africa, Asia, Australasia, N America, S America. Most species sedentary, tropical or subtropical, though a number of migratory species extend to temperate latitudes. Arid desert to humid forest and even moorlands (European cuckoo), but most species typical of light to heavy scrub and woodland, often with an affinity for watercourses. Size: 7–26in (17–65cm) long and 1–25oz (30–700g). Sexes usually similar in size, males sometimes slightly larger. A family characteristic is that sizes and weights are unusually variable within each sex. Plumage: generally subdued grays and browns, underparts often barred and/or streaked, tail sometimes conspicuous with spots or flashes when opened. Voice: generally simple flutes, whistles and hiccups exemplified by the disyllabic note which gives the

group its name. Also many harsh notes, especially by fledglings. In at least some species, voice differs between the sexes. Eggs: parasitic species may lay 10–15 per season, although more may be stimulated by unusually high losses; nonparasitic species 2–5; weights from 0.3–2.5oz (8–70g). The eggs of nonparasitic species are very heavy relative to female body-weight. Incubation period 11–16 days; nestling period 16–24 days. Egg color variable due to mimicry of host eggs in parasitic species. Diet: almost completely insectivorous, with most species taking noxious prey (eg hairy caterpillars) unavailable to other groups of birds. Larger forms take some smaller vertebrates; one genus (*Eudynamys*) largely vegetarian.

Species include: **Black-billed cuckoo** (*Coccyzus erythrophthalmus*), **European cuckoo** (*Cuculus canorus*), **Great spotted cuckoo** (*Clamator glandarius*), **Groove-billed ani** (*Crotophaga sulcirostris*), **Klaas's cuckoo**

(*Chrysococcyx klaas*), **koel** (*Eudynamys scolopacea*), **Pheasant coucal** (*Centropus phasianinus*), **roadrunner** (*Geococcyx californianus*).

Turacos
Family: Musophagidae
Twenty-two species in 5 genera.
Central and southern Africa. Evergreen forest, wooded valleys. More rarely savanna. Size: 14–30in (35–75cm) long, weight 8–34oz (230–950g). Plumage: either dark glossy green with red patches on wings and head crest, or duller gray or blue-gray; sexes similar. Voice: one- or two-syllable barks with some longer wailing notes. Eggs: 2–3, usually glossy white or pale blue/green; weight 0.7–1.6oz (20–45g); incubation period 21–24 days; nestling period 10–12 days. Diet: fruit, some invertebrates.

Species include: **Great blue turaco** (*Corythaeola cristata*), **Guinea turaco** (*Tauraco macrorhynchus*), **Violet**

plantain-eater (*Musophaga violacea*), **White-bellied go-away bird** (*Corythaixoides leucogaster*).

Hoatzin
Family: Opisthocomidae
Sole species *Opisthocomus hoazin*.
Northern S America. Rain forest. Size: 24in (60cm), weight 28oz (800g). Plumage: dark brown on back, buff below, shading to chestnut on abdomen and sides; facial skin electric blue; head quills chestnut with dark tips; tail with a broad buff tip. Voice: various calls, including a clucking courtship call, a mewing feeding call, a wheezing alarm call, and a sharp screech like a guinea fowl. Nests: twigs and sticks, in trees or large bushes, usually over water. Eggs: 2–3 (occasionally 4 or 5), buff, dappled with brown or blue spots; weight 1oz (30g); incubation period 28 days; chicks start to feed themselves at 10–14 days. Diet: leaves, flowers and fruits of marsh plants.

The cuckoo egg develops very rapidly and, even if some host eggs were already incubated when parasitism occurred, is generally the first in the nest to hatch. At this point the cuckoo nestling displays an adaptation at least as remarkable as those of its mother. The tiny pink body thrashes about in the nest until a hollow in its back comes into contact with another object, either another egg or another small chick. The cuckoo then begins to climb the inside of the nest, using surprisingly powerful legs, until it reaches the rim and ejects its little load into oblivion. Within a short time it begins again, repeating the task until all other objects have been ejected from the nest. What the cuckoo has done, of course, is to eliminate any possible competition and ensure that its innocent foster parents concentrate their reproductive efforts on one thing—the raising of the voracious cuckoo!

This pattern is not invariant among the cuckoos. Many species, for instance the Great spotted cuckoo and the koel, do not show ejection behavior and share the nest with offspring of the host species, in these species usually crows. However, the aim is the same and only the methods are different. The rapidly growing and more active cuckoo nestling either tramples the crow chicks to death underfoot or, more subtly, monopolizes the food brought to the nest by its foster parents.

In an evolutionary sense it is surprising that cuckoo nestlings succeed in obtaining parental care from foster parents, when selection against this behavior must be very strong indeed (see pp84–85). Mimicry of egg color and size may increase the chances of host acceptance, and appear to be very finely tuned to the resident host population. For example, the Brown babbler is a central African host species which lays clear blue eggs over most of its range, but in one part of northern Nigeria lays pink or mauve eggs. Incredibly, its cuckoo parasite has evolved to faithfully mimic these changes in coloration. The accuracy of this kind of local mimicry is presumably dependent upon the high degree of breeding site tenacity in both migratory and nonmigratory cuckoos: a female which tried to breed other than close to where she was hatched might find her eggs a discordant mismatch to those of the resident hosts!

Even after hatching, the cuckoo nestling must continue the deception to be able to obtain food from its foster parents. This trickery seems to be achieved by the cuckoo exploiting the signals that usually pass between parent and offspring in the nest.

About 45 species have no other habit of reproduction than to place their eggs in the nests of another species of bird. The European cuckoo female defends a territory within which she keeps a close eye on the comings and goings of the resident songbirds. In fact she is concerned only with one of her resident species, for her eggs are characteristic in color and will closely match the eggs of only one potential host species. Some of these territorial females also allow a second, subordinate female to use the territory, but perhaps only if these are dependent upon an entirely different host species, thereby avoiding competition for host nests. When a suitable nest becomes available, usually one in which laying has just begun, the cuckoo flies warily down, takes one host egg in its bill, and quickly deposits a single egg in the nest. The stolen host egg, and the mimicry of the egg color, ensure that the clutch appears untouched when the rightful owner returns. This delicate operation successfully completed, the cuckoo eats the stolen egg as reward for its stealth!

I

The Great spotted cuckoo produces a passable imitation of the begging calls of nestling magpies and its wide open gape is even more vivid than those of the host nestlings. The motivation to respond to these stimuli is so strong in small songbirds that, once it has left the nest, the fledgling European cuckoo may be fed by passing birds that are neither true nor foster parents! This huge adoptee could in fact be quite a hazard to foster parents or others which attempt to feed it. A cuckoo's bill is powerful compared with that of a dunnock or Reed warbler host and capable of causing injury if the nestling is too eager to seize offered food. For this reason, the acceptance of food in the cuckoo is quite unlike that in other nestlings which close the bill rapidly over that of the parent as the food is transferred. The parasite, in deference to its tiny guardians, keeps its huge gape open until well after the parents have safely departed!

The remarkable behavior of such cuckoos tends to obscure the fact that about two-thirds of the species appear to be nonparasitic in breeding habits, mating monogamously and remaining together while the offspring are reared. The Pheasant coucal is one such species—producing one or two grotesque black nestlings which, in common with many cuckoos, excrete a foul liquid when they suspect the presence of a predator. However, our knowledge of most species is extremely poor, and some of these may turn out to be parasitic at least in certain circumstances.

One of the most remarkable things about the cuckoos is that even the nonparasitic members turn out to be unusual in other ways, and the roadrunner is just such a bird. This "outlier" of the cuckoo family, living in the desert chapparal of southwestern North America, was once heavily persecuted in the belief that it was harmful to populations of gamebirds. In fact it eats an assortment of large invertebrates and is also a voracious predator on small lizards. Travelers' tales have embellished the reputation of the roadrunner: in one popular story the bird delicately wields a cactus leaf, teasing an angry rattlesnake until it strikes and becomes impaled on one of the bird's thorny weapons.

Rather more firmly established is the fact that this species displays a physiology which is most unusual among birds—it is to some extent cold-blooded! When air temperatures become very low, as in deserts during the night, most birds need to increase metabolism to maintain their internal body temperature at a constant, high level. This of course means burning internal food reserves at an increasing rate. The roadrunner takes a more economical course—it simply allows its body temperature to fall slightly, turning down the "central heating" with no ill effects, and a saving in energy costs. The bird does in fact go into a slight torpor and may not be able to respond as quickly to sudden danger, but for a bird which has few predators this slight disadvantage may be relatively unimportant.

When the first rays of light break the cool of the desert night, the roadrunner displays a neat trick for warming up. Areas of skin on the back, just between the wings, are darkly pigmented and absorb the energy of sunlight, warming the skin and underlying blood vessels. To hasten this process, the bird fluffs the feathers covering the patches so that the light penetrates more effectively, and with this mechanism the bird can save up to about 50 percent of the energy it would otherwise use to warm up to a working temperature.

Thankfully, and unlike many other groups of fascinating and understudied birds, the cuckoos do not seem at great risk from man's activities. Many species are characteristic of scrub, secondary forest,

9

T.B

and other types of disturbed ground which, if anything, increase under human interference.   JAH

For all its weird and wonderful animal species Africa contains only one large family of birds totally restricted to that continent—the **turacos**. This group is so poorly known that for years it labored under the name of "Plantain-eaters," until reports filtered through that they rarely or never ate plantains or bananas. Subsistence through the aeons of time would, in any case, have been difficult for plantain-eaters because it was man, comparatively recently, who introduced these fruits to Africa!

The turacos are, to be sure, committed frugivores, taking a wide variety of fruits, including certain berries highly poisonous to man, as they forage through the dense foliage in parties of up to a dozen birds. The few reports that there are describe the nestlings also as being fed largely on a fruit diet supplemented by the occasional invertebrate, especially snails. This is unusual among young birds, most of which are fed on a high protein diet of invertebrates during their growth spurt between hatching and independence. The turaco life-style is a half-way house towards that of an even more specialized vegetarian, the hoatzin, and this fact, along with a general resemblance in form, has prompted some students to suggest a common ancestry. In fact, there are almost as many ideas about the evolutionary origins of the turacos as there are species within the family. Evidence from their feather parasites suggests an affinity with the fowls (Galliformes), while eye-lens proteins appear similar to those of songbirds (Passeriformes), and the structure of the foot places them close to the cuckoos (Cuculiformes).

One characteristic which the turacos seem to share with no other living birds is the possession of two vivid feather pigments—a green turacoverdin and a red turacin. The latter is known to be a copper compound and colors the crimson wing flashes and head ornamentations found in most turaco species. The turacoverdin has not been fully investigated, but may also be a copper compound and produces the rich green body feathers of 14 species. Most birds' feathers produce their colors by refracting light with specialized feather structures (iridescence) and turacoverdin is the only green pigment found in birds. The lengthy period of about a year taken by a young turaco to develop full adult coloration may perhaps be related to the difficulty of acquiring the relatively scarce copper for the pigment.

The common observation that turacos forage in groups might suggest that these birds, like some others in the tropics, are social breeders, organizing themselves so that individuals other than the parents contribute to the nesting chores of incubation, brooding, and feeding the hungry young. Our knowledge of their breeding habits is, however, so poor that this mode of reproduction has been confirmed in only a single species. In captivity, turacos will nest in simple pairs, although their success rate is low, perhaps due to unknown dietary deficiencies. Monogamy seems to be the rule, and the close similarity between the sexes is typical of other monogamous bird species—the only sexual difference seems to be one of bill color.

For several weeks before egg-laying, the male regurgitates gifts of fruit pulp for his female. Once reproduction proper has begun, both birds contribute equally to incubation, brooding, and feeding of the two or three chicks. These nestlings are covered in a fine down, of varying color and thickness, and they advertise their hunger with a large orange-red gape. Parents respond by regurgitating the fruit/insect mixture directly into the throat and, unlike some birds, this operation takes place in silence, perhaps because of the high density of predators in the forest habitat. Yet another affinity with the peculiar hoatzin emerges once the young have recovered from hatching and increased their strength with a few

▲ **Eclipsed by acacia blossom,** the Go-away bird (*Corythaixoides concolor*) is uniformly gray. The tall crest is the most distinctive feature of these African birds.

▶ **Elegant coiffure** of the Angola red-crested turaco (*Tauraco erythrolophus*). The green coloration is due not to iridescence, as in most birds, but to a green pigment peculiar to turacos—turacoverdin.

The Remarkable Hoatzin Chick

High above the shallow, muddy waters of a South American river, a newly-hatched hoatzin chick weakly lifts its head above the nest rim while its parents are away foraging. The hoatzin chick is naked and ugly and, like many other young birds, it appears to be virtually helpless. The latter could hardly be further from the truth. Upon the noisy return of its clumsy parents, the dark-skinned nestling leaves the nest, climbing gingerly among the thin branches, to intercept any tender young leaves which the parent may be carrying back to its hungry brood.

Two unique events are occurring here! The hoatzin is the only tree-living bird species which feeds its young on foliage to any great extent. Indeed, the adult hoatzin is one of the strictest vegetarians of the bird world, and its plant-crushing crop has evolved to be extremely large—about one-third of body-weight! The hoatzin is also the only tree-living bird in which the chicks habitually leave the nest very soon after hatching. Such a lightly muscled body hardly has the strength to balance on the swaying twigs, but the task is eased by the use of tiny claws emerging from the "elbow" bends of the unfeathered wings.

These appendages are not at all unique among birds—very young European coots bear single claws to aid their frequent climbs back into nests that may tower high above the water surface, and some species of geese carry sharp spurs on the wing-edge even as adults. Many species of animal in South America show similar adaptations to a precarious life over water: the American monkeys and anteaters possess gripping tails as an added insurance against a hazardous fall. The hoatzin chick has an additional safety net. Even if it should fall into the brown waters several feet below, all is not lost—the leathery bundle simply swims to the nearest branch and begins a slow deliberate climb back up to parental care!

meals. The silky nestlings are endowed with tiny claws on their wing-joints and can use these, and their adaptable foot structure, to leave the nest and sit on the periphery or even on adjoining twigs. In fact the young leave the nest for good, at an age of about four weeks, several days before they can fly. Independence from parental feeding seems to be gained at about six weeks, although the offspring continue to beg long after this age. If social breeding does occur in turacos it might even be expected that, as in other co-operative breeders, some offspring remain within the parental home range for much of the early part of their lives.

JAH

The strange unbirdlike **hoatzin** has defied conventional methods of classification for generations, and has traditionally been aligned with the Galliformes— an assemblage of "fowl-like" birds whose relationships to each other are not fully understood.

With its stout legs, coarse plumage, and weak flight, it certainly resembles a domestic hen rather more closely than a typical cuckoo. It has long been put in its own, single-species family, and, in the past, because of its superficial resemblance to reconstructions of the extinct bird *Archaeopteryx*, the hoatzin was often labelled as a "living fossil." In fact, probably nothing could be further from the truth.

Early birds, in common with many of their reptilian ancestors, were probably insect eaters, whereas the hoatzin is one of the most refined and specialized herbage eaters in the whole bird class. Many features of its appearance and biology seem to be consequences of its highly specialized way of life, rather than any evolutionary "hangover" from the distant past. Recent investigations of its biochemistry suggest that the hoatzin has closer affinities with the cuckoos than with any other group of birds.

JAH

Cuckoo in the Nest

The evolution of parasitism in birds

Although about two-thirds of the family are nonparasitic, cuckoos are infamous for their ability to divert the normal parental energies of a host species to their own ends. The mechanisms by which they accomplish this trickery may be fascinating but the selection pressures causing the evolution of the habit itself are equally intriguing.

There are two sides to this evolution, that of the cuckoo and that of its host, and of the two the former is the easier to visualize. Many bird species seem to be limited, in their reproductive capacity, not by the number of eggs they can lay but by the number of chicks they can successfully feed through to independence—increasing the number of eggs laid would not increase the number of chicks eventually reared. Imagine, however, that in a population of birds a parasitic mutant arises which can somehow foist its offspring successfully onto others. The major limitation of reproductive capacity is at a stroke removed and this mutant female is limited only by the number of eggs she can lay. If she is thus able to increase her fecundity, this mutant will increase in frequency in the population through time and the population will evolve towards a parasitic habit.

This scenario need not apply only to cuckoos. Females of such diverse species as House sparrow, starling, Redhead duck, and moorhen have been shown to deposit eggs in nests which are not their own, although these are usually nests of their own, more rarely of other, species. Parasitic females may lay in territories very close to their own and also complete a "legitimate" clutch of their own which they care for in the normal way. The adaptations of these part-time parasites are unlikely to be as perfect or extreme as those of the specialist cuckoos, but in one study of magpies in Spain it was unexpectedly found that an introduced swallow nestling repeatedly tried to eject the host eggs from the nestcup, exactly in the manner of a European cuckoo!

One evolutionary "half-way house" between these habits and full-scale cuckoo parasitism is the Black-billed cuckoo. In most years, pairs of this species build a nest and raise a brood of 2–4 nestlings exactly in the manner of any "ordinary" bird. When food is unusually abundant, however, each female also attempts to parasitize the nests of others in addition to raising a brood via her own parental care. Many of these parasitic eggs are foisted upon other Black-billed cuckoos but some are deposited in the nests of other species. What ecological factors have caused the evolution of this mixed policy? The interesting features of these cuckoos is that they have very large eggs, relative to body size, and that these large eggs have an extraordinarily fast development time, hatching in only 11 days—the shortest incubation period of any bird! Rapidly hatching eggs are of course essential for successful parasitism because the host's nest will already contain developing eggs when discovered by the cuckoo. If the cuckoo's eggs hatch much later than those of the host their chance of success will be very small. In comparison with other bird species showing longer incubation periods, the Black-billed cuckoo's efforts at parasitism are more likely to succeed, and the habit will become fixed in the population.

The more difficult evolutionary problem is understanding just how the host species continues to be fooled by the cuckoo's tactics. Any female songbird, a dunnock or Meadow pipit for example, which accepts a cuckoo's egg into her nest will leave no offspring that year. Other females, which may be able to discriminate and throw out cuckoo eggs or nestlings, will of course leave a reduced but significant number of offspring and so it is precisely these types which we should see in the population. Intensive study of several cuckoo species has shown that, within many species of host, there are discriminating and non-discriminating females. How then do non-discriminating females remain in the population in the face of their inability to reproduce themselves? One possible explanation has been proposed, which does however require that the cuckoo be even more cunning than we imagined. She must ensure that the discriminating birds leave no more offspring than the gullible hosts, and one way in which she could do this is to visit each nest she laid in and destroy the contents of any that had rejected her offspring.

Cuckoos are very difficult to watch, especially after egg-laying, but there is some evidence to support the foregoing. In an observation on Klaas's cuckoo, one host nest which rejected the cuckoo egg was quickly destroyed, probably by the cuckoo: the host birds (obviously discriminators) set about building a new nest and laying a fresh clutch nearby. This nest was also found and destroyed, although this time no cuckoo eggs were laid. Other observations on several species of cuckoo show that it is only the females which commonly eat eggs, as one would predict if they do so only to regulate the evolution of host discrimination.

JAH

▲▶ **The exploited Reed warbler.** TOP The imperfect mimicry of this cuckoo's egg, being pinkish when the Reed warbler's are green, does not prevent incubation and hatching. ABOVE The cuckoo hatches first and, naked though it is, maneuvers the other eggs until they fall out of the nest—it even has a hollow in its back into which the egg fits snugly. RIGHT The dainty Reed warbler then begins to bring food to the voracious maw of the cuckoo. The cuckoo's bill is so large relative to the Reed warbler that the cuckoo leaves the bill open till well after the "mother" has departed to avoid the risk of serious injury to the Reed warbler.

▼ **Half-way house.** These young Black-billed cuckoos are actually being reared by their true mother. This species though, does sometimes resort to parasitism.

OWLS

Order: Strigiformes
Families: Strigidae, Tytonidae.
One hundred and thirty-three species in 24 genera.
Distribution: worldwide except Antarctica and some remote islands.

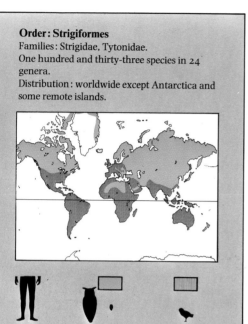

Typical owls   **Barn owls**

▶ **Full frontal.** All of the owls' characteristic features are evident here as a Great horned owl flies towards the camera. Superb nocturnal predator though it obviously is, this specimen is in fact a juvenile.

▼ **Diminutive predator.** A Saw-whet owl, one of the smaller owls, with a short-tailed shrew. Note the typically large head in relation to the size of the body.

Less than three percent of all bird species are active at night and over half of these are owls—they are the nocturnal counterparts of the day-hunting hawks and falcons. Although the largest species is one hundred times the weight of the smallest, all owls are instantly recognizable as such—a uniformity which stems from their unique adaptations for their role as nocturnal predators. New species are still being discovered at the rate of one every decade.

Owls occur wherever there are animals on which they can prey. Most are associated with trees, but others are adapted to living in grasslands, deserts, marshes or even arctic tundra. The diets, biology and behavior of many tropical owls are unknown, but about 80 of the 133 species of all owls are thought to be primarily night-hunting and most of the rest can hunt at any time but do so especially at dusk and dawn.

All owls are easily recognized by their shape: an upright stance, short tail, large head and dense covering of feathers giving them a neckless, rounded outline. Equally characteristic are the huge frontally placed, often orange or yellow eyes, which stare out from saucer-shaped disks of radiating feathers. Daytime-hunting species have smaller eyes and ill-defined facial disks. Many owls have flexible tufts of feathers above the eyes used in visual communication; these "ear tufts" have no connection with hearing. All owls have powerful, usually feathered legs with sharp curved talons for gripping prey. The short hooked beak is curved downwards and may be hard to see among the feathers.

Birds active only in darkness do not require striking plumage; owls mostly spend the day roosting in quiet places, often pressed tight against a tree-trunk, and so both sexes are usually similarly patterned with various somber shades of brown to aid concealment. If discovered by small birds, owls are mobbed to advertise their presence and to persuade them to move on.

Owls which live in open habitats are paler than those from woodland: desert forms are often sandy-colored and the Snowy owl is mainly white to match its arctic surroundings. Some woodland owls have two distinct color-phases—gray in northern coniferous forests, brown in deciduous woods further south. With few exceptions, juveniles look similar to adults. In most owls the female is larger than the male, although the difference is not usually as marked as in some of the day-hunting birds of prey.

Most owls are "typical" owls of the family Strigidae. The largest genus (*Otus*) contains 33 screech or scops owls—a far-flung group, though absent from Australia; all are small to medium-sized, unspecialized "eared" owls of tropical woodland or scrub. Most are nocturnal and feed on insects, but the few temperate species switch to rodents in winter. The 12 eagle owls are the nocturnal equivalents of the large day-hunting eagles and buzzards. They are absent from Australia and the Pacific Islands. Between them they occupy most habitats apart from arctic tundra, where they are replaced by the equally large and powerful Snowy owl, a species which often hunts by day.

The seven large fishing owls of Asia (*Ketupa*) and Africa (*Scotopelia*) are the only food specialists among the owls—the nocturnal counterparts of the osprey and fish eagles and equivalent to the fish-eating bats of tropical America. They occur from cold northern forests to equatorial jungles. The twelve pygmy owls (*Glaucidium*) are shared equally between Eurasia, Africa and the

The 2 Families of Owls

[R] Rare. [E] Endangered.

Typical owls

Family: Strigidae

One hundred and twenty-three species in 22 genera.

Almost cosmopolitan, except Antarctica. Chiefly woodlands and forests; some grasslands, deserts and tundra. Size: 4.7–28in (12–71cm) long and weight 1.4–141oz (40–4,000g). Sexual dimorphism slight but females usually larger. Plumage: patterned brown or gray; one white, several black and white. Voice: a wide range of shrieks, hoots and caterwauls. Nests: chiefly holes, or abandoned nests of other species; a few on the ground and in burrows. Eggs: 1–14 depending on food supply, usually 2–7, white and rounded; weight 0.2–3oz (7–80g); incubation period 15–35 days; nestling period 24–52 days, but young may leave nest before able to fly (15–35 days after hatching). Diet: mostly small ground-living rodents, also birds, reptiles, frogs, fish and crabs (fishing owls), earthworms and large insects (especially small owls).

Species include: **African wood owl** (*Ciccaba woodfordii*), **Barking owl** (*Ninox connivens*), **Barred owl** (*Strix varia*), **Black and white owl** (*Ciccaba nigrolineata*), **Blakiston's fish owl** (*Ketupa blakistoni*), **Boobook owl** (*Ninox novaeseelandiae*), **Brown fish owl** (*Ketupa zeylonensis*), **Burrowing owl** (*Athene cunicularia*), **Eagle owl** (*Bubo bubo*), **Elf owl** (*Micrathene whitneyi*), **Giant scops owl** (*Otus gurneyi*), **Great gray owl** (*Strix nebulosa*), **Great horned owl** (*Bubo virginianus*), **Hawk owl** (*Surnia ulula*), **Laughing owl** (*Sceloglaux albifacies*) (possibly extinct), **Least pygmy owl** (*Glaucidium minutissimum*), **Little owl** (*Athene noctua*), **Long-eared owl** (*Asio otus*), **Long-whiskered owlet** (*Xenoglaux loweryi*), **Madagascan scops owl** (*Otus rutilus*), **Oriental hawk owl** (*Ninox scutulata*), **Oriental scops owl** (*Otus sunia*), **Pearl-spotted owlet** (*Glaucidium perlatum*), **Pel's fishing owl** (*Scotopelia peli*), **Powerful owl** (*Ninox strenua*), **Pygmy owl** (*Glaucidium passerinum*), **Saw-whet owl** (*Aegolius acadicus*), **Scops owl** (*Otus scops*), **Screech owl** (*Otus asio*), **Short-eared owl** (*Asio flammeus*), **Snowy owl** (*Nyctea scandiaca*), **Sokoke scops owl** [R] (*Otus ireneae*), **Spectacled owl** (*Pulsatrix perspicillata*), **Spotted eagle owl** (*Bubo africanus*), **Tawny owl** (*Strix aluco*), **Tengmalm's owl** (*Aegolius funereus*), **Ural owl** (*Strix uralensis*). Threatened species: 3.

Barn and bay owls

Family: Tytonidae

Ten species in 2 genera.

Europe except far north, SE Asia, Africa, N America to Canadian border, S America, Australia. Open areas, including farmland, scattered woodland, and forests. Size: 9–21in (23–53cm) long, weight 6.3–45.5oz (180–1,280g). Females usually slightly bigger than males. Plumage: orange-buff to blackish brown above, white, rufous or blackish-brown below; a striking facial "disk." Voice: shrill hissing, screeching or whistling. Nests: in barns, holes in rocks or trees, or on the ground (grass owls). Eggs: usually 2–6, sometimes up to 11, white, elliptical; most weigh 0.65–1.5oz (17–42.5g); incubation 27–34 days; nestling period 49–56 days. Diet: small mammals and birds, fish, frogs, lizards and large insects.

Species include: **African bay owl** (*Phodilus prigoginei*), **Barn owl** (*Tyto alba*), **Common bay owl** (*Phodilus badius*), **Grass owl** (*Tyto capensis*), **Madagascar grass owl** [E] (*T. soumagnei*), **Masked owl** (*T. novaehollandiae*), **Sooty owl** (*T. tenebricosa*).

Americas. They include the sparrow-sized Least pygmy owl of tropical South American forests, which shares with the Elf owl of the American West the distinction of being the smallest owl. Both are closely related to the Long-whiskered owlet of the Peruvian Andes, not discovered until 1976. Most medium-sized owls of Indonesia and Australasia are hawk owls (*Ninox*). Of these only the Oriental hawk owl of the Asian mainland has a wide distribution; most of the other 15 species are confined to single islands and their ranges do not overlap. In Australia, where most owl genera are absent (eg *Bubo, Otus, Strix* and *Glaucidium*), three *Ninox* species do exist side by side, including the small Boobook owl which also occurs in New Zealand and New Guinea. The five *Ciccaba* owls are rarely-seen medium-sized owls of the tropical forests of Africa and the Americas. In temperate woodlands they are replaced by the 11 *Strix* species, including the extensively studied Tawny owl, whose range extends from Britain across Europe and northwest Africa to the mountains of Burma and China. The five *Asio* species fall into two ecologically distinct groups: "long-eared," found in broad-leaved or coniferous woodland, and "short-eared" which frequent open country.

The genus *Athene* contains four species and takes its name from the Greek goddess of wisdom Pallas Athene. The Little owl, which sometimes hunts by day, is a familiar sight in open habitats from western Europe and North Africa across to China. In the late 1800s it was introduced into Britain and New Zealand. The only New World representative is the Burrowing owl, a long-legged, daytime-hunting, terrestrial species of open treeless grasslands. The genus *Aegolius* is a basically New World family of four geographically-separated, small, nocturnal, forest owls. The most widespread is the Boreal or Tengmalm's owl. Like several other owls of northern coniferous forests (eg the Great gray and the Hawk owl) its range extends in a belt right across the Old World.

The **barn** and **bay owls** form the other family (Tytonidae). They are distinguished from the typical owls by their heart-shaped rather than round faces, middle and inner toes of equal length (the inner is shorter in strigids), serrated middle claws and wishbones fused to the breastbone. The rodent-hunting Barn owl of open country is one of the most widely distributed of all birds (see box), found on every inhabited continent. The other seven barn owls occur in Africa, islands in the Indian Ocean and Southeast

▶ **Representative species of owl.** (1) Elf owl (*Micrathene whitneyi*) in the roosting posture. (2) Barking owl (*Ninox connivens*) with nestlings at the nest-hole. (3) White-faced scops owl (*Otus leucotis*) listening for prey. (4) Tengmalm's owl (*Aegolius funereus*) about to catch a vole. (5) Common bay owl (*Phodilus badius*). (6) Spectacled owl (*Pulsatrix perspicillata*). (7) Malaysian eagle owl (*Bubo sumatranus*). (8) Spotted wood owl (*Strix seloputo*) being mobbed by passerines. (9) Pel's fishing owl (*Scotopelia peli*) with fish.

Asia, and in Australasia. The little-known Common Bay owl is found in Asian forests from India to Java and Borneo; the African Bay owl is known only from a single specimen collected in the Congo in 1951.

In spite of their general resemblance, owls are not closely related to the hawks and falcons; both groups evolved to exploit similar food supplies and so possess the same basic anatomical features for a predatory way of life. Study of egg-white proteins suggests that the nearest relatives of owls are another nocturnal order—the nightjars and allies (see pp96–101). Nightjars use their huge mouths to snap up insects in flight, oilbirds find ripe fruit by smell, but owls are unique among nocturnal birds in using vision and/or hearing to locate their food.

The adaptations needed for hunting at night limit the kinds of food that owls can exploit efficiently. There are no carrion-feeding owls equivalent to vultures and kites (although some do take carrion occasionally), no soaring forms, and owls seldom pursue and capture birds in flight—a common specialization among day-hunting birds of prey.

Owls catch most of their prey on the ground in the open. Woodland owls have short, rounded wings and when hunting sit quietly on a low perch watching and listening for small mammals. On hearing a likely noise they rapidly rotate their head until the sound registers equally in both ears; they are then directly facing it. When the source of the sound is pin-pointed, the owl glides silently down towards it; at the last second it swings its feet forwards to hit the prey, often killing it outright. Many owls of open country hunt mainly in flight. They have long wings which enable them slowly to quarter the ground like the day-hunting harriers, with little expenditure of energy. Long-eared owls spend about 20 percent of the night hunting. Once prey is located, it is pounced on from a low height in the manner of perch-hunting owls; about one in five attempts is successful. Owls are opportunistic hunters and will often try to catch prey any way they can: insects (and sometimes birds) may be chased in flight, birds are grabbed while roosting, several species (eg Little and Burrowing owls) bound across the ground in search of invertebrates, and Tawny owls will plunge into water to catch frogs. The specialist fishing owls swoop down to pluck fish from the water surface. Roadsides also provide good hunting areas for owls and in developed countries many are killed by traffic.

Unlike hawks and falcons, owls carry all but the largest prey in their bill and swallow it whole, head first. Sorting out what is nutritious takes place internally and any indigestible remains such as bones and fur are regurgitated as pellets, which provide a good record of what owls eat (see box). Owls have no crop in which to store food but sometimes cache prey.

Owls feed on a wide variety of animal prey; what they eat depends mainly on their size and the habitat they occupy. Tawny owls living in woodland feed mainly on mice and voles, but in the towns they feed on birds, especially house sparrows. Small owls are mostly insectivorous; medium-sized ones feed mainly on small rodents or birds; the largest species take mammals (up to the size of hares or even small deer) and medium-sized birds—including other owls and birds of prey!

Owls are well insulated by their dense covering of feathers and get by on about 30 percent less food than most other birds of equivalent size. They can have a substantial impact on prey populations: in one study, a pair of Tawny owls, consuming a maximum of seven 0.7oz (20g) rodents per day, removed 18–46 percent of the Bank voles and 28–70 percent of the Wood mice

Man's Friend—The Barn Owl

The Barn owl's nocturnal life-style, ghostly white appearance and association with ruins or churches where it likes to nest, have earned it a place in the folklore of many cultures but, as its name suggests, it is best known for its association with farmers. Wherever crops are grown, large populations of rats and mice build up and these attract the rodent-hunting Barn owl. It is found almost everywhere between latitudes 40°N and 40°S, and its range also extends into northwestern Europe and to the tip of South America.

In the Netherlands, farmers actively encourage owls by installing special "owl doors" to allow them easy access to their buildings, and by providing food in hard weather, which otherwise causes heavy losses. Unfortunately, this close association with agriculture was almost the Barn owl's undoing in western Europe, and they suffered more from poisoning by agricultural chemicals than other owls. In Malaysia, Barn owls and chemicals are actually used together to control the plagues of rats which cause severe damage in oil-palm plantations. Formerly rare, Barn owls have invaded the plantations since nest-boxes were erected for them to breed in. The owls can now raise several families per year and often congregate in flocks of up to 40 birds. Each owl family eats about 1,300 rats per year, which can slow the recovery of rodent populations that have first been reduced by poisoning.

Not every pest-control scheme involving Barn owls has had such a happy outcome. In the 1950s they were introduced into the Seychelles, again to control rats. Unfortunately, the owls found the native birds easier to catch and in 12 years they exterminated the White tern from two islands, reduced the numbers of the rare Blue pigeon, and competed for nest sites with the endangered Seychelles kestrel. They now have a bounty on their heads and are killed at every opportunity.

▲ **Nocturnal killer.** The Barn owl's oval facial disk is characteristic of many owls, and is thought to aid in the fine location of sound.

The Barn owl's range extends from northwestern Europe to the tip of South America, and throughout the world this species is an important predator of agricultural pests.

ciency). Extra food is also needed to grow the new feathers and to compensate for the reduced insulation properties of their plumage. In tropical regions, breeding is geared to rainfall—small species have young in the nest when the onset of the rainy season produces a flush of insects. Many owls have only a single brood per year, but some open-country species can breed whenever rodents are abundant, and may raise several broods in a year. Most owls can breed in their first year if conditions are suitable.

Many owls adopt another family-planning measure. Single eggs are laid at intervals of two or more days but incubation begins with the first, so that the earliest chick to hatch may be up to three weeks older than the last. If food is plentiful, all the chicks survive, if not, the youngest die and are eaten by the rest. In this way, brood size is adjusted to the food available.

Owls are not great nest-builders: most breed in holes in trees, rocks or the ground, but some open-country owls line depressions in the ground and Burrowing owls can dig their own underground nest chambers (although they usually take over prairie dog lairs). Small species appropriate old woodpecker holes. Large owls unable to find appropriate old woodpecker holes, and most woodland owls, readily occupy nest-boxes provided for them. Large owls unable to find appropriately sized natural fissures take over abandoned tree-nests of crows or birds of prey.

Incubation tends to be by the female alone, with the smaller male providing all the food from before egg-laying until the young—initially born blind, helpless and covered in sparse grayish-white down—no longer need brooding or their prey torn up for them. This division of labor allows the inert female to accumulate fat reserves and remain on the nest even when the male finds hunting difficult as, for example, in wet weather. In many species, the larger female vigorously defends the young against intruders, including humans (some people have even lost eyes to them). Other species have threat displays in which the female tries to make herself look larger and even more fearsome. To further reduce the chances of predation, the young of open-nesting owls grow faster than those which are reared in holes and leave the nest before they are fully feathered.

Fledged young beg loudly for food and are often dependent upon their parents for several months before they disperse. Newly independent owls suffer a high mortality:

present in their hunting range in each two-month period.

Periodic fluctuations in the numbers of rodents have striking effects on the owls themselves. In years when they are scarce, many owls either do not breed or lay reduced numbers of eggs; Snowy owls and Short-eared owls lay 2–14 eggs, depending on prey availability. Generally, breeding is timed so that food is most plentiful when the young are learning to hunt for themselves and the adults are undergoing their annual molt (which reduces their hunting effi-

over half the young Tawny owls die in their first year, many of starvation, but once settled they can expect to live for at least four or five years and some have survived for more than 15. Larger species probably live even longer—a captive Eagle owl survived 68 years.

Most owls are territorial and non-migratory, especially those living in the tropics or woodland. Here pairs often spend all their lives in strictly defended territories, switching to alternative prey if one kind becomes unavailable; the populations of such species remain stable over long periods. Northern owls and those of open country which feed mainly on rodents have a narrower range of quarry available to them. They usually defend territories in the breeding season but their populations tend to fluctuate in parallel with those of their prey. Some are found far outside their normal ranges if food supplies fail. Large numbers of Snowy owls sometimes appear in the USA when lemming or hare populations have crashed in the Arctic. The birds are often very tame when in unfamiliar surroundings: North American bird-banders catch the impressive looking Great gray owl by casting out a dead mouse attached to a fishing line (without a hook)—a hungry owl will pounce on it and can be reeled in! A few owls undertake regular north–south migrations, like the Scops owl, which exploits the summer flush of insects in southern Europe; the Short-eared owl is nomadic, settling wherever prey is temporarily abundant.

Owls which are territorial throughout the year live in pairs but forage alone so as not to interfere with each other's hunting. The rest usually live alone outside the breeding season, except some owls of open country which congregate in areas where prey is plentiful; these often roost communally but disperse at dusk to hunt alone. Only the Burrowing owl is colonial.

Breeding territories tend to be smaller where more prey is available. In Britain, Tawny owls defend 30–50 acres (12–20ha) in open deciduous woodland where small rodents are abundant but over 100 acres (40ha) in more sterile conifer plantations. The huge Eagle owl takes bigger, less common prey and needs a correspondingly large territory: their nests are usually spaced 2.5–3mi (4–5km) apart. To communicate over such long distances at night, owls have well-developed vocabularies and they are much more vocal than day-hunting birds of prey. The familiar territorial hooting of many owls is equivalent to the song of other birds serving to warn off rival males and to attract a mate. The hoots of male Eagle owls can be heard 2.5mi (4km) away and like many other owls the pair frequently answer one another in a duet, probably to

▲ **Owls' eyes.** The large wide-set eyes of these young Tengmalm's owls help them to see in poor light. Tengmalm's owls are found in North America, Europe and Asia.

◄ **Owl pellets:** the content of a pellet from a Long-eared owl.

► **The gape, stare and ear tufts** of a Malaysian fishing owl (*Ketupa ketupa*) give it an eagle-like appearance. Fish owls of Africa and Asia feed mainly on fish which they strike with their talons on the surface of the water. They also hunt crabs and crayfish in the shallows, and may take small mammals and insects.

Owl Pellets

Owls usually bolt their prey whole and much of what is indigestible, such as fur, bones, teeth, claws, beaks or the head capsules and wing-cases of insects, are compressed into a sausage-shaped pellet which is cast back out through the mouth. To ease the pellet's passage the hard parts are enclosed by the softer fur or feathers. Pellets can be collected, teased apart and their contents identified, to provide a record of what the owl has been eating. Mammals can usually be identified and counted from their skulls, jaws or teeth; birds from their beaks, feet or certain bones. Even the hard remains of earthworms and other invertebrates can often be recognized.

The ease with which pellets can be collected and analyzed depends on the species. Barn owls roost in the same place day after day and it is an easy job to collect the accumulation of pellets at regular intervals. Other species, like the Tawny owl, deposit their pellets at widely scattered nocturnal roosting or feeding sites, making them difficult to find; they also seem better at digesting bones than other owls and sometimes decapitate their prey.

Most owls of temperate regions produce one or two pellets per 24 hours, depending on season. In summer, when nights are short,

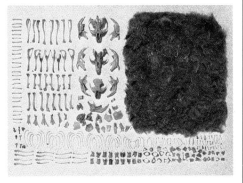

they produce one large pellet at their day-time roosts. In winter they often cast a second, smaller pellet (about 7 hours after the first) while hunting at night.

The size and appearance of pellets is often characteristic of a particular species. In general the largest owls produce the largest pellets. Those of the Eagle owl average 3 × 1.25 × in, those of the Pygmy owl only 1 × 0.4 × 0.3in. Barn owl pellets are black, shiny and hard, those of the Tawny owl gray and crumbly.

Although the analysis of remains in pellets has drawbacks, it provides the best clue to the diets of owls, allowing comparisons to be drawn between different seasons and species.

maintain the pair bond between them. Day-hunting owls are generally less vocal and the Barn owl does not hoot, perhaps because its light color makes it easily visible, removing the need for long-distance vocal communication. All owls can produce loud tongue-clicking sounds when they are frightened or angry.

Many owls will answer imitations of their hoots, and territories can be mapped in this way. Local names for owls often reflect their distinctive calls: the names boobook, and saw-whet are respectively phonetic rendering and description.

Owls sometimes share their habitat with day-hunting birds of prey; on the Galapagos Islands, Short-eared owls hunt both by day and night where the Galapagos hawk is absent, but only at night where hawks are present. Where several owls co-exist they are usually of different sizes and feed on different prey—in Australia three hawk owls occur together: the small Boobook owl feeds on insects and small birds, the medium-sized Barking owl takes small marsupials and birds up to crow-size, and the large Powerful owl catches medium-sized arboreal marsupials. Where owls feed on similar prey in the same habitat, for example Great-horned and Barred owls in parts of North America, they avoid competition for food by defending territories against rival species. Modern forestry reduces the number of nest-sites for owls and in Scandinavia many nest-boxes have been erected for Ural and Tawny owls—these species have increased but they prey upon Pygmy owls, which have consequently become rare.

Like most predators, owls are persecuted by man wherever their presence might conflict with his interests, particularly game preservation. In Europe, Eagle owls have been exterminated in densely populated regions. Ironically, in other areas these owls are used to lure other birds of prey (which mob them) within gunshot range.

Owls did not suffer as much as some birds of prey when toxic chemicals were introduced as pesticides in agriculture. A greater threat is the destruction of their habitats. The Madagascar grass owl, the Sokoke scops owl (discovered in 1965 in coastal rain forest in Kenya), the races of the Madagascan scops owls on the Seychelles and the Comoros, and the Giant scops owl of the Philippines are all endangered for this reason. The Laughing owl of New Zealand may already be extinct. Its decline followed the introduction from Europe of stoats and weasels which destroyed its nests and competed with it for food.   GJMH

A Face for the Night

Why an owl looks like an owl

Owls are generalized predators—their specialization lies not in feeding on a particular type of prey but in catching it in darkness. The modifications which enable owls to do this create their distinctive appearance.

Owls have particularly highly developed hearing and vision, and need oversized skulls to accommodate ear openings and eyes much bigger than those of other birds—the largest owls have eyes comparable in size to those of humans. What, therefore, is the advantage of these large frontally placed eyes?

Large eyes can have large pupils to allow more light to fall on the retina (the light-sensitive layer at the back of the eye). A Tawny owl's eye has 100 times the light-gathering power of a pigeon's and produces a large retinal image to provide the visual acuity necessary to discriminate potential prey. Owls have tubular (rather than spherical) eyes, placed frontally in order to accommodate the huge lens and cornea. Unfortunately, tubular eyes have a reduced field of view and are virtually immobile, giving owls a visual field of only 110° compared with a man's 180° and a pigeon's 340°. To overcome this, owls have remarkably flexible necks, enabling them to invert their heads as well as to look directly behind! Frontally-placed eyes can also provide binocular vision, in which both eyes view the same area from different aspects. This allows better judgment of distance.

Although owls see much better at night than birds active during the day, the popular belief that their eyes are vastly superior to man's in the dark but function poorly in bright light is not correct. The Tawny owl has color vision, sees in daylight as well as a pigeon, and has eyes only some two to three times more sensitive than man's in the dark. Owls can only hunt successfully at night because their visual sensitivity is allied to exceptional hearing. Owls are especially sensitive to sounds with a high frequency component, such as the rustling of dry leaves—some species can even locate and capture small rodents in total darkness just from the noise they make in moving across the woodland floor.

The characteristic facial disks of owls are part of this specialized hearing apparatus. The tightly-packed rows of stiff feathers which make up the rim of this disk reflect high-frequency sounds which are channeled by the mobile facial disks into the ears behind, in the same way that mammals use their large, fleshy external ears. The ear openings themselves are enormous—vertical slits running almost the whole

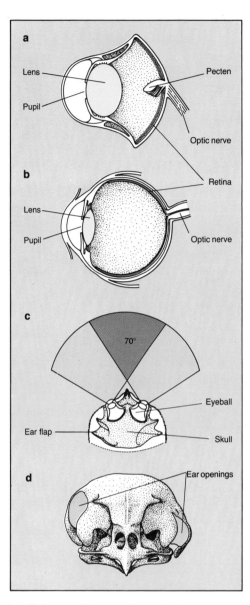

▲ **Owl senses.** The eyes and ears of owls are extremely sensitive. The eye (**a**) differs from the mammalian eye (**b**) in having the retina close to and equidistantly spaced from the lens. The retina is packed with rods (which only detect black and white) and can function at very low light intensities. The pecten is a structure thought to provide nutrients to the eyeball. The owl's field of vision (**c**) is not large, but provides good stereoscopic vision over an angle of 70°. This intense tunnel vision is an adaptation to homing in on its prey. The ears of owls (**d**) are asymmetrically placed to aid in the location of sounds.

▶ **The face mask** of this Short-eared owl shows the barbless feathers characteristic of the area surrounding the ears.

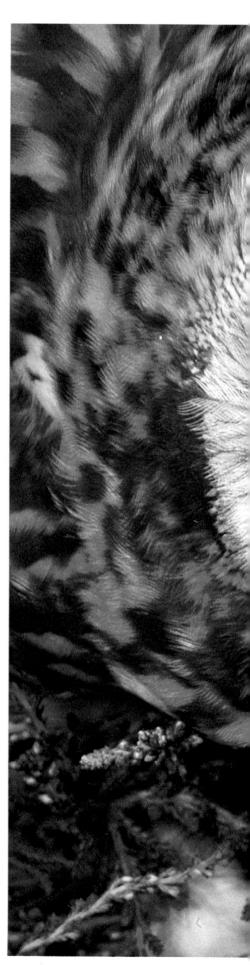

depth of the skull and hidden beneath feathered flaps of skin.

The broad skull helps in sound location— a noise from one side will be louder and perceived fractionally sooner in the ear nearest to it. Owls can locate sounds in the horizontal direction four times better than a cat, but an owl hunting from above needs to pin-point sound in the vertical direction as well as to fix the prey's position exactly. Barn owls can do this with an accuracy of one or two degrees in both horizontal and vertical directions—one degree is about the width of a little finger at arm's length! Owls achieve this by moving their ear flaps to alter the size and shape of the ear openings to make reception different for the two ears. In some highly nocturnal owls (eg Tengmalm's) the ear openings themselves are placed asymmetrically on the skull.

To be able to hear their prey and not frighten it off, owls are equipped to fly silently. From head to toe they are covered with an enormous number of soft, downy feathers. This gives them their characteristic rounded outline and makes them appear much larger than they really are. Long-eared owls are known to have over 10,000 feathers.

The wing feathers of owls lack the hard sheen of other birds and have soft fringes with fluted leading edges to ease the flow of air over them. These adaptations, coupled with extreme lightness in relation to their wing area, enable owls to fly very efficiently and silently over the countryside while hunting. Fishing owls lack these adaptations as their prey cannot hear the owl approaching.

The other prominent characteristics of owls, such as talons, are common to most predatory birds, although in owls the hooked beak is deflected downwards so as not to interfere with the already limited field of view. To grasp and kill prey, the legs and feet are immensely strong and armed with needle-sharp claws. One peculiarity of owls is the reversible outer toe which can point either forwards or backwards to increase the "catching area" of the feet and improve gripping ability. Like mammal-hunting hawks, owls have relatively short legs; these are feathered to the toes, probably to aid thermoregulation, but possibly also to protect against bites from prey. Exceptions are the fishing owls which specialize in catching prey in water and have bare legs and osprey-like feet equipped with spiny soles to grasp slippery fish, and terrestrial species like the Burrowing owl, which have noticeably longer legs. GJMH

NIGHTJARS AND FROGMOUTHS

Order: Caprimulgiformes
Families: Caprimulgidae, Podargidae,
Aegothelidae, Nyctibiidae, Steatornithidae.
Ninety-eight species in 21 genera.
Distribution: worldwide except for the far
North.

Nightjars

Owlet-frogmouths

Frogmouths   **Oilbird**   **Potoos**

▶ **Representative species of the order
Caprimulgiformes.** (1) Tawny frogmouth
(*Podargus strigoides*) on nest showing its large
gape. (2) Standard-winged nightjar
(*Semiophorus longipennis*). (3) Whip-poor-will
(*Caprimulgus vociferus*). (4) Oilbird (*Steatornis
caripensis*) in a cave. (5) Common potoo
(*Nyctibius griseus*) characteristically perched on
a stump. (6) Owlet-nightjar (*Aegotheles
cristatus*). (7) Philippine frogmouth
(*Batrachostomus septimus*) eating a caterpillar.

GOAT herdsmen, flushing the big-mouthed, moth-like nightjars from pastures or hearing their "night-jarring" voices through the wee hours just when the goats were failing to give milk, decided that these strange birds were the culprits, hence the alternative name of "goatsucker." Other species also have mysterious names.

Most **nightjars** look like big soft moths, dressed as they are in variegated patterns of brown, gray, black, and white. Even their comparatively silent and often dancingly graceful flight suggests moths. Their overall appearance is sleek, with the limpid, generally dark eyes and large heads with tiny bills giving them a "baby-faced" charm that big-headed, small-billed birds always seem to possess. Their wings are usually long and tapered, the tail typically long and wide. Males of tropical savanna and desert include several audaciously ornamented forms. These ornaments, elongated wing or tail feathers, are employed in courtship displays, and are molted or broken off after the breeding season. Nightjars have astonishingly large gapes. When one opens its mouth, the whole front of the head becomes a giant glistening cavern fringed with bristles that form an effective insect trap.

The nightjar family is usually subdivided into two subfamilies, the Chordeilinae or nighthawks and the Caprimulginae or nightjars. The former is restricted to the New World while the nightjars, although having a number of New World representatives, are also widespread in Europe, Asia and Africa; the genus *Caprimulgus* itself contains some 45 species.

Being largely insectivorous, nightjars live mainly in tropical climates or migrate to temperate ones only in warm seasons. Nocturnal counterparts of swallows and swifts, they forage mainly in sustained flight. Woodland dwellers, such as the Dusky nightjar, hawk single insects from a perch, returning to it after each sally.

Nightjars are superbly equipped to capture insects on the wing at night. A nightjar can engulf large numbers of mosquitoes in a single snap or wheel about and sweep up a Luna moth having a 4in (10cm) wingspread. Small birds are also sometimes taken by larger species such as the chuck-wills-widow, and probably *not* by accident! There is some indication that these birds can echolocate, thus avoiding collisions with trees while foraging at night. In an experiment, captured Common nighthawks flying in a darkened underground tunnel hung with a complex pattern of wooden and rope obstacles, negotiated the maze without mis-

hap, uttering their "beans" call notes as they flew. However, when temporarily deafened, they struck objects of the maze, and this suggests their difficulties arose from not being able to hear high-frequency sounds reflected from those objects.

There is little information on life span in nightjars. A whip-poor-will ringed as an adult was recovered dead four years later. Since it is a migratory species, it may be safely assumed that many tropical forms live longer. Breeding is generally timed to coincide with surges in insect populations that occur at the beginning of warm or wet seasons. Tropical species may have two broods. Courtship is sometimes elaborate. In the Standard-winged nightjar, the observed clustering of a few nests and the highly ornamented male plumage suggest that the males may have several mates simultaneously. Highly elaborate plumages are useful in mate attraction but impractical in parental care. Clustering of nests of a harem of females permits the male to oversee his mates easily and keep out other males. A male keeps a harem by constant vigil, displaying himself from a prominent perch or in flight. As in birds-of-paradise, the male's role is limited to the mating act.

Nightjars are generally non-social, but

I

3

4

5

2

6

7

T. B.

nighthawks often feed and migrate in large loose aggregations. A few other species may forage in groups, but perhaps due only to swarming of insects.

The poorwill is the *only* species of bird known to become torpid for long periods in winter. A Hopi Indian folk tale was recently confirmed when a hibernating poorwill was discovered three winters in succession in a rock crevice in southern California. Its body temperature was about 64.5°F (18°C). The Hopi Indians called the poorwill *Holchko*—"the sleeping one."

Nightjars are not so much threatened by the advance of civilization as are many other groups of birds. Most thrive in open, often disturbed habitats, but the whip-poor-will, a true forest dweller once common throughout the eastern USA, has completely disappeared from many now heavily disturbed parts of its range. Conservation and management of nightjars requires preservation of habitat and low use of insecticides.

JWH

The **frogmouths** closely resemble true nightjars. They sometimes hunt, adopting a sim-

The 5 Families of Nightjars and Frogmouths   ⓡ Rare.

Nightjars or goatsuckers
Family: Caprimulgidae
Seventy-two species in 16 genera.

Throughout the tropical and temperate world, except New Zealand, southern S America, and most oceanic islands. Mostly forest edge to savanna and desert, a few woodland dwellers; mostly crepuscular and nocturnal. Size: 8–11in (19–29cm) long, weight 1.4–4oz (40–120g). Plumage: concealment patterns of browns, grays and black with patches of white on tail, wings and head; females often differ from males in having less white on the wings, tail or on the head. Some tropical forms with elongate wing or tail feathers. Voice: loud, repetitive trilling or whistled male song; other calls and sounds made with wings. Eggs: 1–2, white or buff-colored, usually with blotches; incubation period 16–19 days; nestling period 16–20 days. Diet: insects.

Species include: **chuck-will's-widow** (*Caprimulgus carolinensis*), **Common nighthawk** (*Chordeiles minor*), **Dusky nightjar** (*Caprimulgus pectoralis*), **European nightjar** (*C. europaeus*), **Little nightjar** (*C. parvulus*), **Pennant-winged nightjar** (*Semiophorus vexillarius*), **poorwill** (*Phalaenoptilus nuttallii*). **Puerto Rican nightjar** ⓡ (*C. noctitherus*), **Rufous nightjar**

(*C. rufus*), **Sooty nightjar** (*C. saturatus*), **Standard-winged nightjar** (*Semiophorus longipennis*), **whip-poor-will** (*C. vociferus*).

Frogmouths
Family: Podargidae
Twelve species in 2 genera.

SE Asia, Australia, Indonesia, Sri Lanka. Mostly confined to tropical rain forest. Size: 9–21in (23–54cm) long. Plumage: brown to gray; most species have at least 2 color phases. Voice: usually a low repetitive booming; Marbled frogmouth has an "ooo" call; young Gould's frogmouths have a soft, kitten-like mew. Nests: twigs in trees. Eggs: 1–3, according to species, white; size 1.5 × 1in; incubation period about 30 days; nestling period about 30 days. Diet: mainly insects but Marbled frogmouth known to take a wide range of small animals, including even small vertebrates such as mice.

Species include: **Gould's frogmouth** (*Batrachostomus stellatus*), **Large frogmouth** (*B. auritus*), **Marbled frogmouth** (*Podargus ocellatus*), **Papuan frogmouth** (*P. papuensis*), **Tawny frogmouth** (*P. strigoides*).

Owlet-nightjars
Family: Aegothelidae
Eight species of the genus *Aegotheles*.
Australia and New Guinea. Tropical

rain forest in New Guinea, open country in Australia. Size: 8–12in (20–30cm) long, weight 1.6–4.1oz (45–115g). Plumage: from ash-gray to black, sometimes with considerable variation within species. Voice: a variety of shrills and churring sounds. Nests: tree hollows lined with leaves and fur, or holes in a cliff face. Eggs: 2–5, white. Diet: mostly insects.

Species: **Archbold's owlet-nightjar** (*Aegotheles archboldi*), **Barred owlet-nightjar** (*A. bennettii*), **Large owlet-nightjar** (*A. insignis*), **Mountain owlet-nightjar** (*A. albertisi*), **New Caledonian owlet-nightjar** (*A. savesi*), **owlet-nightjar** (*A. cristatus*), **Sunda** or **Halmahera owlet-nightjar** (*A. crinifrons*), **Wallace's owlet-nightjar** (*A. wallacii*).

Potoos
Family: Nyctibiidae
Five species of the genus *Nyctibius*.

S and C America, southern N America. Forest. Size: 9–20in (23–50cm) long. Plumage: concealment coloration of barred and mottled gray and browns; soft and fluffy; young mostly white with a few speckled dark patches. Voice: whistles and barking wows; described as "kwak," "kaw," "graw-ar;" the Giant potoo has a loud "baw-woo." Nests: no nest is constructed but egg is laid on broken tree branches, stumps etc. Eggs: usually one,

sometimes two, spotted, size 1.4 × 1in to 2 × 1.5in. Diet: insects.

Species: **Common potoo** (*Nyctibius griseus*), **Giant potoo** (*N. grandis*), **Long-tailed potoo** (*N. aethereus*), **Rufous potoo** (*N. bracteatus*), **White-winged potoo** (*N. leucopterus*).

Oilbird
Family: Steatornithidae
Sole species *Steatornis caripensis*.

S America from Guyana and Venezuela along the Andes to Bolivia; Trinidad. Forested country with caves. Size: about 18in (45cm) long and 14–15oz (400–430g); nestlings up to 50 percent heavier. Plumage: mainly rich brown with a scattering of white spots which are especially large and conspicuous on wing-coverts and outer secondaries; males somewhat grayer and darker than females. Voice: a variety of harsh screams, squawks and clucking calls; also series of short staccato clicks, used for echolocation in darkness. Nests: on ledges in caves from half-light to pitch darkness. Eggs: 2–4, white, 0.6–7.9oz (17–22.5g); incubation period 32–35 days; nestling period 88–125, usually 100–115 days. Diet: exclusively the flesh of fruits from forest trees (the seeds being regurgitated), especially of the palm (Palmae), laurel (Lauraceae) and incense (Burseraceae) families.

▲ **Nightjar courtship.** Some nightjars have dramatic courtship displays. (**1**) The male Common nighthawk dives from a great height, then swoops upward near the female, making a booming sound by the rush of air over the soft inner vanes of certain wing feathers. (**2**) The male Standard-winged nightjar circles his mate in fluttering flight, which causes an updraft that elevates the extended inner primaries into fluttering pennants.

◄ **A European nightjar** ABOVE shows its marbled markings while displaying aggressively on its nest.

ilar manner to nightjars, by hawking after insects, but they are also known to chase insects on branches of trees.

Frogmouths are nocturnal birds similar in color to other Caprimulgiformes. The immature birds tend to have plumages either similar to the adult birds or much paler, with a lot of white specks. They have a very large, sharply hooked beak much bigger than other Caprimulgiformes, with a large gape. However, they have very weak legs and feet. In general, they are considered to be lethargic birds and perhaps the weakest fliers in the order. Their wings are rounded—rather owl-like—and their flight is neither direct nor powerful. They have a distinguishing tuft of bristle-like feathers around the nostrils at the base of the beak, which seem partly to conceal the beak and nostrils. Eye color is brown, red or yellow.

Their hunting method has been described as owl-like, shrike-like or roller-like. It seems that they pounce on their terrestrial prey items from a regular perch. In addition, some species are thought actually to scour the branches of trees for food. Although the majority of frogmouths appear to be catholic in their choice of woodland, the Tawny frogmouth has a distinct preference for eucalypts.

As well as the geographical variation between the two genera, there are also behavioral and physiological differences: *Podargus* has no oil gland while *Batrachostomus* does have one. Some species may be migratory: the Papuan frogmouth has been observed on passage from Cape York in northern Australia to New Guinea.

MEB

The **owlet-nightjars** or moth owls are shy dumpy little birds which look like a cross between an owl and a nightjar. They are typically nocturnal, tree-dwelling birds, usually feeding on flying insects; in Australia they are often found in open country. Owlet-nightjars are closely related to frogmouths.

Owlet-nightjars have relatively large beaks and more forward-facing eyes than the rest of the Caprimulgiformes, which tends to make them seem owl-like, as does their habit of sitting across branches rather than along them. However, they do have typical nightjar features in that they possess long "bristles" around the beak and a wide gape. They fly less erratically than their close relatives.

Males and females are similar. Within a number of species there is considerable variation in plumage, and some color variations

are recognized as separate species by some authorities. The Large owlet-nightjar usually occurs as a light reddish brown phase or in a variegated dark brown and black phase.

Very little is known about the behavior of owlet-nightjars. There is some confusion as to how they catch their prey. Some species are credited with hawking rather like true nightjars, while others are thought to catch their prey on the ground. Analysis of stomach contents has shown that the diet can consist of non-flying prey such as millipedes, ants and also spiders. The fact that they have long, strong legs tends to support the idea that they spend at least some time on the ground chasing insects as well as hawking.

The owlet-nightjar is known to breed from September to December. Some pairs have been known to rear two broods in one season. The nestlings have whitish down which is soon replaced. When they leave the nest they are almost identical to their parents except for a tinge of buff color around the neck. Little is known about the parental care of the young.   MEB

Potoo is a Creole name and refers to the call of the Giant potoo, one of the five species closely related to nightjars. They have concealment coloration, and roost during the day, resting bolt upright on a tree stump or fence post. They feed at night by dashing off from a regular perch to catch flying insects such as moths, beetles, crickets and termites.

Potoos differ from nightjars in not having facial bristles or the usual comb on the middle claw. However, they do have modified cheek feathers on either side of a very large gape. They have long pointed wings and a shortish tail and legs. The bill is small with a downcurved tip. They have a very large gape partly because the upper mandible can be turned up and the lower mandible turned down.

As potoos are nocturnal, one would predict they should have loud distinctive calls which in fact they do. In general, their calls consist of a series of whistles and barking wows. The very loud "baw-woo" of the Giant potoo is often credited to something much larger than a bird, often a cat. During the pre-mating period, quacking sounds are repeated every 10 or 20 seconds.

Potoos do not build nests but lay their solitary egg on a tree stump or even in a crevice in the bark. The egg is oval and spotted. Both sexes appear to take it in turns to incubate and the adults rely on camouflage to avoid detection from natural predators but can often be approached and even touched at this time. Nothing is known about the parental care of the young.   MEB

Discovered in 1799 by Alexander von Humboldt in a cave near Caripe, northern Venezuela, the **oilbird** became famous for its nestlings which, being fed on the oily fruits of palms and other trees, can weigh up to half as much again as the adults. They were regularly collected by the people of the Mission at which Humboldt was staying, and boiled down to give oil for their cooking and lighting. Exploitation by man still continues locally, although in most areas the bird is given legal protection. The English and scientific names (*Steatornis caripensis*—the "fat bird of Caripe") derive from this peculiarity of the nestlings.

The oilbird is related to the large, worldwide group of nightjars and related birds, but it is so specialized, and peculiar in so many ways—in its anatomy, behavior and ecology—that it is placed in a family of its own. Oilbirds are large birds, with long wings, ample tail, very short legs, a strong hawk-like bill surrounded by long whiskers, and large eyes. They are the only nocturnal fruit-eating birds in the world. They spend all day, even during nesting, deep within caves, coming out at nightfall to forage and returning to their caves before daylight. They are highly social, and large caves may contain thousands of birds. The essential requirement of large caves, with ledges on which they can roost and nest, restricts them to mountainous areas, especially limestone formations. In Trinidad, however, they also occupy a few of the large sea caves on the island's north coast.

The most immediate impression made on an intruder into an oilbird cave comes from the unearthly snarling screams uttered by the birds as they mill around in the darkness overhead, a noise that can be almost deafening in a large colony. Not surprisingly, they have been thought of by native peoples liv-

Whip-poor-will—Nightjar Music

The whip-poor-will is a widespread species from southern Canada to Central America. The whip-poor-will of the eastern USA has a clear, slightly warbled song, that of the geographically separated whip-poor-wills of the southwestern USA and Mexico have a guttural quality, yet both species clearly say "whip-poor-will."

In many birds with stereotyped vocalizations song is an inherited trait. It may offer clues to relationships. Nightjars communicate mostly by voice, and males of a given population all sing basically the same songs.

A little known species, the Sooty nightjar of mountainous Costa Rica and Panama, has only recently been tape-recorded. Its voice is strikingly similar to that of the western whip-poor-wills, being higher-pitched but containing the same syllables. Based on this close resemblance and its general physical similarity to the whip-poor-will, the Sooty nightjar perhaps should be regarded as merely a Central American subspecies of the whip-poor-will. The Puerto Rican nightjar was originally described as a separate species, but is currently regarded as a form of the whip-poor-will. However, its "will-will-will-will" song does not support that merger!

The Little nightjar is widespread in tropical South America. Birds from eastern Peru sing a charmingly guttural song (rather froglike), while birds in Venezuela sing a complex series of clear resonant "tick-tock" notes—possibly more than one species is "hidden" under the name Little nightjar.

Based on physical appearances, the chuck-will's-widow of the southern USA and the Rufous nightjar of northern South America are each other's closest relative; voice evidence strongly supports this.   JWH

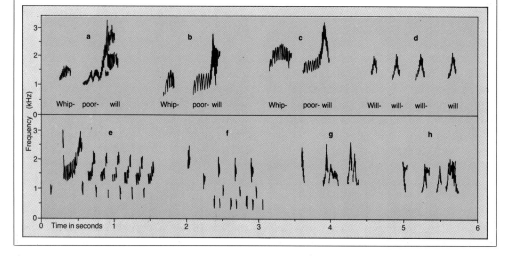

▲ **A Tawny frogmouth** and young, showing the way in which the markings of the bird mimic closely the texture of bark. Adults typically roost in this stiff, upright posture with the beak and forehead bristles pointing obliquely up.

▶ **A plump owlet-nightjar** at the entrance to its nesting hollow in a tree. As with the nightjars, the color is a remarkable match for its surroundings. Owlet-nightjars roost during the day in hollow trees and tree-holes. At dusk they become active, leaving the roost to forage in forest and woodland.

◀ **Sonograms** or voice prints of the songs of nightjars. (**a**) Eastern whip-poor-will (*Caprimulgus vociferus vociferus*). (**b**) Western whip-poor-will (*C.v. arizonae*). (**c**) Sooty nightjar. (**d**) Puerto Rican nightjar. (**e**) Little nightjar. (**f**) Venezuelan little nightjar. (**g**) Chuck-will's-widow. (**h**) Rufous nightjar.

clicking as they emerge into the open air and, while outside the cave, use what is evidently very sensitive night vision to find their way about. There is some evidence that, in locating some of their food trees, they also use the sense of smell. Many of the fruits of the trees at which they feed are aromatic, and oilbirds have an unusually large and sensitive organ of smell.

Adult oilbirds occupy their nests continuously, returning to them to roost even when they are not breeding. The nests are built of regurgitated fruit matter and grow year by year, in the form of a truncated cone with a saucer-shaped depression in the top. The nesting cycle is extremely long. It is usual for the eggs to be laid at intervals of three days or more, an extreme of nine days being recorded. Incubation starts with the first egg, so that they hatch, after the long incubation period of about 33 days, in the sequence in which they were laid. At hatching, the young are sparsely down-covered, but in their second week a second and much thicker generation of down feathers grows. This is succeeded by plumage of adult type, which begins to appear at the age of about five weeks. There is no distinct juvenile plumage, nor any other visual character obviously distinguishing a recently fledged young bird from an adult, doubtless because such a distinction would be without function in a dark cave. By about the 70th day, the nestling reaches its maximum weight, and for the remaining 30 or so days it loses weight as the plumage finishes its growth, until both wing-length and weight reach the adult condition and the young bird is able to fly. During the nestling period, both parents feed the young, on the same fruits that they themselves eat.

In Trinidad, where oilbirds have been most thoroughly studied, the breeding season is long, lasting for most of the year. It is just possible for a pair of birds to fit two breeding cycles into a year and some do so, but most pairs nest only once per year. In other areas, especially the Andes of Ecuador and Peru, there is evidence that the birds leave their caves for part of the year, perhaps in consequence of seasonal changes in the availability of fruit; but it is not known where they go. Possibly, colonies alternate between two caves some distance apart, where seasonal fruit regimes are complementary. What is certain is that some oilbirds, probably young birds, at times wander far from their caves. Stragglers have reached Panama, and even the island of Aruba off the coast of Venezuela.

ing near the caves as devils or lost spirits rather than birds. Among the Spanish-speaking people of South America they are generally known as *guácharo* ("the one who cries"), and in Trinidad as *diablotin* ("little devil"). These loud cries are calls of alarm and of communication with each other, probably also serving to indicate the position of the calling bird to others flying near it. Its other main call—a staccato click which can always be heard when the birds are flying round and undisturbed in the darkness of their caves—is used for echolocation; by picking up echoes from the cave walls and other surrounding objects the oilbird is able to avoid obstacles in pitch darkness. Their echolocation is, however, much less highly developed than that of bats; the clicks are not supersonic, and echoes are not reflected from very small objects. When oilbirds leave their caves at night they stop

DWS

SWIFTS

Families: Apodidae, Hemiprocnidae
Order: Apodiformes (suborder: Apodi).
Seventy-four species in 10 genera.
Distribution: see map and table.

  Swifts Crested swifts

Swifts
Family: Apodidae
Seventy-one species in 9 genera.
Distribution: worldwide except high latitudes and some islands.
Habitat: aerial feeders rarely coming to rest.
Size: 4–12in (10–30cm), weight 0.3–5oz (9–150g).
Plumage: most species dull black or brown, many with conspicuous white or pale markings.
Voice: shrill piercing screams.
Nests: in rocks, crevices or caves; a variety of materials cemented with saliva.
Eggs: 1–6, white, weight 0.04–0.35oz (1–10g); incubation period 17–28 days; nestling period 34–72 days.
Diet: flying insects, other airborne arthropods.
Species and genera include: **Alpine swift** (*Apus melba*), **Black swift** (*Cypseloides niger*), **Chimney swift** (*Chaetura pelagica*), **Common swift** (*Apus apus*), **Edible-nest swiftlet** (*Collocalia inexpectata*), **Palm swift** (*Cypsiurus parvus*), **swallow-tailed swifts** (*Panyptila*), **White-throated spinetail swift** (*Hirundapus caudacutus*), **White-throated swift** (*Aeronautes saxatilis*).

Crested swifts
Family: Hemiprocnidae
Three species of the genus *Hemiprocne*.
Distribution: SE Asia.
Habitat: woodland.
Size: 6.5–13in (17–33cm), weight 2.5–4oz (70–120g).
Plumage: mainly soft gray or brown, with white stripes on sides of head and crest on front of crown.
Nest: tree bark and feathers glued to a branch.
Eggs: 1, white, weight 0.2–0.35oz (6–10g).
Diet: flying insects.
Species: **Crested tree swift** (*Hemiprocne longipennis*), **Lesser tree swift** (*H. comata*), **Whiskered tree swift** (*H. mystacea*).

◄► **Precarious perches.** Swifts are only agile in the air; grounded, they are extremely ungainly birds. ABOVE A Northern white-rumped swift (*Apus pacificus*) perched on a rock. RIGHT A Common swift clinging to a house wall.

S WIFTS are a symbol of summer over much of the world, wheeling and darting through the air, never alighting on the ground or on vegetation. Several species, such as the Common swift of Europe, regularly breed in or on buildings even within large cities; indeed, hardly any breeding records exist of this common species in "natural" sites in Britain. In the primeval forests of Europe, such as those remnants still to be found in Poland, nests have been found in high, broken-off hollow branches and down the trunks of ancient hollow trees.

Swifts rely on catching insect prey on the wing, which restricts their winter range to areas where the temperature allows insects to keep on flying in some numbers (see box). At such times most species have to retreat far from the temperate parts of their range. Common swifts from Britain winter in East Africa, Chimney swifts from Canada in the upper Amazon Basin and White-throated spinetail swifts from China and Japan in Australia. Such long-range migrations are easily within their flying capability for, of all groups of land birds, they seem to be most at ease in the air and would, in any case, fly hundreds of miles every day while feeding, even if they were not migrating. In experiments, nesting Alpine swifts have successfully returned home from 1,000mi (about 1,620km) in three days and a ringing record from Britain has shown a newly fledged young Common swift reaching Madrid from Oxford in only three days.

Most swifts seem ungainly and primitive in the hand or when inadvertently brought down to earth—none will willingly settle on the ground. They have short, weak beaks which open very wide to reveal a huge gape. This allows them more easily to catch insects in flight. Most species have rather dull plumage, although several have this shot through with blue, green or purple gloss. Many have forked tails, although the spine-tailed swifts have the shafts of their tail feathers extending beyond the vane to form a row of spines. These help the birds when they are clinging to vertical surfaces, by giving them support. All species have very short legs (Apodidae means "lacking legs") but very strong feet for grasping vertical surfaces when breeding or roosting. For instance, Chimney swifts are so named for their habit of breeding and roosting inside tall chimneys, which must be a recent adaptation.

Swifts are almost always seen in flight and appear to fly very fast indeed. Their silhouette, with the wings making a thin crescent and their bodies a small cigar through it, would seem to be built for speed, but this is not the case. The long, thin wing is an adaptation for efficient gliding flight—like a sailplane—and most of the time swifts are not flying particularly fast. Indeed, while they are feeding this would be very inefficient for they must see and snatch their prey on the wing and too fast a speed would make this much more difficult. However, during displays they can fly very fast and are often able to take advantage of the wind to cover the ground very rapidly even when their airspeed is not exceptional.

The temperate, migratory species that have been studied in detail are long-lived and faithful both to their breeding site and

to their mate. They have to undertake their breeding attempt quickly as there may only be sufficient aerial food for them for 12–14 weeks, even in areas where they commonly breed. For instance, Common swifts arrive in Britain to breed in early May and leave at the end of July. The males generally arrive first and take possession of the breeding site. This is nowadays almost always in a roof and the birds will make a small ring of material, taken in flight and glued down with saliva, at the place where the eggs will be laid. The chicks are brooded by one or other of the parents for the first few days after hatching and food is brought to them as "boluses"—gobs of insects stored in the parent's throat. These can weigh up to 0.06oz (1.7g) and may contain over 1,000 tiny insects and spiders. In fine weather, feeds may be brought in every 30 minutes or so and thus the parents may provide 1–1.4oz (30–40g) of food in a single day. In such circumstances, the minimum nestling period is roughly five weeks but, should the weather be bad, it may reach eight weeks.

Individual Common swifts undoubtedly recognize each other by voice—their shrill piercing screams—but apparently not by sight. Colonial breeding can lead to several dozen pairs breeding in a single roof-space or, more often, in adjacent buildings. In this species the first-year birds seldom return to the breeding grounds and many do not breed until their third or fourth year. The pre-breeding birds form the large screaming parties which display in mid-summer and often fly up to occupied nesting sites in a very excited state—much to the annoyance of the resident birds.

It has been proved that the Common swift regularly spends the night on the wing. Birds have been watched rising in the evening long past the time when they are capable of finding their way into a nest. They have been seen from planes and gliders and regularly tracked by radar. They may well never come to land at all except when breeding and so complete a nonstop flight of 312,500mi (500,000km) between fledging late one summer and their first landing at a potential nesting site two summers later!

The other 70 or so species of swift include some swiftlet species (*Collocalia*) whose colonies in vast Asian caves may contain several hundred thousand individuals. These birds include species that make their nests entirely from dried saliva and stick it to the roof and walls of the caverns. They are of economic importance, for the nest is the source of "Bird's nest soup." The collection of the nests is a very hazardous under-

taking, involving ropeways and ladders up to 330ft (100m) high. The crop of nests taken may be very valuable and very considerable—more than 3.5 million nests were exported in one year from Borneo to China. These Edible-nest swiftlets use echolocation to find their way round the interior of their nesting caves—it is much too dark for them to be able to see. With such vast colonies, the droppings (guano) also accumulate in the caves and are mined from the floor for use as a fertilizer.

In order to provide the material for the nest, even those species that only use the saliva as cement to glue together other nesting material have much enlarged salivary glands during the nest-building phase of the breeding season. The glands of the Chimney swift, which glues its nest of twiglets to a vertical wall, undergo a 12-fold enlargement. This swift, and the other species which use twigs for nest-building, break them from trees in flight. Other materials are gathered while they are being blown about—feathers, seeds, grasses, straw—during World War II, even the tinsel strips used to confuse enemy radar were incorporated into swift nests.

The varied shapes of, and construction methods used for, nests are often particular to individual species. For instance the Palm swift of the Old World is only found where the Fan palm grows. Its nest is made along the vertical channel on the inside of one of the palm's leaves, from feathers and fibers, and has a small lower rim. This is for the bird to perch on, as it incubates while clinging vertically to the nest into which its two eggs are firmly cemented.

In the New World, the palm swifts belong to a different genus (*Tachornis*) and build their nest inside the vegetation hanging from the crown of the palm trees. In this case, the bag-shaped nest is glued to the leaf and the bird enters along the leaf side and lays its eggs in a cup formed inside the lower, outer edge. Very complex nests are also built by two more New World species, the swallow-tailed swifts, which may form a tube 28in (70cm) long hanging vertically from a rock face. The birds have a nest at the top of the tube, close to the point of attachment. These nests may be very durable and used year after year.

The setting of the Chimney swift's nest, down a vertical chimney, is obviously the equivalent of nesting in a hollow tree and the species still does this too. Several other species will fly down to nest underground in potholes—even 230ft (70m) below ground—and the Black swift has been described as nesting in sea-caves whose entrances are covered by each successive wave. At least three different species habitually nest in the vertical faces of cliffs behind waterfalls and have to fly in and out through the falling water.

These varied nesting sites and structures are a particularly interesting illustration of how a group of aerial birds, without the opportunity for collecting much nesting material, has managed to make use of safe

▲ **Representative species of swifts and some typical nests.** (1) Seychelles cave swiftlet (*Collocalia elaphra*), a colonial cave-nester. (2) Common swifts (*Apus apus*) mating on the wing. (3) Palm swift (*Cypsiurus parvus*) in flight. (4) Alpine swift (*Apus melba*) chasing an insect. (5) Crested tree swift (*Hemiprocne longipennis*) perching on a branch while incubating its egg. (6–9) Nests. (6) Lesser swallow-tailed swift (*Panyptila cayennensis*) builds a tubular nest attached to a tree trunk or rock. (7) Fork-tailed palm swift (*Tachornis squamata*) builds a bag-shaped nest hanging from a fan frond of a palm. (8) Edible-nest swiftlet (*Collocalia inexpectata*) builds cup-shaped nests largely of saliva. (9) Palm swift (*Cypsiurus parvus*) glues its nest to the underside of a palm leaf; the eggs also may need to be glued to the nest.

Survival in Cold Weather

Birds, like the Common swift, that feed on flying insects, may have a considerable problem in the northern part of their range: when the weather turns cold, wet and windy their food may become very scarce—even nonexistent. Outside the breeding season, the birds may make good their escape by flying south to warmer areas but this is not possible while they are nesting.

Detailed studies have shown a range of adaptations to overcome this problem. The adult birds are able to store a considerable amount of subcutaneous fat which they can utilize while food is scarce. They can roost at the nesting site for several days on end with a very slow metabolism and a depressed temperature. Swift eggs are capable of withstanding chilling much more than those of most species; the parents may even practice a rather crude form of birth control, for many observers have reported eggs being removed from the nest-cup in times of cold weather.

Much the most interesting adaptation is the ability of the young to withstand long periods of starvation and cold. Young which have not been fed for a week or more at some stage of the nestling period may still fledge successfully if conditions improve and their parents start to feed them again. Indeed, fasts of up to 10 days have been reported with weight losses of more than 50 percent. The young may be so cold and torpid that they seem dead even to the experienced observer. In such circumstances, the fledging period will approach 60 days instead of the five weeks to be expected in summers with consistently good weather.

Torpidity has been recorded for several other species of swift and also for nightjars and hummingbirds. In Europe, swallows have also been found in a similar state and it is suspected that this may have given rise to theories of hibernation in birds. A record of eight White-throated swifts in a torpid condition during January in California was probably an immediate response to poor weather locally and not an example of true hibernation—so far the only bird which seems to approach true hibernation is the poorwill (see p98).

nesting sites. Most of them are very inaccessible to mammalian or reptilian predators: this safeguards not only the egg and young but also the vulnerable parents. None of the adult swifts are at all maneuverable when on the ground or perched.

The nest of the **crested swifts** is a tiny structure with paper-thin walls stuck on the side of a thin branch. The nest is only about 1in (2.5cm) across and just big enough to take a single egg, glued in with saliva for safety. It is not strong enough to take the weight of the incubating adult or of the developing youngster, so the perched adults incubate sitting along the branch, and the nestling, quite soon after hatching, takes to perching on the branch also. Food is brought to the nestling in boluses and the construction of the nest and the wing structure of the bird point to a fairly close relationship with the true swifts. However, the feeding behavior recalls a shrike or flycatcher, since a perched bird flies out to catch a particular insect and then returns to the perch. CJM

HUMMINGBIRDS

Family: Trochilidae
Order: Apodiformes (suborder: Trochili).
Three hundred and fifteen species in 112 genera.
Distribution: throughout Americas from Strait
of Magellan to Alaska. Also W Indies,
Bahamas, Juan Fernandez islands. Many
species migratory.

Habitat: wherever nectar-producing flowers
blossom, from sea level to 15,000ft (4,500m).

Size: 2.3–8.5in (5.8–21.7cm)
long and 0.07–0.7oz (2–20g).

Plumage: most have glittering blue or green
plumage often with brilliant iridescent areas in
other colors mostly on head, throat or breast;
males often more brilliant, some with crests or
elongated tails.
Voice: most calls high pitched, brief. Flight calls
characteristic of each species, uttered by both
sexes. Male advertising song, a brief warble or
one or two notes frequently repeated.
Nest: in most species, a small cup nest astride
a horizontal twig or stalk. In hermit
hummingbirds and cave-nesting species, a
hanging nest attached by cobweb beneath a
large leaf or to a rock surface.
Eggs: 2 (occasionally 1) elongated white eggs,
0.3 × 0.5in to 0.5 × 0.8in, weight about 13
percent of female's; incubation period 14–23
days, nestling period 18–38 days.
Diet: mostly nectar and small insects.

Species and genera include: **Andean hillstar**
(*Oreotrochilus estella*), **Anna's hummingbird**
(*Calypte anna*), **barbthroats** (*Threnetes*), **Bearded
helmetcrest** (*Oxypogon guerinii*), **Black-throated
mango** (*Anthracothorax nigricollis*), **Blue-chested
hummingbird** (*Amazilia amabilis*), **Blue-throated
hummingbird** (*Lampornis clemenciae*), **Costa's
hummingbird** (*Calypte costae*), **emeralds**
(*Amazilia*), **fairies** (*Heliothryx*), **Fiery-tailed
awlbill** (*Avocettula recurvirostris*), **Giant
hummingbird** (*Patagona gigas*), **Green-backed
firecrown** (*Sephanoides sephanoides*), **hermits**
(*Phaethornis*), **incas/starfrontlets** (*Coeligena*),
lancebills (*Doryfera*), **Marvelous spatuletail**
(*Loddigesia mirabilis*), **metaltails** (*Metallura*),
Mountain avocetbill (*Opisthoprora euryptera*),
pufflegs (*Eriocnemis*), **Purple-throated carib**
(*Eulampis jugularis*), **Purple-throated mountain
gem** (*Lampornis calolaema*), **Rufous-breasted
hermit** (*Glaucis hirsuta*), **saberwings**
(*Campylopterus*), **sicklebills** (*Eutoxeres*),
sunangels (*Heliangelus*), **sunbeams** (*Aglaeactis*),
Sword-billed hummingbird (*Ensifera ensifera*),
thornbills (*Chalcostigma*), **violetears** (*Colibri*).
Threatened species: 6.

Hummingbirds are unique for their
agility in flight, extremely brilliant
iridescent plumage, long bills and generally
small size. To many Europeans they first
became known as decorative objects on the
ornate hats worn by women in the 19th
century, when many thousands were
imported for this purpose. This unhappy
relationship between humans and hummingbirds has long since ceased.

Most hummingbirds are immediately
recognizable by their small size, long thin
bills, brilliant plumage and ability to hover.
Nearly all these characteristics are adaptations for securing their main nourish-
ment: nectar.

The hummingbirds' long bill enables
them to reach nectar inside flowers; in addition they have long extendable tube-like
tongues up which the nectar is drawn. Nectar is usually extracted while the hummingbird hovers in front of the flower; it hovers
forward while inserting its bill and backwards when removing it. This ability to
hover forwards and backwards is unique
among birds and the structure of the hummingbird's wings differs from that of all
other birds except their closest relatives, the
swifts. The hummingbirds' wing consists
mainly of elongated "hand" bones to which
the flight feathers are attached, and the
whole wing can rotate as a wrist does. In
flight, a hummingbird's wing is only visible
as a blur, because of the speed of its wing
beat, between 22 and 78 beats per second,
with the highest rate in the smaller species.

Hummingbirds' feet and legs are
peculiarly small because in most species
they are used only for perching. The exceptional species are a few that live in the high
Andes, the Bearded helmetcrest, the
thornbills and the Andean hillstar, all of
which occasionally walk about, gleaning
insects off bare ground and rock, and have
relatively larger legs and feet.

The bills of hummingbirds vary greatly in
length and shape, according to the flowers
at which they feed. The hermits, which
inhabit tropical and subtropical forest, all
have long, slightly curved bills (except for
two species with long straight bills), the
degree of curvature matching the shape of
the flowers at which they feed. The mostly
smaller emeralds have straight bills varying between 0.7–1in (1.8–2.5cm). The
thornbills, living in the temperate Andes,
have short bills of 0.3in (0.8cm) and take
many insects. The sharp, strong, medium-
length bills of the two fairy hummingbirds
are used to pierce the corollas of flowers and
so steal the nectar. The Fiery-tailed awlbill

and the Mountain avocetbill have bills that
curve upwards, presumably to match some
flower corolla, but this has not yet been
investigated.

Hummingbird plumage is extremely
varied, but in general green, usually a glittering green, is a common color for the
upperparts, while the underparts are often
paler, particularly in females.

In about a third of the family the sexes
are alike; these include most of the larger
duller hummingbirds such as hermits,
saberwings and incas, but also the brilliant
violetears, emeralds and others. In the
remainder of the family the sexes are different, as males have many adornments
which females lack, such as ear tufts, crests
and greatly elongated tails. Many males
have patches of brilliant iridescent feathers,
usually on the crown, throat or upper
breast; these are most often green, blue or
purple, but also red or yellow.

The majority of hummingbird species
occur in Central and South America with
the greatest diversity within the latitudes
10°N to 10°S of the equator. In this broad
latitudinal belt, as one passes from near sea
level in the tropical Amazon forests up the
slopes of the Andes through subtropical and
temperate zones to the open bush and grasslands of the paramo, a different assemblage
of up to 20 hummingbird species is found
in each altitudinal belt until the paramo,
which supports around five species. In the
temperate latitudes of Chile and Argentina
there is only one species of hummingbird to

▲ **Hummingbird nests** are small delicate cups fixed by cobwebs to a twig, often in a fork, as here. A female Anna's hummingbird is feeding her young. Note the lichen-encrusted bark on the outside of the nest.

◄ **Gleaming like pyrites,** the yellow-green iridescence of a male Allen's hummingbird (*Selasphorus sasin*). This species nests up the west coast of Mexico into California. The male has a dramatic display flight involving a dive from about 100ft (30m) above the female.

be found, the Green-backed firecrown.

North of Mexico, 13 species of hummingbirds breed, the number decreasing from the southwest to the northwest of the subcontinent. All these hummingbirds migrate south to winter in Mexico or Central America, except for Anna's, Costa's and the Blue-throated hummingbirds, some individuals of which remain in the southern USA while others migrate.

Some hummingbirds have an extremely wide distribution, such as the tropical Black-throated mango, found from Panama to Paraguay; others have a very restricted range, such as the Marvelous spatuletail—known only from one valley in the Andes of Peru. Two new species of hummingbird, with very restricted ranges, have been discovered in Peru in the 1970s, a sunangel at subtropical levels and a metaltail at temperate levels.

Hummingbirds feed mainly on nectar taken directly from flowers, but all species that have been studied also take small insects.

Within the hummingbird family two major strategies for nectar-feeding are employed. A large number of species with medium-length bills defend from other hummingbirds a dense patch of flowers capable of supplying most of an individual's nectar needs. The defended flowers may or may not be exploitable by insects, and are usually produced by trees or shrubs and herbaceous plants growing in the open and receiving full sunlight. These plants typically have relatively brief but intense flowering periods, so the territory holder must periodically abandon one nectar territory and take up a new one. Emeralds, pufflegs, sunangels and sunbeams are some of the many territorial hummingbirds.

The other main nectar-feeding strategy is non-territorial and has been termed "trap-lining." This term is borrowed from the human trapper who sets traps over a wide area which are then periodically visited. Trap-lining hummingbirds have long bills and the flowers they visit have evolved characteristics that make their nectar available only to long-billed hummingbirds and not to insects or short-billed hummingbirds. This type of flower is usually produced by vines, epiphytes (ie plants that grow on other plants), understory trees and herbaceous plants of forest and shady areas. Typically, these plants have a long flowering season and produce a few flowers at a time, so providing a long-term food source for their hummingbirds. Typical trap-lining hummingbirds are the hermits, the swordbills, and some incas.

In addition to these two major feeding strategies there are also small trap-lining hummingbirds with shorter bills, which feed at small dispersed patches of unspecialized flowers.

Hummingbirds catch their animal food by either hawking for flying insects or by gleaning resting insects or small spiders from the vegetation or spiders' webs. Most straight-billed hummingbirds use both methods, but the curve-billed hermits catch most of their insects and spiders by picking them off the tips, edges and undersides of leaves.

Because hummingbirds are so small they need a high intake of food to maintain their body temperature, particularly at night. Food intake varies with temperature and activity but typically a hummingbird takes over half its body-weight in food a day. If a hummingbird needs to conserve its energy it becomes torpid at night, its body temperature, normally above 105°F (41°C) falling to near air temperature. Nightly torpidity is usually a response to low night temperatures but it can also be a response to insufficient food reserves.

The breeding seasons of hummingbirds are closely tied to the flowering seasons of their major nectar sources. In temperate latitudes this corresponds to the northern and southern springs; in arid areas, rain which stimulates plant growth may be more important than length of day. Thus in California, Anna's hummingbird breeds from November to March, the main rainy season. In high rainfall areas of the tropics and subtropics such as Trinidad and Costa Rica, hummingbirds start nesting at the end of the wet season and beginning of the dry season when many trees and shrubs flower; but they also continue breeding into the follow-

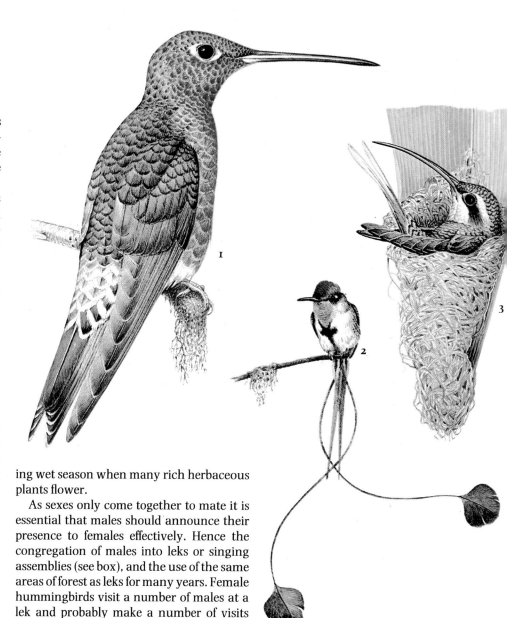

ing wet season when many rich herbaceous plants flower.

As sexes only come together to mate it is essential that males should announce their presence to females effectively. Hence the congregation of males into leks or singing assemblies (see box), and the use of the same areas of forest as leks for many years. Female hummingbirds visit a number of males at a lek and probably make a number of visits to the lek before selecting a mate. Mating

Hummingbirds and Their Flowers

When a hummingbird inserts its bill into the corolla of a flower, its forehead, beak and chin may become well dusted with pollen, some of which will be transferred to neighboring flowers of the same species, so achieving cross-pollination.

From the plant's point of view, hummingbirds are very desirable pollinators because they are long lived and can fly long distances in all weather conditions. For this reason, many plant families of the Americas have evolved flower characteristics which make their nectar available only to hummingbirds and not to insects. Such characters are long tube-like corollas with narrow openings and the absence of landing platforms which insects require. These flowers are oriented well away from leaves and entangling vegetation so that the feeding hummingbird can hover in front of or below them. They are usually colored red or orange, because hummingbirds, but not insects, can distinguish these colors. The nectar in hummingbird flowers is abundant but not very concentrated compared with that of bee-pollinated flowers, as bees are more efficient at

collecting small quantities of concentrated nectar.

It is generally the larger hummingbirds with longer bills, such as the hermit hummingbirds, that get most of their nectar from hummingbird flowers at which insects cannot feed. The smaller, shorter-billed hummingbirds, such as emeralds, do much of their feeding at less specialized flowers which they may share with insects.

Two hummingbirds with highly specialized bills—the swordbill with a bill up to 4in (10.5cm) long, twice as long as that of any other hummingbird, and the sicklebill with a deeply curved sickle-shaped bill—have a particularly high degree of co-evolution with certain plants. Bird and plant are interdependent: the swordbill with a climbing Passion flower, which has a corolla tube of 4.5in (11.4cm) and produces up to 17fl oz of nectar a day, and the sicklebill with certain heliconias whose sickle-shaped corollas fit its bill exactly. The larger sicklebills, which weigh about 0.4oz (12g), prefer to perch while feeding, and the flowers of the heliconias at which they feed are arranged to make this possible.

▲ Representative species of hummingbirds showing the variety of bill shapes. (1) Giant hummingbird (*Patagona gigas*). (2) Spatuletail (*Loddigesia mirabilis*). (3) Long-tailed hermit (*Phaethornis superciliosus*) in its nest attached to a drooping leaf. (4) Bee hummingbird (*Mellisuga helenae*). (5) Amethyst woodstar (*Calliphlox amethystina*). (6) Frilled coquette (*Lophornis magnifica*). (7) Ruby-topaz hummingbird (*Chrysolampis mosquitus*). (8) Bearded helmetcrest (*Oxypogon guerinii*). (9) White-tipped sicklebill (*Eutoxeres aquila*). (10) Sword-billed hummingbird (*Ensifera ensifera*).

▶ In-flight refueling. OVERLEAF With perfect control, a male Broad-billed hummingbird (*Cynanthus latirostris*) approaches a flower. The bird sucks-up nectar provided by the flower, while in return it transfers pollen dusted onto its bill to other flowers, so achieving cross pollination for the plant—nature in harmony.

takes place on the lek perch and also occasionally nearby.

Although mating has been observed infrequently, the males of the four species of hermit frequently "false mate" with leaves near their lek perches, performing the same display to the selected leaf before mounting it, as they perform to females.

Most hummingbird songs are very simple, high-pitched and unmelodious to our ears. The more elaborate and attractive songs, such as that of the barbthroats, are warbles lasting 4–5 seconds. Many songs are just repeated single notes, each lasting only a quarter of a second.

In spite of the simplicity of the song, careful analysis has shown that it varies between leks or singing assemblies, and even between groups of males within a lek. Young males joining a lek copy the song-type of the males near whom they settle.

Only the female hummingbird builds the nest, incubates the eggs and feeds the young. In all but three or four species, male hummingbirds do not even know the whereabouts of nests. Most hummingbird nests are small open cups fixed by cobwebs astride a twig. Although small, the cups are deep and have relatively thick walls of moss lined with vegetable down to assist the female in keeping the eggs and small young warm. Hermit hummingbirds build hanging nests attached by cobwebs to the underside of large leaves such as palms and ferns. Some hillstars, metaltails and lancebills build hanging nests attached by cobwebs to the ceilings of caves, shafts or rocky overhangs.

Occasionally, two females lay in the same nest. This has been recorded among barbthroats and Rufous-breasted hermits, but there are no records of more than two young surviving from these double clutches. The nestlings are fed by regurgitation, usually while hovering. The mother inserts her bill into the nestling's throat and pumps in nectar and insects.

After leaving the nest the fledgling hummingbird is fed by its mother for as long as 20–40 days. A second nesting attempt is usual and a third is not uncommon in the long tropical breeding season. A nest that has been successful may be used again when refurbished or a new one built nearby.

Where the sexes are different, most young hummingbirds fledge into the female plumage, but in a few, such as the Mountain gem, males fledge directly into male plumage. Males which fledge into female plumage acquire their adult plumage at 2–10 months after fledging. Young male hummingbirds start to sing, either alone or at the edge of singing assemblies, a few months after independence. Females probably make their first attempt to nest when about one year old. In captivity, hummingbirds live for about 10 years. In the wild, a Blue-chested hummingbird (identified by its unique song) lived for 7 years.

Most hummingbirds inhabiting humid tropical and subtropical areas, where there are no seasonal extremes, are resident all the year round, making only short local movements when foraging. But in areas where latitude, altitude or drought cause a dearth of flowers at certain times of year seasonal migrations are undertaken. Thus in the highlands of Costa Rica at 10,000ft (3,000m) four species breed but only one is present throughout the year. Anna's hummingbird, which breeds in winter and early spring in California and adjacent areas, moves in midsummer high into the mountains, away from the heat and the drought of the lower country.

The first human threat to the survival of hummingbirds came in the 19th century, when stuffed hummingbirds became a desirable decoration on women's hats. During this period, as many as 400,000 skins were being imported in a single year by one London dealer, and the dealers in Paris and New York were equally active. Although most of these skins were destined for a short life on a hat, others were bought by naturalist collectors and museums. There are six species of hummingbird now in museums that are known only from these trade skins: three from Colombia, two from Brazil and one from Bolivia. Whether they are extinct or not remains to be seen; some are believed to be hybrids and not true species. The fact that new species of hummingbird have been discovered within the last 10 years suggests that some of these six "extinct" species may yet be found. The main threat to the survival of hummingbirds now comes from the destruction of forest and the replacement of other natural vegetation by crops.

The species of hummingbirds most threatened are the larger hummingbirds with long specialized bills who need the flowers with which they have coevolved to survive (see box). The smaller hummingbirds, which are mainly territorial and less specialized, can adapt to feed on many garden and wayside flowers or second-growth shrubs. These are the species that learn to come to feeders put out by people. These feeders, containing a sugary solution accessible only through a narrow tube, are put out by many people in North America and by a few in Central and South America. Originally, the feeder tube was surrounded with an artificial flower, but soon such enticement proved unnecessary and hummingbirds came to undecorated feeders, and the territorial species even set up feeding territories based on them.

The provision of suitable nest-sites and nest materials are also crucial if hummingbirds are to continue to live in man's altered environment. For the hanging nest of the hermit hummingbirds, a suitable tapering leaf, such as the tip of a palm leaf, is essential, and the nest-site must be low off the ground (2–10ft; 0.5–3m), as nests in higher sites are liable to be overturned by the wind.

Of the nest materials, the soft down from seeds or furry leaves is essential for most species, but may be missing from some man-made habitats. Building hummingbirds very often reuse such downy material from old nests, which suggests that it is relatively rare and could be a limiting factor. Finally, hummingbirds must have a plentiful supply of cobwebs, which are used in the nests of all species.   BKS

TROGONS AND MOUSEBIRDS

Orders: Trogoniformes, Coliiformes
Families: Trogonidae, Coliidae.
Forty-three species in 8 genera.
Distribution: see map and table.

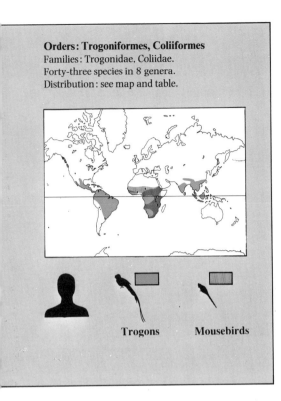

Trogons   Mousebirds

▶ **Clinging Speckled mousebirds** showing the versatile use of their claws—the outer toes are reversible, enabling them to grip like parrots.

▼ **Jewel of a bird.** Many birds have bright iridescent patches of color but the Resplendent quetzal glows from head to foot. Its tail can be as long as 24in (60cm). The Guatemalan currency is named for this dramatic bird.

TROGONS are some of the most brilliantly colored birds in the world. According to Guatemalan Indian legend, the male Resplendent quetzal, most brilliant of all, with glittering metallic green above and crimson below, received its stunning plumage during the Spanish conquest of South America. After a particularly gruesome battle, huge flocks of quetzals (which were then only green) flew down to keep a watch over the dead Mayas, thus staining their breasts red.

The feathers of the Resplendent quetzal's head are bristly and upstanding, forming a narrow ridged crest. The bright green middle wing-coverts are very long, overlapping onto the flanks, while the green uppertail coverts are so elongated that they extend far beyond the normal tail length, forming a graceful curving train which hangs below the bird when perched. Climax cloud forests appear to be essential for the existence of the Resplendent quetzal which ranges along a 1,000mi (about 1,600km) stretch from southern Mexico to western Panama. Unfortunately, the species has much decreased as a consequence of habitat destruction, and there are few areas where it can now be claimed to be abundant. Especially important to the quetzal are the trees of the laurel family, and it is particularly fond of the *Ocotea* fruit.

Unlike other species of trogon, the Resplendent quetzal has a well-marked display flight in which the male flies high above the forest canopy, circling around before dropping back into the foliage, giving distinctive "wac-wac" call notes. The nest chamber is a roughout in a rotting tree trunk, often at some considerable height. Both sexes incubate and tend the young. Outside the breeding season, Resplendent quetzals are mainly found singly, although small flocks are occasionally reported.

The rare Eared trogon is found in western Mexico in mountain pine or pine-oak forest. It normally perches in the middle and upper branches of a tall tree, or flies with a fluttering undulating flight, high up. The small brush-like ear tufts of this trogon are unique, but not easily seen and it differs from other similarly plumaged trogons by having a black rather than a yellow bill. The head and upper parts are glossy green and it is scarlet below, showing a good deal of white on the underside of the square-ended black tail.

The 15 species of the genus *Trogon* range from southern Mexico to northern Argentina. They are birds of similar appearance, glossy green or greenish-blue above, and either scarlet, pink or yellow below. The Collared trogon has the largest range of all New World trogons, also occurring in the tropical forest zones of Trinidad and Tobago as well as on the subtropical slopes of the Andes up to 8,000ft (about 2,500m).

There are three species of trogon found in Africa, of which the Narina trogon is the commonest and most widespread, being found from lowland forest up to almost 11,000ft (3,300m) in montane forest. The male is bright glossy green above and on the throat and breast, with a scarlet belly. The Bar-tailed trogon has a darker head and a narrowly barred whitish underside to the tail. The Yellow-cheeked trogon is a larger bird with brighter red underparts and is a little known species of primary evergreen forest.

The 11 species of Asian trogons belonging to the genus *Harpactes* range from western India to southeast China, Indo-China, Malaya and Indonesia. Like the New World and African trogons they have colorful plumages, short rounded wings, a long square-tipped tail and very short, weak legs. The bill is short and broad, and is cobalt blue in most species, as is the bare patch of skin around the eye. Unlike the New World trogons, which include a very high proportion of fruit in their diet, the oriental trogons feed mainly on large insects and small vertebrates, which they snatch from leaves as they swoop past. Several species are widely distributed, such as the Orange-breasted trogon, which lives in evergreen forest from Burma to Malaya, from Thailand and southwest China to Java.

The Malaysian region is by far the richest in trogon species, with eight present in Sumatra and six in Borneo. The largest species, Ward's trogon, is found in forest above 5,900ft (1,800m) in northeast Burma and northwest Tonkin, also in Bhutan and Assam.   PRC

Mousebirds are so called because of their curious way of moving through the thick foliage of their African forest environment— they crawl around the branches, sometimes resting on the leg rather than the foot, as well as pulling themselves up by their bill, parrot-fashion. These habits are reflected in the anatomy of the foot: normally the bird holds the center two toes forwards and the other two splayed out partly sideways, but the latter are very mobile and can be held forwards or backwards.

All species are rather loosely feathered in gray or brown, though several have a single distinctive marking such as a chestnut rump

(Red-backed mousebird), a blue back to the head (Blue-naped mousebird), or a red mask (Red-faced mousebird).

Mousebirds are common—sometimes very common—and widespread over the African continent. They live in small flocks from about 6–20 birds. They tend to clamber about in dense bushes and then fly to the next, only a very short distance away. They have short rounded wings and are not strong fliers; flight is usually a series of rapid, whirring wing beats followed by a longish glide. Members of the flock keep in contact with a series of short whistles or twitters.

Mousebirds not only live in flocks by day, but they roost together at night, often tightly packed. They have also been reported as sleeping hanging head downward in a tight cluster. At least some species appear to allow their body temperature to fall at night, warming themselves up again in the morning; presumably by doing this they help to conserve energy by reducing overnight heat loss. This habit might point to a relationship with the nightjars, swifts and hummingbirds, some of which have the same ability.

Mousebirds have short, stubby, finch-like beaks and feed mainly on berries and fruits, though they sometimes also take animal matter; they use their feet to help hold food items. They are considered serious pests in gardens and orchards.

Their breeding biology is not particularly well known. In at least some species, both sexes incubate the eggs, though in the Speckled mousebird the female does most of the brooding of the young. The young are naked in the early stages; although they remain in or near the nest until they are able to fly, the larger young may clamber around in the branches close to the nest.

CMP

The Trogon and Mousebird Families   ▣ Vulnerable.

Trogons
Family: Trogonidae
Thirty-seven species in 7 genera.
Southern half of Africa, India and SE Asia; Malaysia, Philippines, Arizona, southern Texas, Mexico, C and S America, W Indies. Forest, woodland and second growth, also montane forests to 9,850ft (3,000m). Size: 9–15in (23–38cm) long. Plumage: soft and dense, with adult males having the breast and abdomen bright pink, red, orange, or yellow and the head and upper parts often brilliant metallic green. Females duller. Voice: a variety of simple calls,

including hollow whistles, hoots, coos, churring and squeaky notes. Eggs: 2 to 4, white or buff to greenish blue; incubation period 17–19 days; nestling period 17–18 days. Diet: insects, spiders, small frogs, lizards, snails, also berries and small fruits.

Species include: **Bar-tailed trogon** (*Apaloderma vittatum*), **Collared trogon** (*Trogon collaris*), **Cuban trogon** (*Priotelus temnurus*), **Eared trogon** (*Euptilotis neoxenus*), **Hispaniolan trogon** (*Temnotrogon roseigaster*), **Narina trogon** (*Apaloderma narina*), **Orange-breasted trogon** (*Harpactes oreskios*), **Resplendent quetzal** ▣

(*Pharomachrus mocino*), **Whitehead's trogon** (*Harpactes whiteheadi*), **Yellow-cheeked trogon** (*Apaloderma aequatoriale*).

Mousebirds
Family: Coliidae
Six species of the genus *Colius*.
Africa south of the Sahara (not in Madagascar). Open woodland and bushy country; avoids dense forest. Size: 12–14in (30–35cm), but much of this is due to long tail which may be 8–10in (20–25cm); weight about 1.6–1.9oz (45–55g). Plumage: light brown or gray, lighter below; loose

crests; some have bright face or neck marks (red or blue); tail strongly graduated. Sexes similar. Voice: a single whistle-like note or a series of more twittering notes. Nests: in an open cup, sometimes bulky and untidy, usually in a thick thorny bush. Eggs: usually 2–4, whitish with blackish or brownish streaks; size usually in range 0.7–0.8 × 0.5–0.6in.

Species include: **Blue-naped mousebird** (*Colius macrourus*), **Red-backed mousebird** (*C. castanotus*), **Red-faced mousebird** (*C. indicus*), **Speckled mousebird** (*C. striatus*).

KINGFISHERS

Family: Alcedinidae
Order: Coraciiformes (suborder: Alcedines, part).
Eighty-six species in 14 genera.
Distribution: cosmopolitan except very high latitudes.

Habitat: interior of rain forests, woodlands far from water, desert steppe, grassy savannas, streams, lakeshores, mangrove, seashores, gardens, mountain forest, oceanic islands.

Size: 4–18in (10–45cm) long (excluding any tail streamers) and weight 0.3–18oz (8–500g); in many species females slightly larger than males.

Plumage: azure blue above and reddish below; also light and dark blue, green, brown, white and black; bill and legs vermilion, brown or black. Males and females similar in most species, pronounced differences in a few others.
Voice: loud song of ringing notes in slowing tempo and falling cadence, or single loud coarse cry, or occasional weak, quiet notes.
Nests: in earthen holes excavated by the birds, including termitaria on ground or in trees, and tree holes.
Eggs: clutches vary from 2–3 in tropics up to 10 at high latitudes; white; weight 0.07–0.4oz (2–12g). Incubation period 18–22 days; nestling period 20–30 days.
Diet: terrestrial arthropods and small vertebrates, aquatic insects and fish.

Species and genera include: **African dwarf kingfisher** (*Ceyx lecontei*), **African pygmy kingfisher** (*C. pictus*), **Amazon kingfisher** (*Chloroceryle amazona*), **Beach kingfisher** (*Halcyon saurophaga*), **Belted kingfisher** (*Megaceryle alcyon*), **Black-capped kingfisher** (*Halcyon pileata*), **Blue-breasted kingfisher** (*Halcyon malimbica*), **Common paradise kingfisher** (*Tanysiptera galatea*), **Crested kingfisher** (*Ceryle lugubris*), **Eurasian kingfisher** (*Alcedo atthis*), **Giant kingfisher** (*Megaceryle maxima*), **Gray-headed kingfisher** (*Halcyon leucocephala*), **Green kingfisher** (*Chloroceryle americana*), **Green-and-rufous kingfisher** (*C. inda*), **Laughing kookaburra** (*Dacelo gigas*), **Mangrove kingfisher** (*Halcyon chloris*), **Oriental dwarf kingfisher** (*Ceyx erithacus*), **paradise kingfishers** (*Tanysiptera*), **Pied kingfisher** (*Ceryle rudis*), **Pygmy kingfisher** (*Chloroceryle aenea*), **Ringed kingfisher** (*Megaceryle torquata*), **Ruddy kingfisher** (*Halcyon coromanda*), **Shovel-billed kingfisher** (*Clytoceyx rex*), **Stork-billed kingfisher** (*Halcyon capensis*), **Tuamotu kingfisher** (*Halcyon gambieri*), **Variable dwarf kingfisher** (*Ceyx lepidus*), **woodland kingfishers** (*Halcyon*).

THE Eurasian kingfisher is a vibrant bird, both in looks and behavior. A stab of electric blue contrasted with the warm chestnut orange of the underparts is the usual image that it presents. And then it is gone, leaving behind the impression of a living cobalt and azure jewel.

Kingfishers are small-to-large, monogamous, more-or-less solitary, bright-plumaged birds of forests, savannas and waterside situations. The great majority of species are tropical, but one or two species from each subfamily have extended as migrant breeders into temperate latitudes.

Primitive species are forest-dwelling predators feeding mainly on forest-floor insects; more specialized types plunge into shallow water for small animals, flycatch for airborne insects, forage in leaf-litter for earthworms, prey on birds and reptiles, and deep-dive for fish from a perch or (particularly the Pied kingfisher) from hovering flight.

Like other birds of their order, kingfishers are large-headed, short-necked, stout-bodied and short-legged, with weak, fleshy feet having the second and third toes partly joined. The bill is straight, strong and long, flattened from top to bottom in insectivorous species and from side to side in fish-eating species. The extraordinary Shovel-billed or Earthworm-eating kingfisher has a short, wide, conical bill. Other forms have the bill sharp-pointed and dagger-like, but in the adult African dwarf kingfisher it is blunt-tipped (sharp in the juvenile). For no obvious reason, several not-closely related lineages of kingfishers are three-toed, having lost the fourth toe. Plumage and other characters show that three-toed species are very closely allied with some four-toed species in the genera *Ceyx* and *Alcedo*, and that the three-toed kingfishers do not comprise a single natural assemblage as they were

formerly held to do. Although colorful, the colors are in general muted, with shades of blue and red predominating. Shoulders and rump are usually shining azure blue, and a dark cap and back are commonly separated by a white or pale collar. Juveniles of paradise kingfishers are dusky, differing markedly from their adults, but in other species juveniles are bright in plumage, though duller than adults. There is little geographic variation within a species, and color conservatism has led to allied species looking much alike. Notable exceptions are the Variable dwarf kingfisher, whose subspecies on islands from the Philippines to the Solomons vary from red to blue or yellow, Africa's Gray-headed kingfisher and the much larger Black-capped kingfisher of China. Although the last two differ in appearance, biochemical and biological characteristics, as well as the geographical relationship of their ranges, suggest very strongly that they are of immediate descent from a common ancestor.

The evolutionary history of other groups of kingfisher species is better understood than for most groups of birds. The family almost certainly arose in tropical rain forest, partly in the northern Australasian region (insectivorous woodland kingfishers, subfamily Daceloninae), and partly in adjacent Indonesia, Borneo and Southeast Asia (forest insectivores, evolving into waterside fishers, subfamily Alcedininae). Both subfamilies extended into Asia and repeatedly invaded Africa, on as many as 12 separate occasions; the Alcedininae invaded the New World to give rise to the Green and Giant kingfishers there (exclusive fishers, subfamily Cerylinae). The several Pacific archipelago species of woodland (*Halcyon*) kingfishers have clearly evolved from the wide-ranging complex formed by the

Mangrove and Beach kingfishers and the more southerly Sacred kingfisher. African mangrove, Woodland and Blue-breasted kingfishers are similarly of recent descent from a single ancestor; their habitats keep them apart, though they are acquiring sufficient ecological differences to permit some degree of geographical overlap. Belted, Ringed, Giant and Crested kingfishers respectively in North America, tropical America, Africa, and southern Asia, are all very closely allied and it is thought that the Giant and Crested descended from small populations of the first two which crossed

the Atlantic (Belted kingfishers occasionally still arrive in Europe as vagrants). Species multiplication is also demonstrated by the four green kingfishers of the neotropics. Long ago, their common ancestor there separated into two geographically distinct populations which duly happened to evolve differences of size, enabling them to overlap as distinct species. Later, each of the two species repeated the separating process, and the

▶ ▼ **Representative species of kingfishers.**
(1) Pied kingfisher (*Ceryle rudis*) hovering.
(2) Blue-breasted kingfisher (*Halcyon malimbica*).
(3) Belted kingfisher (*Megaceryle alcyon*).
(4) Amazon kingfisher (*Chloroceryle amazona*).
(5–7) Kingfisher bill-types. (5) Shovel-billed kingfisher (*Clytoceyx rex*). (6) Laughing kookaburra (*Dacelo gigas*) with a long bill flattened top to bottom. (7) African mangrove kingfisher (*Ceyx pusillus*) with a long bill flattened side to side.

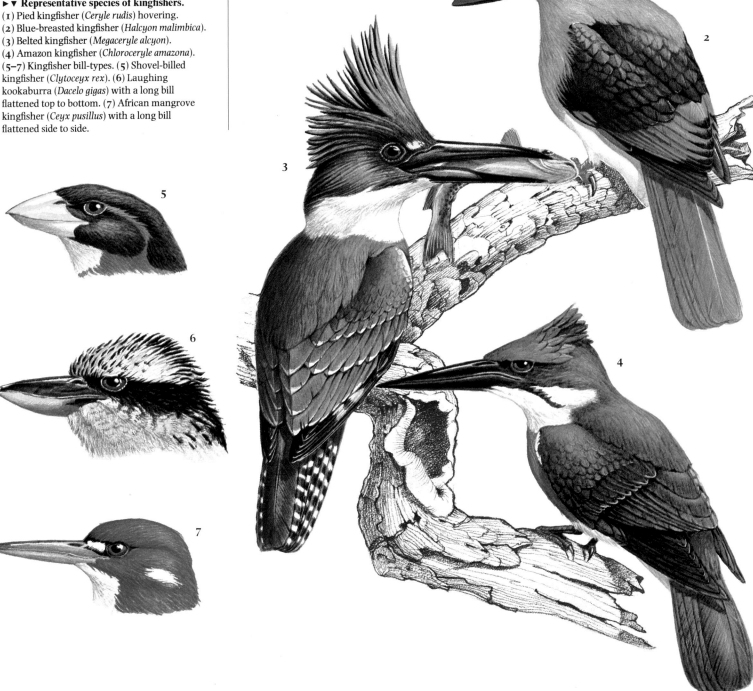

result today is four species all occupying much the same range, having body-weights close to the proportions 1:2:4:8, with the smallest and second-largest (American Pygmy and Green-and-rufous kingfishers) being almost alike in appearance and the largest and second-smallest (Amazon and Green kingfishers) also being remarkably similar.

All fishing kingfishers take a certain amount of invertebrate prey in addition to fish; Eurasian kingfishers, for instance, have about 21 percent of insects in their diet, mainly aquatic but some caught on dry land. Pied kingfishers, fishing from hovering flight more than from a perch, are in that sense at the pinnacle of evolution of the family; in Africa they live entirely upon fish (but in India take insects and crabs too, and can even "hawk" for flying termites). Not having to rely on a perch means that they can fish far from shore: on Lake Kariba they fish up to 1.9mi (3km) offshore at dawn and dusk, catching sardines, a deep-sea fish which rises to the surface at those times. In Natal, 80 percent of their fish food consists of *Sarotherodon mossambicus*, mainly in the 0.035–0.07oz (1–2g) weight class, and on

▲ **The Laughing kookaburra** is obviously a kingfisher, although it lives in wooded country and eats insects and some reptiles.

◄ **The kingfisher's dive.** (1) The kingfisher has spotted a fish and tenses for the dive. (2) A 45° plunge with powerful wingbeats takes him to the water. (3) The kingfisher enters the water, having made last-second adjustments to its aim by fanning the tail feathers. (4) With eyes closed, the fish is seized. (5) The kingfisher, its eyes still closed, emerges from the water with the fish. (6) The kingfisher returns to its perch and swallows the fish head-first after beating it against the branch.

Lake Victoria they prey almost exclusively on fish from the genera *Haplochromis* and *Engraulicypris*. When they forage close to the shore, they dive from hovering flight in windy conditions when ruffled water seems to make fishing from a perch unrewarding. Only when the surface is calm do they fish from perches to a greater extent than from hovering. A Pied kingfisher flies low over the water to a desired hunting station, then rises up to 33ft (10m) and hovers on rapidly beating wings with the trunk held almost vertically and the bill pointing acutely down, keeping station for 5–10 seconds, then diving steeply to

▲ Bringing it back home. A Eurasian kingfisher returns with a fish in its beak to its nest in a bank. There may be as many as 6–7 young, each of which will eat 15 or more fish a day. Thus each parent may need to catch 50 fish each day for the young—as well as those they need for themselves.

penetrate possibly 6.5ft (2m) underwater, occasionally catching more than one fish at a time. Similar behavior is exhibited by the Belted kingfisher of North America.

Most kingfishers are monogamous and territorial, a pair defending an area of woodland on a stretch of river against incursion by other birds of the same species. Several species are migratory, both in the temperate zone and within the tropics; others are sedentary. What little is known suggests that most species breed at the end of their first year, and are quite long-lived. Woodland kingfishers (*Halcyon* species) have a ter-

ritorial advertising display, singing loudly and repeatedly from a conspicuous treetop perch, spreading the wings widely, with the patterned undersides facing forwards, and rotating the body about the vertical axis. Other species have little by way of any courtship display. Both sexes dig the nest tunnel and the male takes a minor role in incubation. The eggs hatch at about daily intervals, in the sequence of laying, so nestlings vary considerably in size. They are fed by both parents equally.

Laughing kookaburras in Australia and Pied kingfishers in Africa have a more complex social system than solitary monogamy. Each has adult helpers at the nest, and in Pied kingfishers there are two kinds of helpers: primary helpers (those helping their own parents) and secondary helpers (those helping an unrelated pair). "Helping" includes defense of territory and feeding the young in the nest and after fledging. This species breeds in loose colonies, the only kingfisher to do so.

Kingfishers have not, in general, come into direct conflict with man. As fish-eaters a few species have occasionally been viewed as pests on fishing streams and dealt with accordingly; but usually they are treated with respect—and often with admiration. Formerly, great numbers of Eurasian kingfishers were shot or netted to make fishing "flies" from their feathers, and in earlier times (in Britain at least) superstition caused the destruction of many, for a dried kingfisher corpse in the house was supposed to avert thunderstorms and keep out moths! Today, man's harmful effects upon kingfishers are more accidental than deliberate, in the pollution of fresh waters and the modification of habitats, especially rain forest. Bird-catchers destroy many; at Jatinga in Assam great numbers of migrating Eurasian, Stork-billed, Ruddy, and Oriental dwarf kingfishers are killed (and presumably eaten) when they are attracted to light beacons around the village at night. In some Mediterranean countries, many kingfishers are killed by netting, shooting and liming, although they are not target species.

Few populations are at great risk. So many species are confined to tropical rain forests, however, or to small Pacific islands or archipelagos, that their fate depends entirely on the preservation of their habitats. Almost certainly extinct is the distinctive race of the Tuamotu kingfisher, which lived until about 1922 on the island of Mangareva, 800mi (about 1,250km) from Tuamotu in the central Pacific.   CHF

MOTMOTS AND TODIES

Families: Motmotidae, Todidae
Order: Coraciiformes (suborder: Alcedines, part).
Thirteen species in 7 genera.
Distribution: see map.

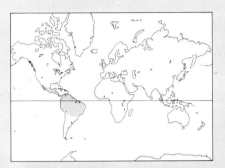

Motmots   Todies

Motmots

Family: Motmotidae
Eight species in 6 genera.
Distribution: C and S America.
Habitat: forests below the canopy.
Size: most 11–18in (28–45cm), but Tody
motmot only 6.5in (17cm); this length includes
long tails in all species except Tody motmot.
Plumage: all species bright green above (some
with blue in wings and tail), several with green
or brown crowns; a mixture of browns and
greens below depending on species; several
have a black spot on the breast and most have
a black mark through the eye; all with very
long, graduated tails with (except for Blue-
throated and Tody motmots) bare shafts just
before the end of the longest (central) tail
feathers, so that the tips appear like "rackets".
Sexes similar.
Voice: a wide range of hoots and squawk-like
notes, many far-carrying.
Nests: sometimes in crevices in rocks, but
mostly in burrows in banks excavated by the
birds themselves.
Eggs: 3–4, white, incubated by both sexes.

Species include: **Blue-crowned motmot**
(*Momotus momota*), **Blue-throated motmot**
(*Aspatha gularis*), **Keel-billed motmot** (*Electron
carinatum*), **Tody motmot** (*Hylomanes momotula*).

Todies

Family: Todidae
Five species of the genus *Todus*.
Distribution: confined to the larger islands of
the Caribbean.
Habitat: forest and woodland, often along
streams.
Size: 4.3–4.7in (11–12cm).
Plumage: all species iridescent green above,
with red throats; underparts vary with species.
Sexes similar.
Voice: a harsh chatter, often a di-syllabic *cherek*.
Nest: a burrow in a bank.
Eggs: 2–5, white, roundish.

Species: **Broad-billed tody** (*Todus subulatus*),
Cuban tody (*T. multicolor*), **Jamaican tody**
(*T. todus*), **Narrow-billed tody** (*T. angustirostris*),
Puerto Rican tody (*T. mexicanus*).

A COLORFUL bird sitting on a branch in a
South American forest, swinging from
side-to-side a long tail, shaped at the end like
the flights of a pair of darts, is almost
certainly a **motmot**—a close relative of the
kingfishers. Motmots are medium-sized
insectivorous birds that are usually found in
pairs, well separated from their neighbors.

All species are bright green or turquoise
green on the back and tail, several are also
green beneath; others have brown underparts. Some have brown heads, but the
crowns of most species are turquoise, blue
or black. All have black marks through or
near the eye and in many this mark is
highlighted by thin turquoise stripes above
and below. Several have a black spot on the
breast.

The most distinctive feature of most motmots is their long, highly graduated tail. In
all species except the Blue-throated and Tody
motmots the vanes of the two longest (central) tail feathers are missing for 1in (2.5cm)
or more a short way from the tip, leaving
the bird with "racket" tips to the feathers.
Some reports describe the birds as stripping
the barbs off the feathers themselves, but it
seems as if the barbs are anyway weakly
attached to the quill at this point and that
they work loose shortly after the feather is
fully grown; doubtless they are more likely
to break loose while the bird is preening,
which probably explains the different
accounts. It is not known why the feathers
should be like this except that they are
extensively used in display.

Motmots have longish, powerful bills

which are slightly downcurved and which
have sharp serrations along the edges; the
bill of the Keel-billed motmot is strongly
keeled. The birds feed on large insects and
lizards and use their powerful bills for crush-
ing their prey; they also sometimes feed on
berries. They sit around on perches beneath
the forest canopy and sally forth, flycatcher-
like, to catch flying insects or to pounce on
small animals on the ground.

All motmots nest in holes, usually in a
bank or sometimes in a burrow dug in the
ground; they dig the burrows themselves.
At the end of the burrow they excavate a
largish chamber in which the female lays
the eggs. Both sexes incubate the eggs and
feed the young. The young do not leave the
nest until they are fully able to fly, but their
elongated tail feathers have not developed
at this time.   CMP

Todies are close relatives of the motmots of
Central and South America: both groups
have many characteristics in common, but
todies are considerably smaller.

Todies are confined to the larger islands
of the Caribbean, where each species has a
limited distribution. The Cuban tody lives on
Cuba and the Isle of Pines, the Puerto Rican
tody on Puerto Rico, the Jamaican tody on
Jamaica; Hispaniola has two species, the
Narrow-billed tody at low altitudes and the
Broad-billed tody in the mountains. The
Narrow-billed tody is also found on Gonave,
off Hispaniola.

All are a brilliant, iridescent green above,
with a bright red throat. The color of their

◄ **Tody on a twig.** A diminutive Jamaican tody devouring an insect on its perch. The bird will beat the butterfly against the branch to knock the wings off and then either swallow the body or take it back for the young.

▼ **Attentive motmot.** A Blue-crowned motmot in characteristic pose, waiting for prey to appear. The powerful beak has sharp serrations along the edges, enabling it to grip prey firmly.

underparts varies from species to species; they may be pale—whitish or grayish—and some have a pink or yellow wash on their flanks. Unlike the motmots, todies have short tails. All have long, straight bills which vary somewhat in width; they are usually black above and red or orange-red below. In flight, both sexes may make a whirring noise. This is apparently made by the wings and may be associated with court-ship display.

The todies are also like miniature versions of their mainland motmot cousins in their ecology. They live in wooded country, usually in forests and frequently along the edges of streams or rivers. They spend much of the day, either alone or in pairs, sitting still, perched on small twigs from which they sally out to catch small passing insects; occasionally they may pounce on tiny lizards or other small animals, and they also hover briefly to pluck prey from leaves. They are extremely tame and approachable.

During the breeding season they use their beaks to excavate tiny burrows in a bank of a stream or road. They lay their eggs in a chamber at the end. Both parents incubate and care for the young. When the young hatch they are naked, and remain in the nest until they can fly.   CMP

BEE-EATERS

Family: Meropidae
Order: Coraciiformes (suborder: Meropes).
Twenty-four species in 3 genera.
Distribution: Eurasia, Africa, Madagascar, New
Guinea, Australia.

Habitat: mostly open country: woodlands,
savannas, steppe; 6 species in rain forest.

 Size: 6.5–13.5in (17–35cm)
long (including tail
streamers), weight 0.5–3.0oz
(15–85g).

Plumage: mostly green above, buff below; some
species black or blue or carmine with black eye
mask, black gorget, and colored throat. Males
and females very similar; some males brighter
than females, with longer tail streamers.

Voice: rolled liquid syllables, melodious *en
masse* or hoarse cawing.

Nests: unlined chamber at end of a tunnel 2–
3in (5–7cm) in diameter and up to 10ft (3m)
long, dug in cliff or flat ground.

Eggs: 2–4 in tropics, up to 7 in Eurasia; white;
weight 0.12–0.16oz (3.5–4.5g); incubation
period 18–23 days; nestling period 27–32
days.

Diet: airborne insects, mainly wasps and bees.

Species include: **Black bee-eater** (*Merops
gularis*), **Blue-bearded bee-eater** (*Nyctyornis
athertoni*), **Blue-cheeked bee-eater** (*Merops
persicus*), **Carmine bee-eater** (*M. nubicus*),
Celebes bee-eater (*Meropogon forsteni*),
European bee-eater (*Merops apiaster*), **Little bee-
eater** (*M. pusillus*), **Little green bee-eater**
(*M. orientalis*), **rainbowbird** (*M. ornatus*), **Red-
bearded bee-eater** (*Nyctyornis amicta*), **Red-
throated bee-eater** (*Merops bullocki*), **Swallow-
tailed bee-eater** (*M. hirundineus*), **White-fronted
bee-eater** (*M. bullockoides*).

► **Adorning a bank,** a colony of Carmine bee-
eaters. Some of the nest-holes are visible here.
This is the southern race (*Merops nubicus
nubicoides*) which lacks the greenish blue throat
of the northern race.

Bee-eaters do indeed eat bees, and this has brought them into conflict with bee-keepers. The bees are caught usually on the wing, and are taken to a perch to be relieved of their venom and sting before being swallowed—this involves beating the bee against a hard object.

Bee-eaters are highly colored birds: most are green above and green, buff or chestnut below, but one is predominantly black, one blue, one pink and gray, and one carmine. All have a black eye mask, most have a black band on the upper breast, and the intervening chin and throat are strikingly bright yellow, red, reddish, blue or snowy, often with a cheek stripe of contrasting color. Wings are rounded (in forest dwelling bee-eaters) or long and pointed (in open country species, particularly those that hunt or migrate long distances). In most species the wings are green with a broad black trailing edge. The tail is quite long, not much patterned, but often with slightly or greatly elongated central feathers, or elongated outer feathers in the Swallow-tailed bee-eater. In other respects, all species are physically much alike: large-headed, short-necked birds with a long, slender, downcurved bill, very short legs and weak feet. When perched, all move the tail backwards and forwards through a small arc—these are balancing movements which have come to have a social function. All sunbathe using a number of postures, the commonest being to sit back-to-the-sun with mantle feathers acutely raised.

The bee-eater family is essentially tropical, and its more primitive members inhabit Southeast Asian rain forests: this and other clues suggest that bee-eaters arose there, and spread to Africa, where they proliferated. Repeated intervention of rain forest between northern and southern tropical savanna isolated ancestral populations and

allowed them to differentiate. Northern and southern Carmine bee-eaters are thought to have diverged from a common ancestor only about 13,000 years ago, and the northern tropical Red-throated bee-eater and southern tropical White-fronted bee-eater diverged about 75,000 years ago.

The commonest prey of most bee-eaters are honeybees. When readily available—near their hives or around flowering trees and herbs—they seem to be taken in preference to other equally abundant flying insects. All four species of honeybee are eaten, and the geographical ranges of honeybees and bee-eaters coincide so closely as to suggest that honeybees have always

▷ **Poised with prey,** OVERLEAF a European bee-eater prepares to swallow a cicada. Note the subtle color scheme: lilac-blue breast, russet back of the head, yellow throat patch.

◁ **The rainbowbird,** a bee-eater that lives in Australia and migrates to Indonesia. This species nests in very loose colonies. Sometimes the nests are so far apart that they seem to be solitary.

▽ **Bee-eater at work.** (1) Bee-eaters often perch on bustards to spot their prey, as with this Carmine bee-eater on an Arabian bustard. (2) The pursuit of a bee is usually short and direct but sometimes involves twisting and turning; shown here is a European bee-eater. (3) The bee is caught by an upward movement of the head, as with this Blue-cheeked bee-eater. (4) The bee-eater (as with this Swallow-tailed bee-eater) glides to a perch and rubs the bee on the perch to procure venom discharge and to tear away the poison sacs and sting before (5) swallowing it whole; shown here is a Rainbow bee-eater.

been the birds' staple food. Other insects taken by some species include wasps, hornets, dragonflies and damselflies. The great majority of bees caught are venomous workers. The few non-stinging drones (male bees) taken probably reflects their scarcity outside of the hive. A European bee-eater requires about 225 bee-sized insects to sustain it and its young every day.

Bee-eaters hunt mainly by keeping watch for flying insects from a perch. They sit alertly on a vantage point such as a treetop twig, fence or telegraph wire, turning the head to scan on all sides, then fly out quickly to intercept a passing insect. The prey is seized adroitly in the bill, taken sometimes from below and at other times after a short twisting and turning pursuit; in a graceful glide the bird returns to its perch where it tosses the prey until held in the tip of the bill, and strikes it several times against the perch to left and right. A stinging insect is then held near the tip of its tail, which is rubbed against the perch with the motion of someone using an india-rubber. A bee's bowel fluid is squeezed out, wetting the perch, and its sting and poison sacs are torn away. Several beating and rubbing bouts alternate, and the immobilized insect is swallowed entire.

Like their close allies the kingfishers, bee-eaters excavate nest burrows in soil. Most species dig both in perpendicular banks and in flat ground; but Red-throated and White-fronted bee-eaters nest only in banks. Tunnels decline in flat ground, are horizontal or inclining in cliffs, and end in a broad oval egg-chamber. Red-throated bee-eaters' tunnels have a hump separating entrance tunnel from egg chamber, which helps to prevent eggs from accidentally rolling out. There is no nest lining, but a blackish carpet of trodden-down regurgitated pellets soon accumulates and can almost bury the clutch. Later, nests become fouled with feces, the debris full of scavenging beetle larvae, and a large colony has an ammoniacal stench.

At the end of its first year a bee-eater either breeds or, like many other tropical birds, attaches itself as a helper to a breeding pair. In most species there is little by way of courtship display, although chasing away rival males and adjacent-nesting pairs, and "courtship"-feeding, are commonplace. White-throated bee-eaters, however, have a courtship "butterfly-flight," with raised wings, slow beats and deep-chested appearance. In many bee-eaters, a perched bird also greets its incoming mate by raising its wings, fanning and vibrating the tail, and

calling vociferously. Both sexes—and any helpers—excavate the nest, but the female does most of the incubating. Eggs are laid at 1-day intervals (or up to 2-day intervals in larger species) and incubation begins sporadically with the first egg and fully with the second or third egg. Hence the eggs hatch at about daily intervals, in the laying sequence, and the brood of young are graded in age and size, with the oldest often 2–3 times the weight of the youngest.

Both parents, and any helper(s), feed the young equally, with single insects generally larger than those that the adults themselves eat. The newly hatched young are blind, naked and pink. Their skin soon turns gray, eyes open and spiny, rudimentary feathers appear at about a week; growth is then rapid and the youngsters fledge at a weight up to 20 percent greater than the mean adult weight. After fledging, they and their parents and helpers may all continue to roost in the nest-hole for a few days, but usually start roosting in distant vegetation.

The family group—4 in Black, about 6 in Little, 4–9 in European, or up to 12 in White-throated bee-eaters—stay together in some instances until next year's nesting. After fledging, the young accompany the adults particularly closely for some six weeks, depending on them for food.

Red-throated and White-fronted bee-eaters in Africa have some of the most complex bird societies in the world. The White-throated bee-eater, a Saharan species, has up to six helpers at the nest. Red-throated bee-eaters are densely colonial, with up to 150 birds occupying nest holes in 11–22sq ft (1–2sq m) of cliff face. About two-thirds of nests are attended by a pair only, and pairs at the remaining third have 1–3 helpers which are generally their own progeny from a previous year. White-fronted bee-eaters are similarly colonial, but have 1–5 helpers at a majority of nests, and an individual bird alternates between breeding and helping breeders in successive nestings. Certain pairs and their helpers within a colony form a clan, and a colony may comprise 3–6 clans.

No bee-eater species is greatly threatened, but some may be depleted if commercial bee-keeping is developed in Africa. Bee-eaters were known to the ancient Egyptians as pests at apiaries, and many thousands are killed every year in Mediterranean countries. Since we now know that they consume vast amounts of hornets, bee-wolves and other honeybee-eating insects, it might well benefit bee-keepers in the long run *not* to molest the birds.   CHF

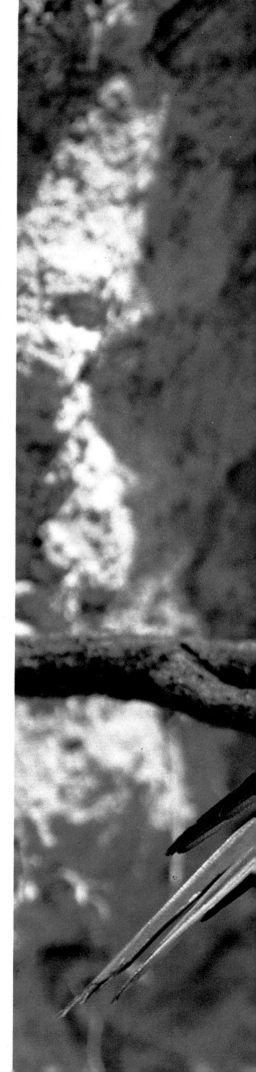

ROLLERS AND HOOPOES

Families: Coraciidae, Leptosomatidae, Phoeniculidae, Upupidae
Order: Coraciiformes (suborder: Coracii).
Twenty-five species in 8 genera.
Distribution: see maps and table.

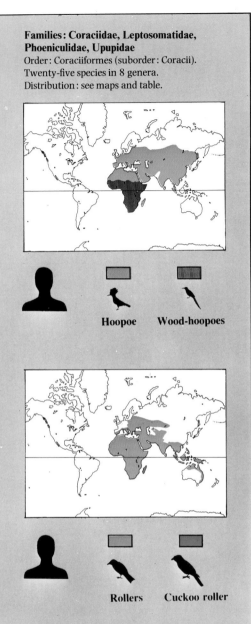

Hoopoe   Wood-hoopoes

Rollers   Cuckoo roller

▶ **The silky plumage** TOP RIGHT of the Lilac-breasted roller, a species of tropical Africa.

▶ **A hoopoe** bringing prey to its young at the nest in a tree-hole. The young hatch at intervals and are at first brooded by the female and fed by the male. Later both sexes take part in feeding.

▶ **A Rufous-crowned roller** (*Coracias naevia*) BOTTOM RIGHT on an acacia tree in Etosha National Park, Namibia. Confined to the southern half of Africa, this species is less noisy and aggressive than other rollers. It occurs singly or in pairs in open woodland.

COLORFUL, numerous and attractive birds, rollers and hoopoes have attracted much attention, principally because of the recently discovered mass-emigration of hundreds of thousands of European rollers from East Africa. Cinnamon rollers, whose diet consists of swarming termites, and Green wood-hoopoes, who have "helpers" at the nest, have also attracted attention.

Rollers are not particularly closely allied with hoopoes. Appearances and ways of life are very different, yet there are underlying affinities of breeding and biology and structure: 22 of the 25 species belonging to these four families breed in the Afro-tropical region and the two most northerly breeding species, European roller and hoopoe, are of immediate descent from relatives in the tropics.

Rollers are so-called because of the spectacular tumbling courtship flight of "true" rollers (*Coracias*) and of broad-billed rollers (*Eurystomus*). The former spend much time aloft, defending their territory with raucous calls and rolling flight; but they feed mainly on the ground, dropping onto small animals from a perch. Broad-billed rollers, by contrast, feed on the wing. For most of the day a pair sits on treetops, eating little, and aggressively chasing other birds away; but in the late afternoon up to 200 gather, dramatically losing their aggressiveness to feed on winged termites. With pointed, quite long wings, large head, short neck and thickset body, they have a fast, wheeling and swooping flight and resemble falcons or huge swifts. One bird can eat up to 800 termites (half the weight of the bird itself) in the 90 minutes before dusk. One African species is resident in rain forests; another is a migrant within the tropical savannas and between Africa and Madagascar. The Oriental species is called dollar-bird because of the coin-sized white "windows" in its wing tips, and migrates between Australia and New Guinea.

All *Coracias* rollers are also strongly migratory. European rollers enter Africa in September, when the closely allied and very similar Abyssinian rollers are also migrating up to 600mi (1,000km) southwards within the northern tropics. But European rollers travel ten times as far, and winter mainly in arid country in Kenya, Tanzania and Namibia. In the first few days of April, huge numbers concentrate in eastern Tanzania, and fly together in a narrow coastal corridor through Kenya and Somalia, where thousands can be seen together, evenly dispersed in the sky from horizon to horizon.

All rollers appear to be monogamous, highly territorial, hole-nesters. Apart from the spectacular rolling flight, the breeding biology of European and Indian rollers is not

unusual. Most African species are curiously ill-known, considering how common and eminently studiable the birds are. Madagascan ground rollers are even less well known; they seem to be mainly active at twilight, feeding entirely on the ground, and nesting in holes in open ground (Long-tailed ground roller), around forest tree roots (Pitta-like and Crossley's ground rollers), or in trees (Short-legged ground roller). There is a strong native tradition that these birds hibernate in the dry season.

The **Cuckoo-roller** is restricted to Madagascar and the Comoro islands, and may well be more closely related to "true" rollers than are the ground rollers. Cuckoo-rollers have the proportions and flight characteristics of "true" rollers but they seek their

food neither in the air nor on the ground, but in the upper story of large forest trees. Chameleons appear to be a staple food item and it is likely that Cuckoo-rollers specialize on them.

Wood-hoopoes comprise one of the very few bird families confined to Africa. Smaller species are rather solitary, but larger ones are gregarious, in parties of 5–12, and make themselves highly conspicuous by periodically interrupting foraging to indulge in noisy mutual displays. Each bird cackles vociferously (they are called *kakelaars* in Africaans, or cacklers), and with each call the head is exaggeratedly bowed and the tail raised high. After a few seconds, they all fly from the nest tree and quietly resume foraging, probing into bark crevices with their long slender bills and often clinging below a horizontal limb or crosswise on a trunk. The bill is straight in some species, downcurved in others, and in the scimitar-bills greatly downcurved, bending through 90 degrees. "Cackling" functions to maintain the identity and cohesion of the group, which is more or less an extended family of parents, helpers and young. Studies in Kenya show that one advantage to the helper, which foregoes breeding in order to help at another adult's nest, is that the helper forms bonds with the young it helps to raise and in a subsequent nesting season those young will assist the former helper, improving its breeding success.

Best known of all these birds is the **hoopoe**, with a vast breeding range in three continents. Being conspicuous and common in gardens and cultivated land, it has a special place in folklore and people's affections.

Hoopoes are small-headed, short-legged perching and ground birds. They forage by walking over turf, probing with their long slender bill for grubs and, like wood hoopoes, taking insects from fissured bark in trees. They fly readily, with irregular, butterfly-like beats of rounded black wings with white bars across the flight feathers, and on perching often momentarily fan the crest. Races vary in the amount of white in the wing, and the depth of body color. Southern African hoopoes are reddish, with little white in the wing, and being readily distinguished in the field from wintering Eurasian migrants, they were formerly held to be a distinct species. Nests are scantily-lined cavities in termite-mounds, old wood-pecker holes, rough stone walls, drainpipes or clefts in trees; the entrance is narrow, so that the bird has to squeeze in, and the hole itself fetid. Young are downy. They have five methods of defense: by spraying excreta; hissing; poking upward with the bill; striking with one wing; and a stinking excretion of the preen gland. Adult hoopoes react to overhead birds of prey by flattening themselves against the ground, with wings and tail spread conspicuously and bill pointing straight up.   CHF

The 4 Families of Rollers and Hoopoes   v Vulnerable.   r Rare.

Rollers
Family: Coraciidae
Sixteen species in 5 genera.

Africa, Madagascar, Eurasia, Australia. Forests, woodlands, savannas. Size: 10–18in (25–45cm). Plumage: muted pink-browns, cinnamon, dark and light blue; sexes alike. Voice: repeated short gruff caws. Nests: in cavities in trees and masonry, or (ground rollers) in tunnel in ground. Eggs: 2–3 near Equator, 3–6 in high latitudes, white; weight 0.35–0.6oz (10–17g); incubation period about 18 days; nestling period 25–30 days. Diet: mainly insects; some small vertebrates.

Species include: **Abyssinian roller** (*Coracias abyssinica*), **Cinnamon roller** (*Eurystomus glaucurus*), **Crossley's ground roller** r (*Atelornis crossleyi*), **dollar-bird** or **Broad-billed roller**

(*Eurystomus orientalis*), **European roller** (*Coracias garrulus*), **Indian roller** (*C. benghalensis*), **Lilac-breasted roller** (*C. caudata*), **Long-tailed ground roller** v (*Uratelornis chimaera*), **Pitta-like ground roller** r (*Atelornis pittoides*), **Purple roller** (*Coracias naevia*), **Racket-tailed roller** (*C. spatulata*), **Scaly ground roller** r (*Brachypteracias squamigera*), **Short-legged ground roller** r (*Brachyptera leptosomus*).

Cuckoo-roller
Leptosomus discolor.
Family: Leptosomatidae.
Sole species
Cuckoo-roller or gourol

Madagascar, Comoro Islands. Forests, scrub. Size: 17in (42cm). Plumage: male, iridescent green back, gray head, white underparts; female,

greenish back, brown head, spotted underparts. Voice: loud "qui-yu," repeated. Nests: in tree cavity. Eggs: 2, cream-buff, rounded ovals. Diet: insects; chameleons and other small vertebrates.

Wood-hoopoes
Family: Phoeniculidae
Seven species of genus *Phoeniculus*.
Subsaharan Africa. Forests, wooded savannas. Size: 9–18in (23–45cm). Plumage: black with green or violet gloss, conspicuous white marks on wing and in long tail, some species with buff or brown head; bill and legs scarlet or black. Voice: repeated fluty notes, or cackling by flock in unison. Nests: in tree cavities, unlined. Eggs: 2–4, blue, spotted; incubation period 17–18 days; nestling period 30 days. Diet: insects.

Species include: **Buff-headed wood-hoopoe** (*Phoeniculus bollei*), **Green wood-hoopoe** (*P. purpureus*), **scimitarbill** (*P. cyanomelas*).

Hoopoe
Upupa epops.
Family: Upupidae
Sole species.
Europe, Africa, Madagascar, southern Asia. Wooded farmlands, orchards, savannas. Size: 11–11.5in (27–29cm) long, weight 1.8–2.8oz (50–80g). Plumage: pink-brown, with black-and-white banded crest, wings and tail. Voice: "hoo-poo." Nest: unlined or simply-lined cavity in tree, masonry or ground. Eggs: 2–5 in tropics, 7–9 in high latitudes; color very variable–yellowish, greenish, brownish; weight 0.1oz; incubation period 15–16 days; nestling period 28 days. Diet: insects, small vertebrates.

◄▼ **Representative species of rollers and hoopoes.** (1) Hoopoe (*Upupa epops*) in defensive posture. (2) Cuckoo roller (*Leptosomus discolor*). (3) Green wood-hoopoes (*Phoeniculus purpurens*) with two performing the calling display. (4) Racquet-tailed roller (*Coracias spatulata*). (5) European roller (*Coracias garrulus*).

HORNBILLS

Family: Bucerotidae

Order: Coraciiformes (suborder: Bucerotes).
Forty-five species in 14 genera.
Distribution: Africa, and S Asia and islands east
to New Guinea.

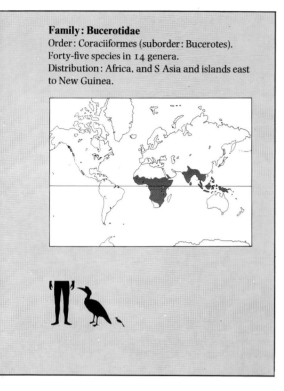

► **Triple-decker bill.** The huge bill of the
Northern pied hornbill (*Anthracoceros
albirostris*), with its casque above the upper
mandible.

▼ **The White-crested hornbill** of Asia. This
species lacks a casque but does have a crest
growing forwards over the bill.

Hornbills are celebrated for their large
bill, often surmounted by a large
casque. They are conspicuous with their
bold colors, varied calls and rushing wingbeats. Their biology is also remarkable, especially the unique breeding habits—the
female seals herself into a nest hole for the
entire nesting cycle.

Hornbills are an Old World group—
unrelated to the toucans of the New
World—with about half the species in Africa
south of the Sahara (not Madagascar), half
in southern Asia, and a single species
extending to New Guinea. The larger forest
species, most of which occur in Asia, are
usually the largest avian fruit-eaters in their
habitat and are probably important dispersers of the seeds of many forest tree species.
More than half the African species inhabit
savanna and woodland, especially the 15
small *Tockus* species, which are mainly
insectivorous, but also the two ground
hornbills, which are among the larger avian
predators.

The large bill characteristic of the family
may be why hornbills are the only birds
with the first two neck vertebrae (axis and
atlas) fused together. The bill is long and
down-curved, often with only the tips of the
mandibles meeting properly, to form dex-
trous forceps. The cutting edges are often
serrated for breaking up food. The casque
surmounting the bill is in its simplest form
a narrow ridge that may reinforce the upper
mandible. However, in many species the
casque is elaborated into a structure that is
cylindrical, upcurved, folded or inflated and
sometimes exceeds the size of the bill itself.

The casque is invariably poorly developed
in young birds. In the adults of most species
it is much larger and more elaborate in
males. In all but one species the structure
is a light skin of keratin overlying a bony
support; it is probably used in recognizing
the age, sex and species of an individual, as
well as for amplifying calls in a few cases.
However, in the largest Asian species, such
as the Great and Rhinoceros hornbills, it
may be used in fighting or to knock down
fruit. Most remarkable is the Helmeted
hornbill, with its straight, short bill supporting a casque containing a block of solid
keratin and together with the skull forming
10 percent of its body weight—possibly a
weighted digging tool.

The wings are broad and, in the larger
species, produce a whooshing noise in flight
as air rushes through the base of the flight
feathers (which lack underwing coverts).
The tail is long in most species, especially
in the Long-tailed hornbill or the White-

crested hornbill, while in the Helmeted hornbill the central pair of tail feathers is up to 3.3ft (1m) in length. In most species of the genus *Rhyticeros* the tail is short and pure white, and the ground hornbills also have short tails.

Notable colors and structures are found on the head and neck. The eye color may differ between species, or between sexes as in the genus *Buceros*. Coloration of the bare skin around the eyes and on the throat may distinguish the species, sex or age of a hornbill and in some species the throat skin is inflated (ground hornbills, *Rhyticeros*, *Aceros*) or hangs as wattles (*Ceratogymna*). Hornbills are also notable for their long eyelashes, and for the rather stubby legs and toes, with broad soles and the bases of the three front toes partly fused.

There is considerable evidence that hornbills are closely related to hoopoes and wood hoopoes (p126) in both their anatomy and their behavior. Hoopoes and the small *Tockus* hornbills that they most resemble are both primarily African groups, which suggests the source and basic form of their common ancestor.

Hornbills in Africa, except ground hornbills, seem more closely related to each other than to those in the Oriental region. The large African species of *Bycanistes* (which have white rumps) and *Ceratogymna* are unusual in that the head and neck of young birds and females are colored brown in contrast to the black of males. In otherwise similar Oriental forms, such as *Anthracoceros*, the young birds resemble males, as in most other hornbills, with brown heads being confined to females in such genera as *Rhyticeros*, *Aceros* and *Penelopides*. The smallest hornbills, in the genus *Tockus*, have diversified into 13 species in Africa, with a further two similar but probably unrelated species in India and Sri Lanka, and the Long-tailed hornbill of Africa is very similar to them.

Among African hornbills only the ground hornbills are apparently allied to Oriental species, although this is far from obvious at first sight. The largest Oriental forest hornbills in the genus *Buceros*, together with the specialized Helmeted hornbill, are derived from smaller *Rhyticeros* species. Some of these share with them the use of preen gland oils to color cosmetically the bill, casque and white areas of plumage with red, orange or yellow. However, only in *Buceros* species and the Helmeted hornbill is the preen gland clothed in a special dense tuft of feathers to improve the application, and this same special feature is found in the ground hornbills of Africa. The ground

▲ **A Southern ground hornbill** and young in Kruger National Park, South Africa.

▶ **A snake-eating Yellow-billed hornbill,** an African species found from Somalia to Kenya and South Africa.

▼ **Displaying ground.** Southern ground hornbills live in cooperative groups of up to eight birds. Social communication is rich.
(1) A female soliciting attention from a male.
(2) A female bringing insects to a male.
(3) A female beating her bill on the ground and flashing the wing feathers.

hornbills are so different from other hornbills in many aspects of their design and biology that this difference may be discounted were it not that they also share a special genus of feather lice with their Oriental relatives.

The larger forest hornbills are mainly fruit-eaters and most travel widely in search of fruiting trees. The irregular fruiting and dispersal of the food source also mean that these species are not territorial and tend to gather in large flocks in search of fruiting trees. The birds use the long bill to reach out to fruits and toss each fruit back into the gullet, where the stubby tongue can assist the swallowing. Undigested remains, such as pips, are regurgitated or defecated, facilitating seed dispersal.

Breeding hornbills have been observed to swallow as many as 69 small fruits and carry them to the nest to be regurgitated for the young. At one nest of a Silvery-cheeked hornbill it was estimated that the male delivered 24,000 fruits, in the course of 1,600 nest visits spanning the 120-day breeding cycle. Any small items of animal food are snapped up if encountered and in several species it appears that animal food is specially sought during breeding, probably as a source of extra protein for the growing young.

Most of the smaller hornbills are primarily insectivorous, taking other small animals and some fruit when available, and most are also sedentary and defend a permanent territory. However, some of the African species which occupy seasonally dry savanna are forced to range widely once the rainy season has passed. Exceptions to these two main feeding strategies are suspected for some large Oriental forest species, such as the White-crested and Helmeted hornbills, which are known to be sedentary—the

The Hornbill Family (Bucerotidae)

☐ Threatened, status indeterminate.

Forty-five species in 14 genera. Africa S of Sahara, S Asia and islands east to New Guinea.
Most species in forest but some, mainly in Africa, occupy savanna. Size: length 15–63in (38–160cm), with elongated tail of Helmeted hornbill up to 20in (55cm) longer; weight 3oz–8.8lb (85g–4kg), and wingspan up to 6ft (180cm). Males usually 10 percent larger than females, with bill 15–20 percent longer. Plumage: mainly areas of black and white, but in some species gray and brown predominate— apparently no plumage pigments other than melanin. Bill, casque, bare facial and throat skin, eyes or feet

often brilliantly colored in black, red, blue, yellow or combinations of these. Juveniles and sex of adults evident from plumage, facial skin, eye, bill or casque color, structure or a combination of these. Voice: considerable range from basic clucks and whistles to soft hooting, deep booming, raucous cackling or high squealing. Eggs: 1–2 in larger species, up to 7 in smaller ones, oval, white with finely pitted shells. Incubation 25–40 days, depending on size. Nestling period 45–86 days, depending on size. Diet: omnivorous; some species largely insectivorous, others largely frugivorous and two predominantly carnivorous.

Species include: in Africa, **Abyssinian ground hornbill** (*Bucorvus abyssinicus*), **Black-casqued hornbill** (*Ceratogymna atrata*), **Dwarf red-billed hornbill** (*Tockus camurus*), **Jackson's hornbill** (*T. jacksoni*), **Long-tailed hornbill** (*Tropicranus albocristatus*), **Red-billed hornbill** (*Tockus erythrorhynchus*), **Silvery-cheeked hornbill** (*Bycanistes brevis*), **Southern ground hornbill** (*Bucorvus cafer*), **Von der Decken's hornbill** (*Tockus deckeni*), **Yellow-billed hornbill** (*T. flavirostris*); in Asia, **Brown-backed hornbill** (*Ptilolaemus tickelli*), **Bushy-crested hornbill** (*Anorrhinus galeritus*), **Celebes tarictic hornbill** (*Penelopides exarhatus*), **Great hornbill** (*Buceros*

bicornis), **Helmeted hornbill** ☐ (*Rhinoplax vigil*), **Indian gray hornbill** (*Tockus birostris*), **Malabar pied hornbill** (*Anthracoceros coronatus*), **Narcondam hornbill** (*Rhyticeros narcondami*), **New Guinea hornbill** (*R. plicatus*), **Philippine brown hornbill** (*Buceros hydrocorax*), **Rhinoceros hornbill** (*B. rhinoceros*), **Rufous-necked hornbill** (*Aceros nipalensis*), **Sri Lankan gray hornbill** (*Tockus griseus*), **White-crested hornbill** (*Berenicornis comatus*), **Wreathed hornbill** (*Rhyticeros undulatus*).

◀ **Sealed inside her nest-hole** until the chicks are half-grown, the female Red-billed hornbill relies on the male to provide food. Here, a male is about to pass fruit through the nest-hole.

▼ **The curious reptilian chick** of a Southern ground hornbill. This large species does not wall itself into a hole but nests in a very large cavity, such as the top of a broken-off tree. Commonly only a single chick is raised and it may remain with its parents for several years.

former probably carefully searching the foliage and forest floor for prey, and the latter possibly excavating prey from rotten wood and loose bark. Only the very large ground hornbills are almost entirely carnivorous, using their pickax-like bills to subdue prey as large as hares, tortoises, snakes and squirrels, together with smaller fare found as they stride over the African veld.

Hornbills reach sexual maturity at between one (*Tockus*) and six (*Bucorvus*) years, depending on their size, but how long they live in the wild is unknown. Breeding seasons depend mainly on the birds' choice of food, with forest fruit-eaters showing little seasonality compared with savanna insectivores, which breed during the warm wet season.

Courtship feeding of females, mutual preening and copulation is all the activity reported to precede breeding in larger forest species. In many species the loud calls function to proclaim defended territories, and in some the calls accompany conspicuous displays. Territory size, in those non-fruiteaters that do not just defend an area immediately around the nest, ranges from 25 acres (10ha) for the Red-billed hornbill to 39sq mi (100sq km) for the Southern ground hornbill.

Hornbills nest in natural cavities, usually in trees but also in rock faces and earth banks. In all species but the two ground hornbills, the female seals the nest entrance—apart from a narrow vertical slit—using mud initially (while working from outside) but later her own droppings, mixed with food remains. In some species the male

assists, by bringing lumps of mud or sticky foods, and in a few, such as *Byncanistes* and *Ceratogymna*, the male forms special pellets of mud and saliva in his gullet and helps to apply these to the entrance. In some genera the male continues to feed the female and their offspring for the rest of the nesting cycle, while in others (*Tockus, Buceros, Rhinoplax, Bycanistes, Ceratogymna, Rhyticeros, Aceros, Penelopides, Anthracoceros*) the female breaks out of the nest when the chicks are about half grown and helps to feed them. In the latter cases the chicks reseal the nest unaided and only break their way out when ready to fly. The vertical slit, with the nest floor sited below it, provides good air circulation through convection and the small opening and wooden walls provide good insulation. The sealed nest, and the long escape tunnel usually present above it, also provide protection from predators.

Food is brought to the nest either as single items held in the bill tip (eg *Tockus, Tropicranus*) or as a gullet-full of fruits which are regurgitated one at a time and passed to the nestlings. Food remains and droppings are passed out of the nest slit, the latter being forcibly expelled. In most species the female undergoes a simultaneous molt of all her flight and tail feathers, which are dropped at the time of egg laying and regrown by the time she emerges. The ground hornbills are an exception to the basic hornbill pattern; the female does not seal the nest (although sitting throughout incubation and the early nestling period, and being fed in the nest), droppings and food remains are not expelled and no unusual feather molt occurs.

Most hornbills are monogamous, with each member sharing all aspects of the nesting cycle. However, in some species, scattered through several genera, cooperative breeding has developed in which some individuals, usually males, although sexually mature, do not breed but help a dominant pair to rear their young. This habit is recognizable by the birds living in groups (of up to 25 in some species) and by the immatures being colored very differently from the adults. It is found in species as diverse in form and size as the Southern ground hornbill, the White-crested hornbill, Bushy-crested hornbill, the Brown-backed hornbill and Philippine brown hornbill.

Several hornbill species have suffered severe reductions in their ranges, especially in Southeast Asia and West Africa. Others, such as the Narcondam hornbill, are endemic to small islands and hence also vulnerable to alteration of habitat. AK

Hornbills in Human Cultures

The conspicuous hornbills have been incorporated into the cultures of many peoples. Many Africans regard hornbills as sacred birds and some species, especially the large ground hornbills, thrive unmolested even in areas of quite high human population density. Members of some West African ethnic groups, such as the Hausa, use stuffed heads of ground hornbills as camouflage when stalking game. Breeding individuals of some smaller species are taken for food or for preparation of medicines.

Hornbills are especially important in certain Southeast Asian societies, notably the Dayaks of Borneo. The great and raucous Rhinoceros hornbill was recognized as the god of war: *Singalang Burong*. Elaborate effigies, which exaggerate the recurved casque, used to be carved in wood and hoisted above longhouses. Today this hornbill is the emblem of the Malaysian state

of Sarawak, and the country is advertised to tourists as the "Land of Hornbills." Its white tail feathers with a single black band once featured prominently in dancing cloaks and head-dresses, as did the similarly colored, greatly elongated central pair of tail feathers of the Helmeted hornbill.

The solid block of "hornbill ivory" forming the front part of the casque of the Helmeted hornbill is unique. It is carved by the indigenous Kenyah and Kelabit people of Borneo into ear ornaments or belt toggles, but in the past was an important item of trade with Chinese visiting Brunei. The Chinese executed exquisite three-dimensional carvings on the casque and worked the ivory (named *ho-ting*) into thin sheets. They also fixed the golden-red pigment derived from the preen gland oil. These sheets were cut into belt buckles that were worn by high officials of the 14th- to 17th-century Ming dynasty in China.

TOUCANS, HONEYGUIDES AND BARBETS

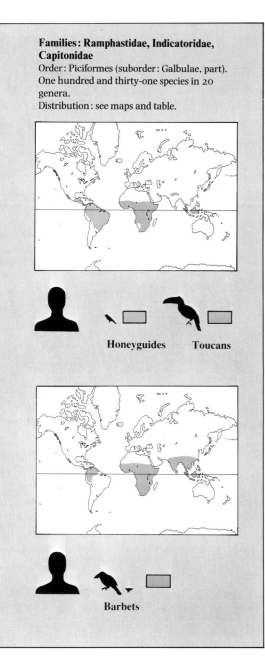

Honeyguides   Toucans

Barbets

► **Representative species of toucans.** (1) An Emerald toucanet (*Aulacorhynchus prasinus*) calling. (2) A Black-billed mountain toucan (*Andigena nigrirostris*) revealing a flash of yellow on its rump as it clambers around in tree branches. (3) A Chestnut-mandibled toucan (*Ramphastos swainsonii*) tossing its head, enabling food held at the tip of the bill to be transferred to the throat. (4) A Toco toucan (*Ramphastos toco*) at full stretch searching for berries. (5) A Guianan toucanet (*Selenidera culik*) examining a possible nest cavity. (6) A Saffron toucanet (*Andigena bailloni*) flying from tree to tree. (7) A Collared aracari (*Pteroglossus torquatus*) preparing to leave its nest-hole.

Toco toucans are so often depicted by artists and designers that they have become a symbol of the warm forests of tropical America. Of all the rich bird life of the Neotropics, probably only hummingbirds are more often illustrated.

The most prominent feature of **toucans** are their bills, often vividly colored, which are much lighter in weight than they appear. A thin horny outer sheath encloses a hollow which is crisscrossed by many thin, bony, supporting rods. Despite this internal strengthening, toucans' bills are fragile and sometimes break. Nevertheless, some manage to survive a long time with part of their bills conspicuously missing. The biggest bill of any toucan is that of the male Toco toucan which accounts for 8in of the bird's total length of 26in (20 of 66cm).

Naturalists have speculated for centuries about the uses of the toucan's exaggerated beak. It enables these heavy, rather clumsy birds to perch inside the crown of a tree, where branches are thicker, and reach far outwards to pluck berries or seeds from twigs too thin to bear their weight. Seized in the tip of the bill, food is thrown back into the throat by an upward toss of the head. This behavior explains the bill's length but not its thickness or bright coloration. The diet of toucans consists mainly of fruit but includes insects, an occasional lizard and eggs and nestlings of smaller birds. The huge, vivid beak so intimidates distressed parents that not even the boldest of them dares to attack the plunderer perching beside its nest. After the toucan flies and is unable to defend its back in the air, an enraged parent may pounce upon it, to withdraw prudently before the larger bird alights. The varied patterns of toucans' bills may help these birds to recognize each other. In Central American forests Chestnut-mandibled and Keel-billed toucans have such similar plumage that they are only readily distinguished by their bills—and voices. The Keel-billed's beak is delicately tinted with all but one of the colors of the rainbow, whereas that of its relative is largely chestnut, with much yellow on the upper mandible. Possibly the bills also play a role in courtship.

Toucans are moderately gregarious and fly in straggling flocks, one after another, rather than in compact bands, like parrots. In flight, the big *Ramphastos* toucans beat their wings a number of times, then close them, whereupon they lose altitude, as though borne downward by their great, forwardly directed beaks. Immediately the black wings are widely spread, the fall is converted into a short glide, followed by more wing beats that recover the lost altitude. Thus the toucan traces an undulatory course from one treetop to another that is rarely far distant. Toucans prefer to remain high in trees, where they hop from branch to branch. They bathe in pools of rain water in hollows high in trunks and limbs—never, apparently, at ground level. They offer food to their companions and, perching well apart, preen them with the tips of long bills.

Toucans are playful birds and often engage in various games. After striking their bills together, two clasp each other's bills and push until one is forced backward from the perch and retreats. Another individual may then cross bills with the winner, and

▲ **Channel-billed toucan.** The ten large toucans of the genus *Ramphastos* all have black or blackish plumage. Other features are more variable. Throats and breasts are yellow or white, upper tail coverts red, white or yellow. But *Ramphastos* toucans are most easily distinguished by their bill colors. This species (*R. vitellinus*) is a medium-sized *Ramphastos* toucan widespread in South America, from the north to southern Brazil.

the victor in this bout may be challenged again. Participants in such a wrestling match reveal no sign of aggression. In another form of play, one toucan tosses a fruit which another catches in the air, then throws it in similar fashion to a third, who may pitch it to a fourth member of the flock.

Toucans are often reported to sleep in holes, but this is only known to occur in the medium-sized aracaris and the Guianan toucanet (see box).

The big *Ramphastos* toucans appear to nest regularly in holes resulting from the decay of tree trunks, the availability of which may limit the number of breeding pairs. A favorable hole, in sound wood with an orifice just wide enough for the adults to squeeze through, may be used year after year. The hole may be only a few inches or 6.5ft (2m) deep. A suitable cavity near the base of a trunk may tempt toucans closer to the ground than is normal. Smaller toucans often occupy woodpeckers' holes, sometimes evicting the owners. They may clean out and enlarge existing cavities, and sometimes try to carve their own holes in soft, decaying wood, but apparently rarely with success. The nest chamber is never lined, but the 2–4 white eggs rest upon a few chips at the bottom, or upon a pebbly bed of regurgitated seeds of various sizes, shapes and colors, which grows thicker as incubation proceeds.

Parents share incubation and are, for birds of their size, impatient sitters, rarely remaining at their task for more than an hour and often leaving their eggs uncovered. Far from trying to repel intruders with their great bills, the least threat causes them to slip out and fly away.

After about 16 days of incubation the nestlings hatch blind and naked, with no trace of down on their pink skins. Like newborn woodpeckers, which they closely resemble, they have short bills with the lower mandible slightly longer than the upper. Around each ankle joint is a pad of spike-like projections, which protects it from abrasion as the nestlings stand on their rough floor, supporting themselves on heels and swollen abdomen. Nestlings are fed by both parents, with increasing quantities of fruit as they grow older, but they develop surprisingly slowly. The feathers of the small toucanets do not begin to expand until they are nearly four weeks old, and month-old *Ramphastos* nestlings are still largely naked. Both parents brood the nestlings, sometimes the male by night, as in woodpeckers. They carry large billfuls of waste from the nest, some, including Emerald toucanets, keeping the nest perfectly clean, whereas Keel-billed toucans permit decaying seeds to remain.

When finally fully feathered, young toucans resemble their parents, but their bills are smaller and less highly colored. Small toucanets may fly from the nest when 43 days old, but the larger *Ramphastos* toucans remain for about 50 days. Aracaris are led back to the nest to sleep with their parents but, as far as is known, other fledglings roost amid foliage.

The biggest toucans, 10 species of the genus *Ramphastos*, are chiefly inhabitants of lowland rain forests, from which they make excursions into neighboring clearings with scattered trees. They are rarely seen at altitudes of 5,000ft (1,500m) above sea level. Their plumage is chiefly black or blackish and their calls are largely croaks and yelps, but the vesper song of the Chestnut-mandibled toucan (*dios te dé*), is almost melodious when heard in the distance.

The 11 species of aracaris are smaller and more slender than the other toucans. They too are inhabitants of warm forests, but rarely venture as high as 4,900ft (1,500m). They have black or dusky green backs, crimson rumps and are usually black on head and neck. Their largely yellow underparts are crossed by one or two bands of black or red. Their long bills are black and ivory white, wholly ivory white or mainly fiery red. Exceptional for this group, the Curl-crested aracari has its crown covered with broad, shiny feathers that resemble curled horny shavings. The calls of the better-known species are sharp and high-pitched for such large birds. They are the only toucans which, as far as is known, regularly

Cooperative Breeding in Aracaris

Aracaris are slender, middle-sized toucans, which inhabit woods amid farmlands. Calling sharply *pitit pitit*, they fly swiftly and directly in small, straggling flocks. At nightfall they retire into old woodpecker holes or other cavities, turning their heads over their backs and their tails forward to cover them, to fit into a narrow space.

In a Panamanian forest six Collared aracaris were once observed to squeeze with difficulty through a narrow orifice in the underside of a thick horizontal branch, 100ft (30m) up in a great tree. As weeks passed the number of birds using this hole for sleeping decreased until only one remained, apparently incubating a clutch of eggs. After the eggs hatched five of the original six birds again slept in this hole, and all brought food to the nestlings, at first chiefly insects grasped in the tips of their great beaks. As the nestlings grew

older the five attendants brought increasing quantities of fruits, some of which they regurgitated.

At about 43 days the first young aracari flew from its high nursery. At nightfall its attendants led it back to sleep with them. While the fledgling tried inexpertly to enter the narrow, downward-facing doorway, a White hawk swooped down, seized the piteously crying young bird in its talons, and carried it off, followed by all the adults.

Three of the attendants at this nest were probably nonbreeding helpers, possibly older offspring of the parents. In the half century since these observations were made no other nest of the Collared aracari has been available for study, and we still do not know whether cooperative breeding, widespread in other families of tropical birds, is usual in any species of toucans.   AFS

lodge in holes throughout the year.

Toucanets of the genus *Aulacorhynchus* (7 species) are small to large with mainly green plumage. Their calls are unmelodious croaks, barks and dry rattles. They chiefly inhabit cool mountain forests, between 3,300 and 10,000ft (1,000–3,000m), and rarely descend into warm lowlands.

The five species of toucanets belonging to the genus *Selenidera* dwell in rain forests at low altitudes from Honduras to northeast Argentina. Their plumage is more variable than that of the foregoing species, and they are the only toucans of which the sexes differ conspicuously in color. The reddish brown

bill of the Tawny-tufted toucanet is prominently striped with black. Little is known of the habits of these small toucans.

Least known of all are the four species of mountain toucans which, as their generic name *Andigena* implies, inhabit the Andes from northwest Venezuela to Bolivia. From the subtropical zone they extend far upward into the altitudinal temperate zone. One of the more colorful is the Black-billed mountain-toucan, whose light blue underparts are exceptional in the toucan family. Its crown and nape are black, its back and wings olive brown, rump yellow, throat white, undertail coverts crimson and thighs chestnut. Although these and many other toucans are becoming rarer as their habitats are destroyed, many remain to be studied by naturalists hardy enough to pass long months in remote forests.   AFS

The dull plumage, remote habitat and retiring disposition of **honeyguides** disguise a family whose behavior is among the most extraordinary—and least known—of any birds. They are named for the habit, of one species in particular (the Greater honeyguide), of guiding people and other large mammals to bees' nests. Experiments have in fact shown that the birds prefer the bees' larvae and even their waxy comb to honey. Honeyguides combine two specializations: the unique one of eating wax and the less unusual one of laying their eggs in other birds' nests.

Honeyguides are probably most closely related to woodpeckers and barbets. They occur only in the Old World tropics, most in Africa but two species in Asia. Their main habitat is broadleaved forest, though in two genera (*Prodotiscus* and *Indicator*) some inhabit more open woodland. Most of the African species form several groups of closely related species which are so similar to each other that even specialists find them very hard to identify, especially in the field.

The 3 Families of Toucans and Their Allies.   v Vulnerable.

Toucans
Family: Ramphastidae
Thirty-eight species in 5 genera.
Tropical America, from S Mexico to Bolivia and N Argentina, excluding Antilles. Rain forests and more open woodlands. Size: 13–26in (33–66cm) long (including bill). Males' bills slightly longer than females'. Plumage: several varieties, black with red, yellow and white; olive brown and blue; chiefly green. Sexes similar in color except in *Selenidera* species. Voice: usually unmusical, often croaks, barks, rattles or high, sharp notes. Nests: in natural cavities in trees; smaller species may occupy woodpeckers' holes, sometimes enlarging them. Eggs: 2–4, white, unmarked; incubation: 15–16 days; nestling period: 43–51 days. Diet: chiefly fruits supplemented by insects and other invertebrates, small lizards, snakes, birds' eggs and nestlings.

Species and genera include: **aracaris** (genus *Pteroglossus*), **Black-billed mountain toucan** (*Andigena nigrirostris*), **Chestnut-mandibled toucan** (*Ramphastos swainsonii*), **Collared aracari** (*Pteroglossus torquatus*), **Curl-crested aracari**

(*P. beauharnaesii*), **Emerald toucanet** (*Aulacorhynchus prasinus*), **Guianan toucanet** (*Selenidera culik*), **Keel-billed toucan** (*Ramphastos sulfuratus*), **Orange-billed toucan** (*R. aurantiirostris*), **Tawny-tufted toucanet** (*Selenidera nattereri*), **Toco toucan** (*Ramphastos toco*).

Honeyguides
Family: Indicatoridae
Fifteen species in 4 genera.
Africa, Asia. Evergreen forest, open woodland. Size: 4–8in (10–20cm) long, weight 0.35–1.9oz (10–55g). Plumage: somber olive, gray or brownish, paler below, often with white sides to the tail; two species have yellow wing patches; one has orange on head and rump; difference between sexes is slight except for one species. Voice: poorly known; males of several species give a simple monotonous song from a high post; one species gives a distinctive chatter when guiding people to bees' nests. Nests: none; in all species whose breeding habits are known the egg is laid in the nest of a hole-nesting bird. Eggs: normally one per nest; white (blue in one species), thick-shelled; incubation: 12–13 days; nestling

period: 38–40 days. Diet: chiefly insects, but all species include some form of wax.

Species include: **Eisentraut's honeyguide** (*Melignomon eisentrauti*), **Greater** or **Black-throated honeyguide** (*Indicator indicator*), **Indian honeyguide** (*I. xanthonotus*), **Lesser honeyguide** (*I. minor*), **Lyre-tailed honeyguide** (*Melichneutes robustus*), **Scaly-throated honeyguide** (*I. variegatus*).

Barbets
Family: Capitonidae
Seventy-eight species in 11 genera.
Africa S of the Sahara, India, Sri Lanka, SE Asia, Philippines, Java, Bali, Borneo, NW S America, Panama, Costa Rica. Primary and secondary tropical forest, plantations, savanna woodland and (in Africa) arid habitats. Size: ranges from 3.5in (9cm) in the tinkerbirds to 13in (33cm) long in the Great barbet. Plumage: Asian and American species are predominantly green with red, blue and yellow markings about the head; some African species are mainly black, red and yellow, heavily spotted or streaked. There are well-

developed differences between sexes only in the S American species. Voice: rapid repetition of a single or series of notes resembling honks, chirps, or the tapping of a hammer; duetting is well developed in the family. Nests: most species excavate holes in decayed trees; others use termite mounds, sand or earth banks, or burrows; no nest lining. Eggs: 2–5, white; incubation: varies, 12–14 days in some species, 18–19 in others; nestling period: 20–21 days, 24–26 days or 33–35 days. Diet: fruit, buds, flowers, nectar, insects; larger species also eat tree frogs and small birds.

Species and genera include: **Black-backed barbet** (*Lybius minor*), **Black-spotted barbet** (*Capito niger*), **D'Arnaud's barbet** (*Trachyphonus darnaudii*), **Great barbet** (*Megalaima virens*), **ground barbets** (genus *Trachyphonus*), **Lineated barbet** (*M. lineata*), **Pied barbet** (*Lybius leucomelas*), **Prong-billed barbet** (*Semnornis frantzii*), **Red-headed barbet** (*Eubucco bourcierii*), **tinkerbirds** (genus *Pogoniulus*), **Toucan barbet** v (*Semnornis ramphastinus*), **White-mantled barbet** (*Capito hypoleucus*), **Yellow-fronted tinkerbird** (*Pogoniulus chrysoconus*).

▲ **Ambidextrous bill**—Cuvier's toucan (*Ramphastos tucanus*). Although often largely fruit-eaters toucans frequently eat other birds' eggs and nestlings, which can be firmly grasped in the bill.

Within each group darker-colored species tend to live in broadleaved forest, paler ones in drier woodland. So cryptic and inconspicuous can they be that a totally new species was described from West Africa as recently as 1981 (Eisentraut's honeyguide). In most species the somber camouflage is relieved only by light sides to the tail which are conspicuous in flight and possibly help to lure potential hosts away from their nests. Only three species depart from this drab uniformity: the Lyre-tailed honeyguide of West Africa, in which the tail of both sexes is curved outwards and the two pin-like outermost feathers make (like those of snipes) a loud tooting noise in diving flight; the Indian honeyguide of the Himalayas, which has orange on the head and rump; and the Greater or Black-throated honeyguide in which the male has a black throat, white cheeks, yellow shoulder-flashes and a pink bill, and which is the only species in which the sexes have a different appearance. All species have zygodactyl feet (ie feet in which the second and third toes of each foot point forward and the first and fourth backward), like woodpeckers, and many also have curiously prominent nostrils, edged with a raised ridge; several species seem to be attracted to wood-smoke, perhaps especially to burning wax, and may have a keen sense of smell connected with locating bees' nests, though this intriguing possibility has not been investigated.

All species, so far as is known, include wax of some kind in their diet, though most eat mainly insects. Birds cannot digest wax without the aid of bacteria in their gut; the existence of these has been reported in Lesser honeyguides but not confirmed in this or any other species. Experiments have shown that both Lesser and Greater honeyguides can certainly digest wax somehow, since they can survive on a diet of pure wax for about 30 days. The small species in the genus *Prodotiscus* eat mainly scale insects, which are thickly coated in wax.

Male Indian honeyguides defend bees' nests, at which they feed, and to which females are admitted if they will mate. This species lacks white in the tail and may not be parasitic, since females bring young to bees' nests and their eggs have never been found despite searches of nests of likely hosts. In several other species males give simple monotonous calls from perches to which females come to mate; some species seem to defend possible hosts against other honeyguides. Honeyguide eggs are laid in holes in trees or banks, in the nests of other species, almost always singly. Young of at least two species hatch with sharp hooks on the tip of the bill, with which they puncture hosts' eggs or kill their chicks. They have an insistent begging call which sounds like several of the host young calling together.

Honeyguides are birds of forest and woodland, and their future is as threatened as that of their habitat. The Greater honeyguide, with its unique mutually beneficial relationship with man (see box), must adapt to changing human behavior as well as to shrinking habitats if it is to survive. AWD

Any visitor to Africa is certain of hearing the monotonous repetitive calls of **barbets** as

Man and the Behavior of the Greater honeyguide

Two species of honeyguide are known to guide people and other large mammals to bees' nests. One, the Greater honeyguide, does this so often that it has been well studied but the other, the Scaly-throated honeyguide, is much less well known. Many African tribes use Greater honeyguides to show them bees' nests, whose honey they relish and which was once their only source of sugar. Greater honeyguides give a distinctive chattering call to attract attention, and then fly towards a bees' nest in short stages, stopping frequently to call and, apparently, to check the progress of the followers. Usually the bird falls silent when it reaches the nest, which is then opened by the men with an ax after stupefying the bees with wood-smoke. Most tribes leave some honeycomb for the birds, believing that if they do not the bird will lead them to a dangerous animal next time; but other tribes say honeycomb spoils the bird and leave it to find its own.

Such bizarre behavior is especially surprising in a nest-parasite, whose opportunities for learning such guiding behavior from adults are at first sight more limited than in most birds. Hand-reared Greater honeyguide chicks eat both the larvae and the wax in the first honeycomb they are given, and develop the guiding call without ever hearing it, directly from the begging call. They do not need wax or grubs in their diet, but some constituent of the honeycomb may play a role, as yet unrecognized, in attaining breeding condition. Wild honeyguides can open bees' nests for themselves (since many species eat beeswax but do not guide), so it is not clear to what extent Greater honeyguides depend on human help for obtaining their honeycomb.

The tradition of using honeyguides is dying out in many parts of Africa as the old lifestyles crumble and refined sugar becomes easily available. AWD

they occur in all the major vegetation zones; 5 African genera (39 species) are recognized and within these there is a greater divergence in size, bill shape and color pattern than is found in Asian and American genera. Adaptation to more arid habitats within Africa is thought to have given rise to the tinkerbirds and ground barbets. Species equivalent to these ecologically do not occur in Asia or tropical America. In these continents the barbets are larger and in the main arboreal, 3 genera (13 species) being recognized in South America and 3 genera (26 species) in Asia (where 2 genera contain only one species each). There are some notable instances of convergence in the family. The Black-backed barbet of Central Africa is similar to the White-mantled barbet of South America, and each continent has a medium-sized brown plumaged species which is highly social.

Barbets are compact, thickset birds with rather large heads. The bill is stout, conical and sharply tipped, being more formidable in the larger species. The *Lybius* species have notched bills that assist in gripping food and in the Prong-billed barbet the tip of the upper mandible fits into a deep cleft in the lower mandible. Many have bristles around the gape and chin and tufts over the nostrils. The legs are short and strong, the feet zygodactylic (ie on each foot the second and third toes point forward, the first and fourth backward). They climb like woodpeckers and their short tail is often used as a support. The large barbets appear heavy and cumbersome in their movements but others (eg the Red-headed barbet and the tinkerbirds) are agile and probe and search much like tits. The wings are short and rounded, and unsuitable for sustained flight. Ground barbets move by inelegant hops.

The *Eubucco* species of South America have green wings, back and tail, and underparts of yellow streaked with green. They differ from each other in the color pattern of their head, throat and breast; the sexes have different appearances. The male Red-headed barbet has the whole head and throat scarlet shading to orange on the breast, and a blue collar on the nape. The female has blue on the side of the head, a gray throat and yellow orange on the upper breast. The sexes of the *Capito* species are also different. Both sexes of the Black-spotted barbet have scarlet on head and throat, black upperparts streaked with greenish yellow and creamy yellow underparts. The female differs from the male in having black spots on the throat and being more heavily spotted black on the under-

parts. Most Asian barbets are predominantly green and differences between species lie in the head colors (brown, red, yellow, orange) and their pattern; the sexes are identical in the field. The Great barbet has a yellow bill, maroon-brown upperparts, a violet blue-black head, multicolored underparts (olive brown, blue, yellow) and red under-tail coverts. In contrast, there is very little green in African barbets, and the majority are patterned black, yellow and red and their plumage is heavily spotted and barred, much more so than in Asian and South American species. Some are a very drab brown (*Gymnobucco* species) and have a tuft of rictal bristles and a head more or less bare of feathers. The sexes are alike in the majority of species.

Most species feed on fruit, much of which is lost when plucked from the tree, but some are more efficient and hold the fruit with a foot when eating. Petals, flower heads and nectar are eaten by some species (for example, the Great barbet, Prong-billed barbet). Most, if not all, species feed insects to newly hatched young and some take insects regularly, particularly termites which may be caught either on the wing or on the ground. Ants and grasshoppers are taken and the larger species (for example, the Lineated barbet) occasionally take lizards, tree frogs and small birds. The Red-headed barbet is mainly insectivorous and feeds in the ground litter. Insect remains are regurgitated as pellets. Fruit-eating barbets often feed in mixed flocks of other species. There are no seasonal migrations; local

▲ **A tight squeeze.** A Yellow-fronted tinkerbird emerges from its nest-hole, which it probably gouged out in a rotten section of the branch.

▶ **Groundhunter.** This Red-and-yellow barbet (*Trachyphonus erythrocephalus*) is one of the three species of ground barbets. Unlike other barbets, which live in tree tops, ground barbets forage on the ground. This species is particularly attracted to stream beds, termite mounds and areas with irregular topography. It excavates nests and roosting sites in the earth walls of ravines.

▼ **Iridescent barbet.** The Golden-throated barbet (*Megalaima franklinii*), a member of the main Asian genus of barbets, is found across a large area of Southeast Asia, from Nepal to Laos and Vietnam. It has well-developed rictal bristles.

movements are governed by the availability of food sources.

The breeding behavior of barbets is varied but little studied. The Prong-billed barbet in Costa Rica lays only one clutch of eggs and has a restricted breeding season beginning in March. Other species are paired throughout the year and have a prolonged breeding season covering both dry and wet seasons in which three or four broods may be raised (for example, the Yellow-fronted tinkerbird) or else breed only in the wet season (for example, ground barbets). The same hole is often used for successive broods and is deepened after each brood. D'Arnaud's barbet, one of the ground barbets, bores a tunnel vertically downwards into level ground and then bores horizontally before forming the nest chamber. The Pied barbet has been known to use deserted nests of swallows and martins when nest-sites are scarce. Both sexes excavate the nest-hole, share in incubation and feeding nestlings, and in nest sanitation. Feces are sometimes swallowed or else pounded with sawdust in the nest-hole into small balls which are then removed. In several of the African species extra helpers, often young of a previous brood, have been recorded feeding nestlings but little detail is known of the cooperative breeding. The African *Gymnobucco* species breed colonially and with other African species are often parasitized by honeyguides.

Because of the difficulty of observing barbets, particularly the forest species, little is known of their courtship behavior, only that the male frequently pursues the female. In ground barbets the male postures with raised crown feathers and struts around the female. Duetting is a common feature of barbets from all three continents. Its exact function is not certain. It occurs throughout the year and there is an immediate response by birds to the play-back of a duet sequence. It probably helps to maintain both territories and family bonds. Barbets are highly territorial and aggressive to other birds (eg woodpeckers, honeyguides) and may then be defending a food source (fruit) or a roosting or nest site. Communal roosting of family parties is frequent, even in aggressive species.

The metallic quality of the voices of several African and Oriental species has earned them names such as stinkerbird, blacksmith and coppersmith.

The young hatch blind and naked and have heel pads. These may be used to enlarge the cramped nest-hole; the honeyguides that are parasitic on barbets also have the pads. LGG

JACAMARS AND PUFFBIRDS

Families: Galbulidae, Bucconidae
Order: Piciformes (suborder: Galbulae, part).
Forty-seven species in 15 genera.

Jacamars

Family: Galbulidae
Fifteen species in 5 genera.
Distribution: Mexico to S Brazil.
Habitat: forest, thickets, savanna.
Size: 5–12in (13–31cm) long.
Plumage: shining iridescent green above, mostly rufous below, or dull brown or blackish; white below. Slight differences between sexes.
Voice: often prolonged and complex song with whistles, squeals and trills.
Nests: in short burrows in ground or termite mounds.
Eggs: 2–4, white, unmarked; incubation period: 20–22 days; nestling period: 19–26 days (in Rufous-tailed jacamar).
Diet: insects caught in the air, including many butterflies, beetles and wasps.

Species include: **Chestnut jacamar** (*Galbalcyrhynchus leucotis*), **Great jacamar** (*Jacamerops aurea*), **Pale-headed jacamar** (*Brachygalba goeringi*), **Paradise jacamar** (*Galbula dea*), **Rufous-tailed jacamar** (*Galbula ruficauda*), **Three-toed jacamar** (*Jacamaralcyon tridactyla*).

Puffbirds

Family: Bucconidae
Thirty-two species in 10 genera.
Distribution: Mexico to S Brazil.
Habitat: rain forest, dry open woodland, shrubbery, savanna.
Size: 5.5–11in (14–29cm) long.
Plumage: black, white, brown, rufous, buff, often barred, streaked or spotted (never brilliant); slight differences between sexes.
Voice: thin and weak to loud and ringing; rarely melodious.
Nests: burrows in ground or cavities carved in termite mounds; occasionally abandoned nests of other birds, sometimes lined (leaves or grass).
Eggs: 2 or 3, occasionally 4; unmarked, white; incubation period: unknown; nestling period: 20 days (White-faced puffbird) or about 30 days (White-fronted nunbird).
Diet: chiefly insects, occasionally small frogs or lizards; rarely fruits.

Species include: **nunbirds** (genera *Hapaloptila*, *Monasa*), **nunlets** (genus *Nonnula*), **swallow-wing** (*Chelidoptera tenebrosa*), **White-fronted nunbird** (*Monasa morphoeus*), **White-whiskered puffbird** (*Malacoptila panamensis*).

A DAINTY, glittering green, iridescent, straight-billed hummingbird the size of a thrush or mockingbird — such would be an apt description of one of the more brilliant **jacamars**. These, however, are more closely related to woodpeckers, toucans, barbets, and puffbirds than to hummingbirds.

The jacamar's long, slender, sharp bill seems poorly fitted for its aerial insect-catching niche and for excavating its nest chamber — a broad, flat bill would seem more efficient. However, the long bill can reach across the wings of a butterfly or dragonfly (which if seized might break and release the insect) to grasp the body firmly. Moreover, it keeps the flailing wings away from the jacamar's face while it knocks its victim against a branch until the wings flutter earthward; it also holds stinging wasps at a safe distance.

Jacamars appear to be charged with irrepressible vitality. While perching on an exposed twig above a stream, path or open space in woods or thicket, they constantly turn their bright-eyed heads from side to side, looking for flying insects which they dart out to seize. The high, thin notes of their calls convey a sense of urgency. For birds that are not true songbirds, their vocal performances are surprisingly complex.

Jacamars nest in tunnels which they dig in vertical banks or sloping ground or in hard, black termite mounds. The Rufous-tailed jacamar, the best-known species, may use both sites in the same locality. The male not only helps his mate to excavate but frequently feeds her, to the accompaniment of much singing. The horizontal burrow, 11–31in (29–79cm) long, according to the species, ends in a chamber where 2–4 white eggs lie on the bare floor, which is soon covered by a growing accumulation of regurgitated beetles' shards and other indigestible parts of insects. By day the sexes incubate alternately, often for an hour or two at a time. The female occupies the nest by night. Unlike most birds of their order (Piciformes), the nestlings hatch with a thin coat of long white down. They are nourished wholly with insects by both parents, and soon become loquacious, practicing songs of the adults while they await their meals. Fledgling Rufous-tailed jacamars do not return to sleep in the burrow, but four young Pale-headed jacamars in Venezuela continued for several months to lodge with their parents in their longer tunnel.

The eight species of *Galbula* are a glittering golden green or purple glossed with green, with chestnut or white underparts. Exceptional in the family is the long-tailed

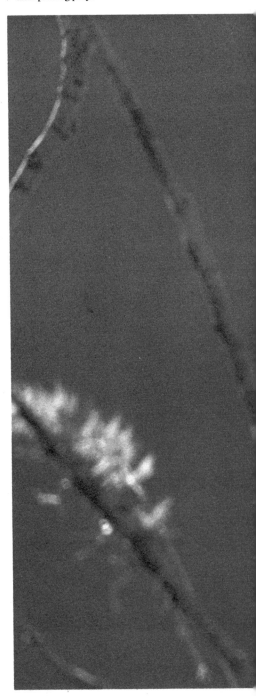

► **Waiting for a butterfly?** Jacamars use their long tapered bills to catch butterflies and insects of similar size. The Rufous-tailed jacamar (*Galbula ruficauda*) is widespread from South Mexico to Brazil.

▼ **Surveying its territory.** A White-eared puffbird (*Nystalus chacuru*) sits ready to leap out after passing prey.

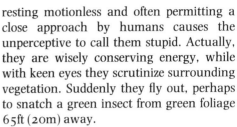

Paradise jacamar of Amazonia and the Guianas with bronzy black plumage.

The Chestnut jacamar has a pink, kingfisher-like bill and the Three-toed jacamar of Brazil is a small bird with a chestnut head and blackish and grayish body. (Other jacamars have four toes, two directed forward and two backward.) The Great jacamar is a stout bird with heavier bill, golden green and rufous, like some of its smaller relatives.

Puffbirds are so named because their large heads, short tails and often loose plumage give them a stocky aspect. Their bills are usually stout and hooked at the end, less often tapering and pointed. Their habit of resting motionless and often permitting a close approach by humans causes the unperceptive to call them stupid. Actually, they are wisely conserving energy, while with keen eyes they scrutinize surrounding vegetation. Suddenly they fly out, perhaps to snatch a green insect from green foliage 65ft (20m) away.

Exceptional in the family are the swallow-wings, which are short-tailed, long-winged, blue-black birds with white rumps and cinnamon chestnut abdomens.

White-whiskered puffbirds are among the few species with sexual differences in plumage, the males being largely chestnut-brown and cinnamon, the females more olive and grayish. Although they live chiefly at mid heights of the rain forest, they nest in short, descending tunnels in the forest floor. On a bed of dead leaves they lay two or three white eggs, which the female incubates through a long morning, the male for the remainder of the time. The blind, wholly naked nestlings are at first brooded by their father and fed by their mother. After daytime brooding ceases, the father helps to feed the nestlings for the remainder of their 20 days underground.

Most social of the puffbirds are the four species of nunbirds. Their pointed, bright red or yellow bills contrast with their somber, black or dark gray plumage. The calls of the White-fronted nunbird are extremely varied, ranging from wooden rattles to notes soft and deep. Up to 10 perch in a row on a high horizontal branch or vine and lift up their heads to shout all together, for 15 or 20 minutes, in loud, ringing voices. Their long burrows in sloping or nearly level ground are lined with dead leaves and have a collar of leaves and sticks around the entrance. Three or four adults, probably parents with older, nonbreeding offspring, feed three nestlings. Blind and naked, the nestlings toddle up the long entrance tunnel to receive their meals at the mouth. When about 30 days old they fly up into the trees.

The four species of *Notharchus*, boldly patterned in black and white, use stout black bills to carve nest chambers deep into hard, black termite mounds. Male and female share this task, and later take turns incubating two or three white eggs on the unlined floor. Their notes are mostly weak and low. Species of *Bucco* and *Hypnelus* also breed in termite nests.

The five species of nunlets are small nunbirds that range from Panama to N Argentina. Unobtrusive forest-dwellers colored gray, brown, cinnamon and white, their habits are little known. AFS

WOODPECKERS

Family: Picidae
Order: Piciformes (suborder: Pici).
Two hundred species in 28 genera belonging to 3 subfamilies.
Distribution: America, Africa, Eurasia.

Habitat: tropical, subtropical and deciduous forest; orchards, parks, grasslands.

Size: ranges from height 3in (8cm), weight 0.3oz (8g), in the Scaled piculet to height 22in (55cm), weight 19.9oz (563g) in the Imperial woodpecker.

▶ **Representative species of woodpeckers.**
(1) A Three-toed woodpecker (*Picoides tridactylus*). (2) A Common flicker (*Colaptes auratus*) in a dance posture. (3) A Green woodpecker (*Picus viridis*). (4) An Olive-backed three-toed woodpecker (*Dinopium rafflesi*) foraging. (5) A Northern wryneck (*Jynx torquilla*). (6) A Great spotted woodpecker (*Picoides major*). (7) A Red-headed woodpecker (*Melanerpes erythrocephalus*) at a nest-hole feeding young. (8) A Yellow-bellied sapsucker (*Sphyrapicus varius*). (9) A Pileated woodpecker (*Dryocopus pileatus*).

WOODPECKERS are unmistakable, thanks to their climbing and pecking habits. Especially impressive however—indeed unique—are their tapping and drumming communication signals, which can be heard in many of the world's woods during the breeding season. With their specialized climbing and pecking methods, woodpeckers are unrivaled as predators on insects that lie hidden under bark, within wood, or, like ants and termites, live in nests with tunnels far below the surface. Woodpeckers also create permanent dwellings for rearing their young and for daily roosting; excavated holes last for years.

Woodpeckers play an important role in the earth's forest eco-systems. They help to control numbers of bark- and wood-boring insects, thereby contributing to the health of the tree trunk and its bark covering. Where woodpeckers have pecked, other smaller birds (tits, nuthatches, treecreepers) can forage successfully for any remaining insects and spiders, and woodpecker holes are used for nesting or roosting by many other hole-nesting insectivores. Owls, martens and other mammals also benefit from using woodpecker holes. Woodpeckers thus help indirectly to exert pressure on the huge populations of insects and mice or voles. They also play an important part in the cycle of decay and regeneration of matter in so far as they peck at huge amounts of dead wood, making it accessible to other decomposing organisms.

True woodpeckers (subfamily Picinae) are small- to medium-sized birds of powerful and stocky build. Their bill is adapted for hacking and chiseling. Their tongue, capable of extreme protrusion (up to 4in, 10cm, in the Green woodpecker), is a highly efficient catching device which enables the bird to extract insects from deep cracks and crevices and from the tunnels bored by insect larvae and made by ants and termites. Woodpecker feet are especially adapted for climbing, with two toes pointed forward and two back. The fourth toe can be bent sideways so that the crampon-shaped claws can always be positioned so as best to suit the curve of trunk or branch. Climbing movements and pecking postures are facilitated by the wedge-shaped supporting tail feathers, the shafts of which have additional strengthening. Such a tail allows the woodpecker's body to be cushioned and permits a good, relaxed posture for pecking or for pauses between bouts of climbing. Special adaptations for pecking, tapping and drumming protect internal organs, particularly the brain, against impact damage. This is absolutely necessary considering the number of pecking blows executed daily (in the Black woodpecker 8,000 to 12,000).

True woodpeckers eat mainly arthropods, particularly insects and spiders, but also take plant food (fruits, seeds, berries) and nestling birds from holes in trees. The Acorn woodpecker eats acorns, storing these for the winter in specially excavated holes. Sapsuckers drill holes in horizontal rows (so-called "ringing" behavior) and then lick up the exuding droplets of sap with the tongue, the tip of which is frayed and brush-like. Great spotted woodpeckers make so-called "anvils" into which they wedge cones in

The 3 Subfamilies of Woodpeckers

True woodpeckers

Subfamily: Picinae
One hundred and sixty-nine species in 23 genera.

America, Africa, Eurasia. Forests; orchards, parks, grasslands, areas of cultivation with hills or earthen banks; up to 16,400ft (5,000m). Size: length 6–22in (15–55cm, weight 0.6–19.9oz (17–563g), Plumage: upperparts usually appropriate to habitat (blackish, brownish, grayish or greenish); head and neck mostly bright colors: red, yellow, white or black patches and stripes; bills are black, gray, brown or bright white. Sexes differ in plumage (sometimes slightly), size, weight. Voice: loud, high-pitched calls; series of calls. Nests: excavated holes. Eggs: 3–11, white. Incubation period: 9–20 days. Diet: insects, spiders, berries, fruits; acorns, seeds; sap, honey.

Species and genera include: **Acorn woodpecker** (*Melanerpes formicivorus*), **Black-backed three-toed woodpecker** (*Picoides arcticus*), **Black woodpecker** (*Dryocopus martius*), **Common flicker** (*Colaptes auratus*), **Gray-headed woodpecker** (*Picus canus*), **Great spotted woodpecker** (*Picoides major*), **Green woodpecker** (*Picus viridis*), **Imperial woodpecker** (*Campephilus imperialis*), **Lewis's woodpecker** (*Melanerpes lewis*), **Olive-backed woodpecker** (*Dinopium rafflesi*), **Pileated woodpecker** (*Dryocopus pileatus*), **Red-bellied woodpecker** (*Melanerpes carolinus*), **Red-headed woodpecker** (*Melanerpes erythrocephalus*), **sapsuckers** (genus *Sphyrapicus*), **Three-toed woodpecker** (*Picoides tridactylus*), **Yellow-bellied sapsucker** (*Sphyrapicus varius*), **Yellow-tufted woodpecker** (*Melanerpes cruentatus*). Total threatened species: 5.

Piculets

Subfamily: Picumninae
Twenty-nine species in 4 genera.

America, Africa, Eurasia. Tropical and subtropical forests, secondary forests, woods: coffee plantations: up to 6,890ft (2,100m). Size: length 3–6in (8–15cm), weight 0.28–0.56oz (8–16g) (0.98oz, 28g, in the Antillean piculet). Plumage: brownish with red, orange, yellow marks; three white stripes on the tail; females have white spots on a black crown. Voice: sharp calls and series of calls. Nests: holes (usually enlargements of existing ones) in rotted tree trunks and soft wood. Eggs: 2–4, white; incubation: 11–14 days. Diet: insects, larvae, ants, termites, wood-boring beetles.

Species include: **Antillean piculet** (*Nesoctites micromegas*), **Scaled piculet** (*Picumnus squamulatus*).

Wrynecks

Subfamily: Jynginae
Two species of the genus *Jynx*.

Africa, Eurasia. Open deciduous forests, grassy clearings, copses, gardens; in Africa up to 10,000ft (3,000m). Size: length 6.3–6.7in (16–17cm), weight 1.05–1.38oz (30–39g). Plumage: chiefly brown. nightjar-like pattern of peppered and blotched markings; dark line through eye; no difference between sexes. Voice: series of calls, up to 18 *kwee* calls. Nests: natural cavities; holes excavated by woodpeckers; nest boxes; no nest material. Eggs: 5–14, white; incubation: 12–13 days; nestling period: 21 days. Diet: ants.

Species: **Northern wryneck** (*Jynx torquilla*), Eurasia migrating to C Africa, SE Asia, Japan; **Rufous-necked wryneck** (*J. ruficollis*), SC and S Africa.

---

holes to peck out the fat-rich seeds. Up to 5,000 cones may be found under a "primary anvil" of which there will be three or four in a territory. The ability to deal with fruits and seeds in "anvils" or to store them in holes is a great aid to survival for woodpeckers in areas of winter cold and consequent seasonal insect shortages.

Woodpeckers catch their prey with a great variety of different techniques, the simplest of which is the gleaning of items from leaf, branch or trunk. Slightly more complicated is probing into bark crevices combined with the scaling of bark. Both sapsuckers and the Three-toed woodpecker obtain insects that lie hidden under bark or within wood by drilling round holes, inserting the tongue and harpooning the item. Other "pecking woodpeckers" and also the large species chisel and lever off large pieces of bark and carve out deep holes in their quest for insects. A Black woodpecker may consume up to 900 bark beetle larvae or 1,000 ants at a single meal. "Ground" woodpeckers mostly peck only funnel-shaped holes in ants' nests, then extend their long "lime-twig" tongue along tunnels and into chambers to spoon up adult ants and pupae. A Green woodpecker needs to eat about 2,000 ants daily, mostly lawn and meadow ants. When this is not possible, in extreme winters such as that of 1962–63, a large part of the population will perish. Some species, for example the Yellow-tufted woodpecker and Lewis's woodpecker and related species of the genera *Melanerpes* and *Centurus*, are able (like flycatchers and tyrants) to take some insects in flight.

▲ **Woodpecker foraging methods:**
(1) gleaning; (2) shooting out the tongue after pecking.

▶ **Takeoff!** OVERLEAF A male Great spotted woodpecker launches itself from its nest while a red-crowned juvenile watches from the hole.

◀ **The naked condition.** Woodpecker young hatch small and naked and require almost four weeks to become ready for flight. For the first few days they huddle like this in a pyramid to share body heat. When an adult brings food—in this case a Common flicker—it wakes the young by touching the swollen white pads to the side of the mouth.

▼ **Not obviously a woodpecker,** the Northern wryneck. The two species of wrynecks belong to a separate subfamily. Although they possess some adaptations of woodpeckers they look more like perching birds and also perch and forage in bushes.

Most woodpeckers are sedentary and may remain in the same territory for a long time. Only a few species, including the Yellow-bellied sapsucker and the Red-headed woodpecker in North America, are migratory. Northern races of the Great spotted woodpecker and the Three-toed woodpeckers undertake far-reaching eruptive movements at intervals of several years, when their main seed-crop diets fail. The Great spotted woodpecker penetrates into central and southern Europe in years of cone shortage; Three-toed woodpeckers invade areas of North America and Europe where the forests periodically suffer from infestations of insect pests.

The great majority of woodpeckers are territorial, living in individual, pair or family territories, in some cases for several years. A ringed Great spotted woodpecker showed fidelity to its 62 acre (25ha) territory for a period of 6 years; in most other species studied most individuals remained in or close to their territory for the whole of their lives. Defending a territory helps to ensure not only breeding success but also adequate food supplies and, above all—especially important for woodpeckers—roosting possibilities in holes affording shelter from the weather. As a rule woodpeckers react aggressively towards intruders of their own kind.

Genuine family territories are found in the Acorn woodpecker. Up to 15 individuals of different generations live in the territory, providing an effective defense of their acorn stores against any competitors.

Woodpecker courtship generally begins with drumming, display ("excitement") flights and prominent calls. These signals are used by both sexes to advertise territory limits and trees with holes, to attract prospective partners to suitable nest-sites (nest-showing), to stimulate the partner sexually and to intimidate rivals. A new nest-hole is not excavated every year and an old one can certainly be used for several years. Black woodpeckers may use the same hole for up to 6 years, Green woodpeckers for up to 10 years or more. However, even these species are forced to excavate new holes when they are evicted by jackdaws or starlings.

Excavation of a hole takes 10–28 days, according to species and method. Both sexes participate. About 10,000 wood chips have been found under a Black woodpecker's hole. When the hole is completed the birds chip off small pieces from the inner wall to serve as a cushion in the nest-scrape for eggs and young.

Copulation usually takes place without any special ceremony. The female assumes a precopulatory posture—crossways on a branch—and the male simply flies onto her back. Lengthy physical contact is avoided. Mutual courtship feeding has been recorded in only a few species, for example the Olive-backed woodpecker of Asia. The glossy white eggs are laid in the early morning, one per day until the clutch is complete. Constant guarding of the nest-hole is typical once the first egg has been laid. In all species of woodpeckers the male spends the night in the nest-hole during both incubation and nestling periods; in the *Melanerpes* woodpeckers, male and female roost there together.

During incubation and brooding, birds of a pair change over at intervals of 30 to 150 minutes. The nest-relief ceremony resembles that of nest-showing: calling, demonstrative tapping, also drumming. The "pecking woodpeckers" collect food in the bill, the "ground woodpeckers" and all large species feed their young by regurgitation. Nestlings give almost ceaseless whirring or rattling food-calls.

The nestling period is 18–35 days. When they leave the nest, young woodpeckers can climb and fly. Soon afterwards they follow the adults through the territory, contact being maintained with calls which in Black, Pileated, Green and Gray-headed woodpeckers are the same as those given to attract a partner or to guide another bird to a hole. In some species both adults tend the young after fledging, in others (eg Great spotted woodpecker and others of the genus *Picoides*, and also Green and Gray-headed woodpeckers) the brood is split, each adult caring for one to three young. The family

breaks up within 1–8 weeks of leaving the nest, adults increasingly using various forms of threat to drive away their offspring (ruffling of crown feathers, wing-spreading, threat calls) which finally move off, eventually to establish their own territories.

The tiny piculets (subfamily Picumninae) climb about tree branches in the manner of woodpeckers or, at times, like titmice and nuthatches. Their flight is undulating. Foraging piculets peck at bark and soft wood to get at ants, termites and wood-boring insects. Their tail, which does not serve as a support when climbing and does not have the stiffened quills of the larger woodpeckers, shows three conspicuous white longitudinal stripes in almost all species. Piculets excavate a nest-hole in tree trunk or branch, or enlarge available holes. During courtship they call and drum. The clutch consists of 2–4 eggs and incubation takes 11–14 days. The young fledge after 21–24 days. Disjunct distribution in Asia, Africa and America indicates the piculets to be of very ancient origin.

Wrynecks (subfamily Jynginae) live in open woods, orchards, parks and meadows with copses. Like woodpeckers they obtain their main food (various kinds of ants) with the help of the tongue. The name wryneck derives from their defense behavior in the nest: when threatened by a predator they perform snake-like twisting and swaying motions of the neck and simultaneously hiss. Filmed sequences show that such behavior is effective in intimidating small predators. A prominent feature in spring is the rather nasal *kwee* call which rises slightly in pitch and which is given by both sexes to attract a partner to prospective nest-holes. The 7 or 8 eggs are usually laid on the bare floor of the nest chamber (after throwing out any nest that may have already been started). Incubation takes 12–14 days and the young spend a further 21 days in the nest, the parents feeding them with adult and pupal ants (about 8,000 individuals daily for all the nestlings); post-fledging care lasts 2 weeks.

From July onwards Northern wrynecks begin their migration south from breeding grounds in Europe and Asia to wintering areas in Africa and Southeast Asia. Populations of the Northern wryneck are threatened and the species has almost completely disappeared from England in recent years. The Rufous-necked wryneck is found in southern Africa, including mountainous regions up to 10,000ft (3,000m). Brown cocktail ants *Crematogaster* make up 80 percent of its diet. DB

Woodland Drumbeats and Dances

The communication system of woodpeckers

Woodpeckers have a varied and highly efficient system of communication comprising visual and acoustic signals. They "speak" to one another by ruffling their crown feathers, spreading wings, swaying the head, hopping and dancing, by giving threat and contact calls, and by tapping and drumming with the bill on tree trunks and branches. Like many other animals woodpeckers use this "language" to express their mood. It is important for other woodpeckers to recognize this because woodpeckers are frequently aggressive. (This is connected with the ownership of trees with holes and of feeding territories, both of which are defended, often in early courtship against the prospective mate.) The contact necessary for reproduction is often made possible

only by a sequence of threat signals that diminish gradually in intensity.

In many species of woodpeckers there is a kind of "threat courtship." An interesting example is the ritualized threat tournament of rival Black woodpecker males. The birds threaten one another at first with *keeyak* calls, then fly to the base of a tree and attempt to drive one another upwards. From time to time they thrust their bills into the air, as if on a command, and wave them about. In these movements the red crown is prominently displayed. The birds then sink into a waiting posture, only to repeat the maneuver after a few minutes. Such a tournament may last for over an hour, until one of the birds gives up. If a male and female meet they threaten one another in similar fashion, but the male's aggression then gradually wanes. This is presumably because the smaller area of red on the female's head and her lower-intensity swaying movements inhibit the male's aggression. Characteristic of this threat ceremony is a very quiet *ryrr* call.

Head-swaying with presentation of the head pattern is found in many species, for example the genera *Colaptes* and *Picus*, many of the sapsuckers and the Pileated

woodpecker. The behavior is especially pronounced in the Common flicker which dances about with wings spread and tail fanned and shows off part of the head which, in the male, bears a moustache-like stripe. If such a stripe is artificially painted on a female she will be treated like a male, ie she will provoke intense aggression.

Multiunit calls, reaching long distances, often combined with demonstrative flights at tree-top height, serve as signals to attract a partner and to advertise trees with holes. In many species drumming and tapping sequences fulfil this function. Some species combine vocal and instrumental (drumming) signals. Each species has its own specific pattern of drumming. In the Black woodpecker long series (43 strikes in 2.5 seconds) function as long-range signals with a great power of attraction while quiet and shorter series are used at close range to advertise the entrance to a hole. When a female has followed a male as far as the hole, or conversely, a male has approached a female showing a nest, the active partner marks the hole entrance with long tapping sequences. Eventually the other bird is attracted nearer and gives threat calls to drive the exhibitor away so that the nest is free for inspection. Woodpeckers sometimes advertise what prove to be unsuitable holes; in such cases the inspecting bird will leave the site, look for another tree, and attempt to lure its future mate to this new site, but success may come only after several days.

The basic scheme of the language of courtship, in a sense its grammar, is found in the majority of woodpecker species: drumming—guiding with calls and special flights—*drumming, tap-drumming, tapping*—hole inspection—agreement over choice of hole.

The Red-bellied woodpecker shows a high degree of ceremony in this sequence. Male and female perform a tapping duet in precise harmony. Where a hole has only been started, they then sit close together on the trunk; if there is a completed hole one bird taps inside, the other outside. Later, there also has to be some understanding between the birds for changeovers during incubation and brooding. Nest-relief has a ceremonial character: the incoming bird gives particular calls, mostly quiet and muttering, or soft and long-drawn. The bird in the hole confirms its readiness for a changeover by tapping on the wall of the nest-chamber and then leaves to allow its mate to take over. In this nest-relief ceremony there is a remnant of antagonistic behavior: when, for example, the bird in the hole is reluctant

▲ **Woodpecker interactions.** (1) Conflict behavior of two female Hairy woodpeckers (*Picoides villosus*) along the boundary of a territory. The owner threatens by jerking her body; the intruder freezes. (2) Red-bellied woodpeckers (*Melanerpes carolinus*) synchronizing behavior: the male taps on the inside, his mate on the outside. (3) An aggressive Downy woodpecker (*Picoides pubescens*) displaying its wings. (4) Male and female Yellow-bellied sapsuckers change place while excavating a hole. The male (right) taps as his mate alights and does a bobbing dance accompanied with "Quirk" notes. This is part of the highly developed ritualized behavior centered on nest-holes or prospective nest-holes.

▲ **Conflict in the desert.** A Gila woodpecker (*Melanerpes uropygialis*) in Arizona invades the territory of another member of the same species sitting on a cactus. This species commonly nests in large cacti.

to leave, its mate uses threat calls and postures to force the other's departure.

If a female dies after the young have hatched the male is able to rear the brood alone, although initially in addition to the feeding of the young his normal response is intense drumming. Such behavior has been observed in the Great spotted woodpecker. After a short time, however, this renewed courtship behavior wanes and the feeding adult becomes noticeably quiet in its territory.

Woodpeckers that have failed to acquire a mate in the breeding season, or have lost one early on, mainly of course males, may drum and call persistently up until the end of the season. Sometimes this enables them to attract another bird, pair up and rear a family in the late spring.

DB

BIBLIOGRAPHY

The following list of titles indicates key reference works used in the preparation of this volume and those recommended for further reading. The list is divided into two sections: general and regional books about birds and books dealing with particular families or groups.

General and Regional

Ali, S. (1977) *Field Guide to the Birds of the Eastern Himalayas*, Oxford University Press, Delhi.

Ali, S. and Ripley, S. D. (1983) *A Pictorial Guide to the Birds of the Indian Subcontinent*, Bombay Natural History Society/Oxford University Press, Delhi.

Ali, S. and Ripley, S. D. (1984) *Handbook of the Birds of India and Pakistan*, Oxford University Press, Delhi.

Baker, R. R. (1984) *Bird Navigation—the Solution of a Mystery?* Hodder and Stoughton, Sevenoaks, Kent.

Baker, R. R. (1978) *The Evolutionary Ecology of Animal Migration*, Hodder and Stoughton, Sevenoaks, Kent.

Blake, E. R. (1977) *Manual of Neotropical Birds, Vol I. Spheniscidae to Laridae*, University of Chicago Press, Chicago.

Blakers, M., Davies, S. J. J. F. and Reilley, P. N. (1984) *The Atlas of Australian Birds*, Melbourne University Press, Melbourne.

Bock, W. J. and Farrand, J. (1980) *The Number of Species and Genera of Recent Birds: a Contribution to Comparative Systematics*, American Museum of Natural History, New York.

Bond, J. (1979) *Birds of the West Indies: a Guide to the Species of Birds that Inhabit the Greater Antilles, Lesser Antilles and Bahama Islands*, Collins, London.

Brown, L. H., Urban, E. K. and Newman, K. (1982) *The Birds of Africa*, vol I, Academic Press, London.

Brudenell-Bruce, P. G. C. (1975) *The Birds of New Providence and the Bahama Islands*, Collins, London.

Campbell, B. and Lack, E. (1985) *A New Directory of Birds*, T. and A. D. Poyser, Stoke-on-Trent.

Clements, J. (1981) *Birds of the World: a Checklist*, Croom Helm, London.

Cramp, S. (1978–85) *Handbook of the Birds of Europe, the Middle East and North Africa: the Birds of the Western Palearctic*, vols I–IV, Oxford University Press, Oxford.

Dementiev, G. P. *et al* (1966) *Birds of the Soviet Union*, vols I–IV, Jerusalem.

Dorst, J. (1962) *The Migration of Birds*, Heinemann, London.

Dunning, J. S. (1982) *South American Land Birds: a Photographic Aid to Identification*, Harrowood, Pennsylvania.

Eastwood, E. (1967) *Radar Ornithology*, Methuen, London.

Ehrlick, P. and A. (1982) *Extinction*, Gollancz, London.

Elkins, N. (1983) *Weather and Bird Behavior*, T. and A. D. Poyser, Stoke-on-Trent.

Falla, R. A., Sibson, R. B. and Turbott, E. G. (1979) *The New Guide to the Birds of New Zealand*, Collins, Auckland and London.

Farner, D. S., King, J. R. and Parkes, K. C. (1971–83) *Avian Biology*, vols I–VII, Academic Press, New York and London.

Farrand, J. J. (1983) *The Audubon Society Master Guide to Birding*, 3 vols, Knopf, New York.

Ferguson-Lees, J., Willis, I. and Sharrock, J. T. R. (1983) *The Shell Guide to the Birds of Britain and Ireland*, Michael Joseph, London.

Finlay, J. C. (1984) *A Bird Finding Guide to Canada*, Hurtig, Edmon.

Flint, V. E., Boehme, R. L., Kostin, Y. V. and Kuznetzov, A. A. (1984) *A Field Guide to Birds of the USSR*, Princeton University Press, Princeton, N.J.

Gallagher, M. and Woodcock, M. W. (1980) *The Birds of Oman*, Quartet, London.

Glenister, A. G. (1971) *The Birds of the Malay Peninsula, Singapore and Penang*, Oxford University Press, Kuala Lumpur.

Godfrey, W. E. (1966) *The Birds of Canada*, National Museum of Canada, Ottawa.

Gotch, A. F. (1981) *Birds—their Latin Names Explained*, Blandford Press, Poole, Dorset.

Gruson, E. S. (1976) *A Checklist of the Birds of the World*, Collins, London.

Halliday, T. (1978) *Vanishing Birds: their Natural History and Conservation*, Sidgwick and Jackson, London.

Harris, M. (1982) *A Field Guide to the Birds of Galapagos*, revised edn, Collins, London.

Harrison, C. J. O. (1975) *A Field Guide to the Nests, Eggs and Nestlings of British and European Birds, with North Africa and the Middle East*, Collins, London.

Harrison, C. J. O. (1978) *A Field Guide to the Nests, Eggs and Nestlings of North American Birds*, Collins, London.

Harrison, C. J. O. (1982) *An Atlas of the Birds of the Western Palaearctic*, Collins, London.

Harrison, C. J. O. (ed) (1978) *Bird Families of the World*, Elsevier-Phaidon, Oxford.

Harrison, P. (1983) *Seabirds—an Identification Guide*, Croom Helm, London.

Howard, R. and Moore, A. (1980) *A Complete Checklist of the Birds of the World*, Oxford University Press, Oxford.

Irby Davis, L. (1972) *A Field Guide to the Birds of Mexico and Central America*, Texas University Press, Austin.

King, A. S. and McLelland, J. (1975) *Outlines of Avian Anatomy*, Baillière Tindall, London.

King, B. Woodcock, M. and Dickinson, E. C. (1975) *A Field Guide to the Birds of South-East Asia*, Collins, London.

Krebs, J. R. and Davies, N. B. (1981) *An Introduction to Behavioral Ecology*, Blackwell Scientific Publications, Oxford.

Lack, D. (1968) *Ecological Adaptations for Breeding in Birds*, Methuen, London.

Leahy, C. (1982) *The Bird Watcher's Companion: an Encyclopedic Handbook of North American Birdlife*, Hale, London.

McFarland, D. (ed) (1981) *The Oxford Companion to Animal Behavior*, Oxford University Press, Oxford.

McLachlan, G. R. *et al* (1978) *Roberts' Birds of South Africa* (4th edn), Struik, Cape Town.

Moreau, R. E. (1972) *The Palaearctic–African Bird Migration Systems*, Academic Press, London.

Murton, R. K. and Westwood, N. J. (1977) *Avian Breeding Cycles*, Oxford University Press, Oxford.

National Geographic Society (1983) *Field Guide to the Birds of North America*, NGS, Washington.

Newman, K. (1983) *The Birds of Southern Africa*, Macmillan, Johannesburg.

O'Connor, R. J. (1984) *The Growth and Development of Birds*, Wiley, New York.

Penny, M. (1974) *The Birds of the Seychelles and the Outlying Islands*, Collins, London.

Perrins, C. M. (1976) *Bird Life: an Introduction to the World of Birds*, Elsevier-Phaidon, Oxford.

Perrins, C. M. and Birkhead, T. R. (1983) *Avian Ecology*, Blackie, London.

Peters, J. L. *et al* (1931–) *Checklist of Birds of the World*, Museum of Comparative Zoology, Cambridge, Massachusetts.

Peterson, R. T. (1980) *A Field Guide to the Birds East of the Rockies* (4th edn), Houghton Mifflin, Boston, Mass.

Peterson, P. T., Mountford, G. and Hollom, P. A. D. (1983) *A Field Guide to the Birds of Britain and Europe* (4th edn), Collins, London.

Pizzey, G. (1980) *A Field Guide to the Birds of Australia*, Collins, Sydney.

Schauensee, R. M. de (1982) *A Guide to the Birds of South America*, Academy of Natural Sciences of Philadelphia.

Schauensee, R. M. de and Phelps, W. H. (1978) *A Guide to the Birds of Venezuela*, Princeton University Press, Princeton, N.J.

Schauensee, R. M. de (1984) *The Birds of China Including the Island of Taiwan*, Oxford University Press, Oxford, Smithsonian Institution Press, Washington D.C.

Serle, W., Morel, G. J. and Hartwig, W. (1977) *A Field Guide to the Birds of West Africa*, Collins, London.

Sharrock, J. T. R. (1976) *The Atlas of Breeding Birds in Britain and Ireland*, British Trust for Ornithology, Tring, Hertfordshire.

Simms, E. (1979) *Wildlife Sounds and their Recording*, Elek, London.

Skutch, A. F. (1975) *Parent Birds and their Young*, University of Texas Press, Austin, Texas.

Slater, P. (1971, 1975) *A Field Guide to Australian Birds*, vol. I, Oliver and Boyd, Edinburgh; vol II, Scottish Academic Press, Edinburgh.

Stresemann, E. (1975) *Ornithology from Aristotle to the Present*, Harvard University Press, Cambridge, Mass.

Tyne, J. van and Berger, A. J. (1976) *Fundamentals of Ornithology* (2nd edn), Wiley, New York.

Warham, J. (1983) *The Techniques of Bird Photography* (4th edn), Focal Press, Sevenoaks, Kent.

Watson, G. E. (1975) *Birds of the Antarctic and Sub-Antarctic*, American Geophysical Union, Washington, D.C.

Weaver, P. (1981) *The Bird-Watcher's Dictionary*, T. and A. D. Poyser, Stoke-on-Trent.

Wild Bird Society of Japan (1982) *A Field Guide to the Birds of Japan*, Wild Bird Society of Japan, Tokyo.

Williams, J. G. and Arlott, N. (1980) *A Field Guide to the Birds of East Africa*, Collins, London.

Wilson, E. (1967) *Birds of the Antarctic*, Blandford Press, Poole.

Families or Groups

Forshaw, J. M. (1978) *Parrots of the World* (2nd edn), David and Charles, Newton Abbot.

Fry, C. H. (1984) *The Bee-eaters*, T. and A. D. Poyser, Stoke-on-Trent.

Goodwin, D. (1983) *Pigeons and Doves of the World* (3rd edn), British Museum (Natural History), London.

Greenwalt, C. H. (1960) *Hummingbirds*, American Museum of Natural History, New York.

Hayman, P., Marchant, J. and Prater, A. (1985) *Shorebirds: an Identification Guide to the Waders of the World*, Croom Helm, London.

Johnsgard, P. A. (1981) *The Plovers, Sandpipers and Snipes of the World*, University of Nebraska Press, Lincoln, Nebraska.

Lack, D. (1956) *Swifts in a Tower*, Methuen, London.

Mikkola, H. (1983) *Owls of Europe*, T. and A. D. Poyser, Stoke-on-Trent.

Short, L. L. (1982) *Woodpeckers of the World*, Delaware Museum of Natural History, Greenville, Delaware.

Soothill, E. and R. (1982) *Wading Birds of the World*, Blandford Press, Poole, Dorset.

Wyllie, I. (1981) *The Cuckoo*, Batsford, London.

GLOSSARY

Adaptation features of an animal that adjust it to its environment. NATURAL SELECTION favors the survival of individuals whose adaptations adjust them better to their surroundings than other individuals with less successful adaptations.

Adaptive radiation where a group of closely related animals (eg members of a family) have evolved differences from each other so that they occupy different NICHES and have reduced competition between each other.

Adult a fully developed and mature individual, capable of breeding but not necessarily doing so until social and/or ecological conditions allow.

Air sac thin walled structure connected to the lungs of birds and involved in respiration; extensions of these can occur in hollow bones.

Albino a form in which all dark pigments are missing, leaving the animal white, usually with red eyes.

Alpine living in mountainous areas, usually above 5,000ft (1,500m).

Altricial refers to young that stay in the nest until they are more or less full grown (as opposed to PRECOCIAL). See also NIDICOLOUS.

Aquatic associated with water.

Arboreal associated with or living in trees.

Avian pertaining to birds.

Beak see BILL.

Bill the two MANDIBLES with which birds gather their food. Synonymous with beak.

Blubber fat, usually that lying just beneath the skin.

Bolus a ball (of food).

Boreal zone the area of land lying just below the north polar region and mainly covered in coniferous forest.

Broadleaved woodland woodland mainly comprising angiosperm trees (both deciduous and evergreen), such as oaks, beeches and hazels, which is characteristic of many temperate areas of Europe and North America.

Brood group of young raised simultaneously by a pair (or several) birds.

Blood-parasite a bird that has its eggs hatched and reared by another species.

Call short sounds made by birds to indicate danger, threaten intruders or keep a group of birds together. See also SONG.

Canopy a fairly continuous layer in forests produced by the intermingling of branches of trees; may be fully continuous (closed) or broken by gaps (open). The crowns of some trees project above the canopy layer and are known as emergents.

Carpal the outer joint of the wing, equivalent to the human wrist.

Casque bony extension of the upper MANDIBLE.

Cecum diverticulation or sac of the hind-gut.

Class a taxonomic level. All birds belong to the class Aves. The main levels of a taxonomic hierarchy (in descending order) are Phylum, Class, Order, Family, Genus, Species.

Cloaca terminal part of the gut into which the reproductive and urinary ducts open. There is one opening to the outside of the body. The cloacal aperture, instead of separate anus and urinogenital openings.

Clutch the eggs laid in one breeding attempt.

Colonial living together in a COLONY.

Colony a group of animals gathered together for breeding.

Comb a fleshy protuberance on the top of a bird's head.

Communal breeder species in which more than the two birds of a pair help in raising the young. See COOPERATIVE BREEDING.

Congener a member of the same genus.

Coniferous forest forest comprising largely evergreen conifers (firs, pines, spruces etc), typically in climates either too dry or too cold to support DECIDUOUS FOREST. Most frequent in northern latitudes or in mountain ranges.

Conspecific a member of the same species.

Contact call CALLS given by males in competition.

Contour feathers visible external covering of feathers, including flight feathers of tail and wings.

Convergent evolution the independent acquisition of similar characters in evolution, as opposed to the possession of similarities by virtue of descent from a common ancestor.

Cooperative breeding a breeding system in which parents of young are assisted in the care of young by other adult or subadult birds.

Coverts the smaller feathers that cover the wings and overlie the base of the large FLIGHT FEATHERS (both wings and tail).

Covey a collective name for groups of birds, usually gamebirds.

Creche a gathering of young birds, especially in penguins and flamingos; sometimes used as a verb.

Crest long feathers on the top of the heads of birds.

Crop a thin-walled extension of the foregut used to store food; often used to carry food to the nest.

Crustaceans invertebrate group which includes shrimps, crabs and many other small marine animals.

Cryptic camouflaged and difficult to see.

Deciduous forest temperate and tropical forest with moderate rainfall and marked seasons. Typically trees shed leaves during either cold or dry periods.

Desert areas of low rainfall, typically with sparse scrub or grassland vegetation or lacking vegetation altogether.

Dimorphic literally "two forms." Usually used as "sexually dimorphic" (ie the two sexes differ in color or size).

Disjunct distribution geographical distribution of a species that is marked by gaps. Commonly brought about by fragmentation of suitable habitat, especially as a result of human intervention.

Dispersal The movements of animals, often as they reach maturity, away from their previous HOME RANGE. Distinct from **dispersion**, that is the pattern in which

things (perhaps animals, food supplies, nest-sites) are distributed or scattered.

Display any relatively conspicuous pattern of behavior that conveys specific information to others, usually to members of the same species; often associated with courtship but also in other activities, eg "threat display."

Display ground the place where a male (or males) tries to attract females.

DNA deoxyribonucleic acid; the key substance of chromosomes—important for inheritance.

Dominance hierarchy a "peck-order"; in most groups of birds, in any pair of birds each knows which is superior and a ranking of superiors therefore follows.

Double-brooded (also triple or multiple brooded) birds which breed twice or more each year, subsequent nests following earlier successful ones, excluding those when the first or all earlier nests fail, in which case the term **replacement nests** applies.

Echolocation the ability to find one's way by emitting sounds and gauging the position of objects by timing the returning echo.

Erectile of an object, eg a crest, that can be raised.

Facultative optional. See also OBLIGATE.

Family either a group of closely related species, eg penguins, or a pair of birds and their offspring. See CLASS.

Feces excrement from the digestive system passed out through the CLOACA.

Fledge strictly to grow feathers. Now usually used to refer to the moment of flying at the end of the nesting period when young birds are more or less completely feathered. Hence **fledging period**, the time from hatching to fledging, and **fledgling**, a recently fledged young bird.

Flight feathers the large feathers of the wing, which can be divided into PRIMARY FEATHERS and SECONDARY FEATHERS.

Fossorial burrowing.

Frontal shield a fleshy area covering the forehead.

Frugivore eating mainly fruits.

Gallery forest a thin belt of woodland along a riverbank in otherwise more open country.

Generalist an animal whose life-style does not involve highly specialized stratagems (cf SPECIALIST), for example, feeding on a variety of foods which may require different foraging techniques.

Genus the taxonomic grouping of species. See CLASS.

Gizzard the muscular forepart of the stomach. Often an important area for the grinding up of food, in many species with the help of grit.

Gregarious the tendency to congregate into groups.

Guano bird excreta. In certain dry areas the guano of colonial sea birds may accumulate to such an extent that it is economic to gather it for fertilizer.

Gular pouch an extension of the fleshy area of the lower jaw and throat.

Habitat the type of country in which an animal lives.

Hallux the first toe. Usually this is small and points backwards, opposing the three forward-facing toes.

Harem a group of females living in the territory of, or consorting with, a single male.

Hatchling a young bird recently emerged from the egg.

Helper an individual, generally without young of its own, which contributes to the survival of the offspring of others by behaving parentally towards them. See COOPERATIVE BREEDING.

Herbivore an animal which eats vegetable material.

Holarctic realm a region of the world including North America, Greenland, Europe and Asia apart from the Southwest, Southeast and India.

Homeothermic warm-blooded, having the ability to keep body temperature constant.

Home range an area in which an animal normally lives (generally excluding rare excursions or migrations), irrespective of whether or not the area is defended from other animals.

Hybrid the offspring of a mating between birds of different species.

Hypothermy a condition in which internal body temperature falls below normal.

Incubation the act of incubating the egg or eggs, ie keeping them warm so that development is possible. Hence **incubation period**, the time taken for eggs to develop from the start of incubation to hatching.

Insectivore an animal that feeds on insects.

Introduced of a species that has been brought from lands where it occurs naturally to lands where it has not previously occurred. Some introductions are natural but some are made on purpose for biological control, farming or other economic reasons.

Irruption sudden or irregular spread of birds from their normal range. Usually a consequence of a food shortage.

Keratin the substance from which feathers are formed (and also reptile scales, human hair, fingernails etc).

Krill small shrimp-like marine CRUSTACEANS which are an important food for certain species of seabirds.

Lamellae comb-like structures which can be used for filtering organisms out of water.

Lanceolate (of feathers) referring to lance-like (pointed) shape.

Lek a display ground where two or more male birds gather to attract females. See DISPLAY.

Littoral referring to the shore-line.

Mallee scrub small scrubby eucalyptus which covers large areas of dryish country in Australia.

Mandible one of the jaws of a bird which make up the BILL (upper or lower).

Melanin a dark or black PIGMENT.

Metabolic rate the rate at which the chemical processes of the body occur.

Migration usually the behavior in which birds fly (migrate) from one part of the world to another at different times of year. There is also local migration and altitudinal migration where birds move, eg on a mountain side, from one height to another.

Molt the replacement of old feathers by new ones.

Monoculture a habitat dominated by a single species of plant, often referring to forestry plantations.

Monogamous taking only a single mate (at a time).

Monotypic the sole member of its genus, family, order etc.

Montane pertaining to mountainous country.

Montane forest forest occurring at middle altitudes on the slopes of mountains, below the alpine zone but above the lowland forest.

Morph a form, usually used to describe a color form when more than one exist.

Morphology the study of the shape and form of animals.

Natural selection the process whereby individuals with the most appropriate ADAPTATIONS are more successful than other individuals, and hence survive to produce more offspring and so increase the population.

Neotropical originating in the tropics of the New World.

Nestling a young bird in the nest, hence **nestling period**, the time from hatching to flying (see FLEDGE).

Niche specific parts of a habitat occupied by a species, defined in terms of all aspects of its life-style (eg food, competitors, predators and other resource requirements).

Nidicolous of young birds which remain in the nest until they can fly. See ALTRICIAL.

Nidifugous of young birds that leave the nest soon after hatching. See PRECOCIAL.

Nomadic wandering (as opposed to having fixed residential areas).

Obligate required, binding. See also FACULTATIVE.

Oligotrophic of a freshwater lake with low nutrient levels; such lakes are usually deep and have poor vegetation.

Omnivore an animal that eats a wide variety of foods.

Opportunistic an animal that varies its diet in relation to what is most freely available. See GENERALIST, SPECIALIST.

Order a level of taxonomic ranking. See CLASS.

Organochlorine pesticides a group of chemicals used mainly as insecticides, some of which have proved highly toxic to birds; includes DDT, aldrin, dieldrin.

Pair bond the faithfulness of a mated pair to each other.

Palaearctic a zoogeographical area roughly comprising Europe and Asia (except the Indian subcontinent and Southeast Asia).

Pampas grassy plains (of South America).

Parasitize in the ornithological sense, usually to lay eggs in the nests of another species and leave the foster parents to raise the young. See BROOD-PARASITE.

Passerine strictly "sparrow-like" but normally used as a shortened form of Passeriformes, the largest ORDER of birds.

Pecten a structure lying on the retina of the eye.

Pigment a substance that gives color to eggs and feathers.

Pod a group of individuals, especially juvenile pelicans, with a temporary cohesive group structure.

Polyandry where a female mates with several males.

Polygamy where a male mates with several females.

Polymorphic where a species occurs in two (or more) different forms (usually relating to color). See MORPH, DIMORPHIC.

Polygyny where a bird of one sex takes several mates.

Population a more or less separate (discrete) group of animals of the same species.

Prairie North American steppe grassland between 30°N and 55°N.

Precocial young birds that leave the nest after hatching. See ALTRICIAL.

Predation where animals are taken by a predator.

Predator birds that hunt and eat other vertebrates hence "anti-predator behavior" describes the evasive actions of the prey.

Preen gland a gland situated above the base of the tail. The bird wipes its bill across this while preening the feathers, so distributing the waxy product of the preen gland over the feathers. The exact function of this is not known; some groups of birds do not possess preen glands.

Primary feather one of the large feathers of the outer wing.

Primary forest forest that has remained undisturbed for a long time and has reached a mature (climax) condition; primary rain forest may take centuries to become established. See also SECONDARY GROWTH.

Promiscuous referring to species where the sexes come together for mating only and do not form lasting pair bonds.

Pyriform pear-shaped.

Quartering the act of flying back and forth over an area, searching it thoroughly.

Race a subsection of a species which is distinguishable from the rest of that species. Usually equivalent to SUBSPECIES.

Radiation see ADAPTIVE RADIATION.

Rain forest tropical and subtropical forest with abundant and year-round rainfall. Typically species rich and diverse.

Range (geographical) area over which an organism is distributed.

Raptor a bird of prey, usually one belonging to the order Falconiformes.

Ratites members of four orders of flightless birds (ostrich, rheas, emu and cassowaries, kiwis) which lack a keel on the breastbone.

Relict population a local group of a species which has been isolated from the rest for a long time.

Resident an animal that stays in one area all the year round.

Roosting sleeping.

Sahara-Sahelian zone the area of North Africa comprising the Sahara Desert and the arid Sahel zone to its south.

Savanna a term loosely used to describe open grasslands with scattered trees and bushes, usually in warm areas.

Scrape a nest without any nesting material where a shallow depression has been formed to hold the eggs.

Scrub a vegetation dominated by shrubs—woody plants usually with more than one stem. Naturally occurs most often on the arid side of forest or grassland types, but often artificially created by man as a result of forest destruction.

Secondary feather one of the large flight feathers on the inner wing.

Secondary forest an area of rain forest that has regenerated after being felled. Usually of poorer quality and lower diversity than PRIMARY FOREST and containing trees of a more uniform size.

Sedentary nonmigrating. See RESIDENT.

Sequential molt where feathers (usually the wing feathers) are molted in order, as opposed to all at once.

Sexual selection an evolutionary mechanism whereby females select for mating only males with certain characteristics, or vice versa.

Sibling group a group containing brothers and sisters.

Sibling species closely related species, thought to have only recently separated.

Single-brooded birds which only make one nesting attempt each year, although they may have a replacement clutch if the first is lost. See DOUBLE-BROODED.

Solitary by itself.

Song a series of sounds (vocalization), often composed of several or many phrases constructed of repeated elements, normally used by a male to claim a territory and attract a mate.

Specialist an animal whose life-style involves highly specialized stratagems, eg feeding with one technique on a particular food.

Species a population, or series of populations, which interbreed freely, but not with those of other species. See CLASS.

Speculum a distinctively colored group of flight feathers (eg on the wing of a duck).

Spur the sharp projection on the leg of some game birds; often more developed in males and used in fighting. Also found on the carpal joint of some other birds.

Staging ground/place an area where birds may pause to feed during migration.

Steppe open grassy plains, with few trees or bushes, of the central temperate zone of Eurasia or North America (prairies), characterized by low and sporadic rainfall and a wide annual temperature variation. In cold steppe temperatures drop well below freezing point in winter, with rainfall concentrated in the summer or evenly distributed throughout the year, while in hot steppe, winter temperatures are higher and rainfall concentrated in winter months.

Stooping dropping rapidly (usually of a bird of prey in pursuit of prey).

Strutting ground an area where male birds may display.

Subadult no longer juvenile but not yet fully adult.

Sublittoral the sea shore below the low-tide mark.

Suborder a subdivision of an order.

Subspecies a subdivision of a species. Usually not distinguishable unless the specimen is in the hand; often called races. See CLASS.

Subtropics the area just outside the tropics (ie at higher latitudes).

Taiga the belt of forests (coniferous) lying below (at lower latitudes to) the TUNDRA.

Tarsus that part of the leg of a bird which is just above the foot. Strictly the tarso-metatarsus, bones formed from the lower leg and upper foot.

Temperate zone an area of climatic zones in mid latitude, warmer than the northerly areas but cooler than the subtropical areas.

Territorial defending an area, in birds usually referring to a bird or birds which exclude others of the same species from their living area and in which they will usually nest.

Thermal an area of (warm) air which rises by convection.

Thermoregulation the regulation and maintenance of a constant internal body temperature.

Torpor a temporary physiological state, akin to short-term hibernation, in which the body temperature drops and the rate of METABOLISM is reduced. Torpor is an ADAPTATION for reducing energy expenditure in periods of extreme cold or food shortage.

Totipalmate feet feet in which three webs connect all four toes. (Most birds have only two webs between the three forward pointing toes, with the hind claws free.)

Tribe a term sometimes used to group certain species and/or genera within a family. See CLASS.

Tropics strictly, an area lying between 23.5°N and 23.5°S. Often because of local geography, birds' habitats do not match this area precisely.

Tundra the area of high latitude roughly demarcated by its being too cold for trees to grow.

Upwelling an area in the sea when, because of local topography, water from deep down in the sea is pushed to the surface. Usually upwellings are associated with rich feeding conditions for birds.

Vermiculation (on feathers) fine markings.

Wattle a fleshy protuberance, usually near the base of the BILL.

Wetlands fresh- or salt-water marshes.

Wing formula statement of relative lengths of wing feathers, especially of primary feathers. Used as a defining characteristic for many species.

Wintering ground the area where a migrant spends the nonbreeding season.

Zygodactyl having two toes directed forwards and two backwards.

INDEX

A **bold number** indicates a major section of the main text, following a heading; a **bold italic** number indicates a fact box on a group of species: a single number in (parentheses) indicates that the animal name or subjects are to be found in a boxed feature and a double number in (parentheses) indicates that the animal name or subject are to be found in a spread special feature. *Italic* numbers refer to illustrations.

Picture Acknowledgments

Key *t* top. *b* bottom. *c* center. *l* left. *r* right.

Abbreviations A Ardea. AN Agence Nature. ANT Australasian Nature Transparencies. BCL Bruce Coleman Ltd. J Jacana. FL Frank Lane Agency. NHPA Natural History Photographic Agency. OSF Oxford Scientific Films. PEP Planet Earth Pictures. SAL Survival Anglia Ltd.

Cover OSF, M. Chillmaid. 1 David Hosking. 2-3 A/J-P. Ferrero. 4-5 A/D. Avon. 6-7 A/M. England. 8-9 Eric Hosking. 10-11 FL. 11t Aquila. 12 ANT. 16t A. 16-17 ANT. 18-19 Tony Tilford, Press-Tige Pictures. 20-21 PEP. 20b J. 22-23 SAL. 23b. 24-25 A. 28t Aquila.

28b BCL. 29, 32b ANT. 32-33 FL. 35 NHPA. 38 BCL. 39 J. 41tAN. 41b A. 44-45 Andrew Henley. 48-49 Fred Bruemmer. 50b, 50-51 A. 53 J. 54 SAL. 55 FL. 56-57 NHPA. 58-59 J. 58b, 59br R. L. Pitman. 59t Chris Perrins. 59bl, 60-61 BCL. 61b AN. 62-63 BCL. 64t Tony Tilford, Press-Tige Pictures. 64-65, 65t A. 66 FL. 66-67 AN. 68 A. 69 ANT. 72-73 A. 73t Heather Angel, Biofotos. 74-75 J. 75b A. G. Wells. 76 A. 77 AN. 78-79, 79b, 82 BCL. 83 Frithfoto. 84t M. King & M. Read. 84c Nature Photographers. 84b BCL. 85 A. 86b Dwight R. Kuhn. 86-87, 90-91 FL. 92 A. 92-93 FL. 93b Frithfoto. 94-95

Aquila. 98 PEP. 100-101 ANT. 101b A. 102 Frithfoto. 103 Aquila. 106 A. 107 BCL. 110-111 A. 112 Michael Fogden. 113 BCL. 116t A. 116-117 NHPA. 118 OSF. 119 A. 120 Heather Angel, Biofotos. 121, 122-123 AN. 124 A. 125t AN. 125b SAL. 128b 128-129 Frithfoto. 130, 131, 132 BCL. 133, Alan Kemp. 136 A. 137 AN. 138-139 A. 139b NHPA. 140t Nature Photographers. 140b A. 141 BCL. 142-143 J. 143t A. 146 Dwight R. Kuhn. 147 Tony Tilford, Press-Tige Pictures. 148-149 NHPA. 151 J.

Artwork

Abbreviations IW Ian Willis. SD Simon Driver. PH Peter Harrison. SM Sean Milne. RG Robert Gillmor. NA Norman Arlott. LT Laurel Tucker. TB Trevor Boyer. AC Ad Cameron. ML Mick Loates.

13t SD. 13 IW. 14-15 RG. 17, 21 IW. 24 SD. 26-27, 30-31 RG. 36-37 PH. 40 IW. 42-43 PH. 44 IW. 46-47 PH. 52 SD. 54-55 IW. 61 SD. 70-71 LT. 76-77 IW. 80-81 TB. 83 IW. 94 SD. 96-97 TB. 99 IW. 100 SD. 104-105 NA. 108 AC. 114-115 SM. 116, 121 IW. 127 SM. 130 IW. 134-135 NA. 144-145 SM. 147, 150 IW.
Maps and scale drawings SD.